STUDENT SOLUTIONS MANUAL

CHAPTERS 1–19

PHYSICS

FOR SCIENTISTS AND ENGINEERS

A STRATEGIC APPROACH

RANDALL D. KNIGHT

D1529854

PAWAN KAHOL and DONALD FOSTER

Wichita State University

PEARSON

Addison
Wesley

San Francisco   Boston   New York
Capetown   Hong Kong   London   Madrid   Mexico City
Montreal   Munich   Paris   Singapore   Sydney   Tokyo   Toronto

Cover Credit: Rainbow/PictureQuest

ISBN: 0-8053-8708-0

PEARSON

Addison
Wesley

6 7 8 9 10 OPM 07 06 05

www.aw-bc.com/physics

Contents

Preface

This *Student Solutions Manual* is intended to provide you with examples of good problem-solving techniques and strategies. To achieve that, the solutions presented here attempt to:

- Follow, in detail, the problem-solving strategies presented in the text.
- Articulate the reasoning that must be done before computation.
- Illustrate how to use drawings effectively.
- Demonstrate how to utilize graphs, ratios, units, and the many other "tactics" that must be successfully mastered and marshaled if a problem-solving strategy is to be effective.
- Show examples of assessing the reasonableness of a solution.
- Comment on the significance of a solution or on its relationship to other problems.

We recommend you try to solve each problem on your own before you read the solution. Simply reading solutions, without first struggling with the issues, has limited educational value.

As you work through each solution, make sure you understand how and why each step is taken. See if you can understand which aspects of the problem made this solution strategy appropriate. You will be successful on exams not by memorizing solutions to particular problems but by coming to recognize which kinds of problem-solving strategies go with which types of problems.

We have made every effort to be accurate and correct in these solutions. However, if you do find errors or ambiguities, we would be very grateful to hear from you. Please contact: knight@aw.com

Acknowledgments

We are grateful for many helpful comments from Susan Cable, Randall Knight, and Steve Stonebraker. We express appreciation to Susan Emerson, who typed the word-processing manuscript, for her diligence in interpreting our handwritten copy. Finally, we would like to acknowledge the support from the Addison Wesley staff in getting the work into a publishable state. Our special thanks to Liana Allday, Alice Houston, and Sue Kimber for their willingness and preparedness in providing needed help at all times.

Pawan Kahol and Donald Foster
Wichita State University
October 2003

CONCEPTS OF MOTION

1.1. Solve:

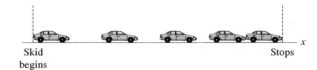

Skid begins   Stops

1.9. Solve: **(a)** Acceleration is found by the method of Tactics Box 1.3. Let $\vec{v}_0$ be the velocity vector between points 0 and 1 and $\vec{v}_1$ be the velocity vector between points 1 and 2.

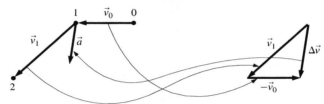

(b) Speed v_1 is greater than speed v_0 because more distance is covered in the same interval of time.

1.11. Solve: The acceleration vector at each location points directly toward the center of the Ferris wheel's circular motion.

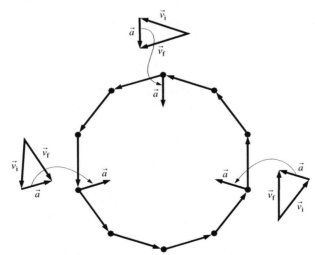

1.17. Model: Represent the car as a particle.
Visualize: The car (particle) moves at a constant speed v so the distance between the dots is constant. While turning v remains constant, but the direction of $\vec{v}$ changes. There will be a $\Delta\vec{v}$ during the turn. Therefore, there is an acceleration during the turn.

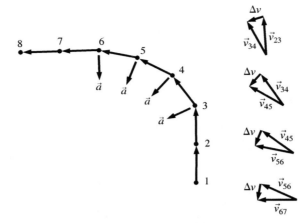

1.19.   Visualize: The bicycle is moving with an acceleration of 1.5 m/s². Thus, the velocity will increase by 1.5 m/s each second of motion.

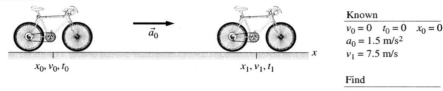

Known
$v_0 = 0$ $t_0 = 0$ $x_0 = 0$
$a_0 = 1.5$ m/s²
$v_1 = 7.5$ m/s

Find
x_1

1.21.   Solve: (a) $9.12 \ \mu s = (9.12 \ \mu s)\left(\dfrac{10^{-6} \ s}{1 \ \mu s}\right) = 9.12 \times 10^{-6} \ s$

(b) $3.42 \ km = (3.42 \ km)\left(\dfrac{10^{3} \ m}{1 \ km}\right) = 3.42 \times 10^{3} \ m$

(c) $44 \ cm/ms = 44\left(\dfrac{cm}{ms}\right)\left(\dfrac{10^{-2} \ m}{1 \ cm}\right)\left(\dfrac{1 \ ms}{10^{-3} \ s}\right) = 440 \ m/s$

(d) $80 \ km/hour = 80\left(\dfrac{km}{hour}\right)\left(\dfrac{10^{3} \ m}{1 \ km}\right)\left(\dfrac{1 \ hour}{3600 \ s}\right) = 22.2 \ m/s$

1.27.   Solve: (a) The number 6.21 has three significant figures.
(b) The number 62.1 has three significant figures.
(c) The number 0.620 has three significant figures. The final zero is significant because it is expressed.
(d) The number 0.062 has two significant figures. The second zero places only the decimal point.

1.29.   Solve: (a) $33.3 \times 25.4 = 846$
(b) $33.3 - 25.4 = 7.9$
(c) $\sqrt{33.3} = 5.77$
(d) $333.3 \div 25.4 = 13.1$

1.35.   Model: Represent the Porsche as a particle for the motion diagram.
Visualize: **Pictorial representation**

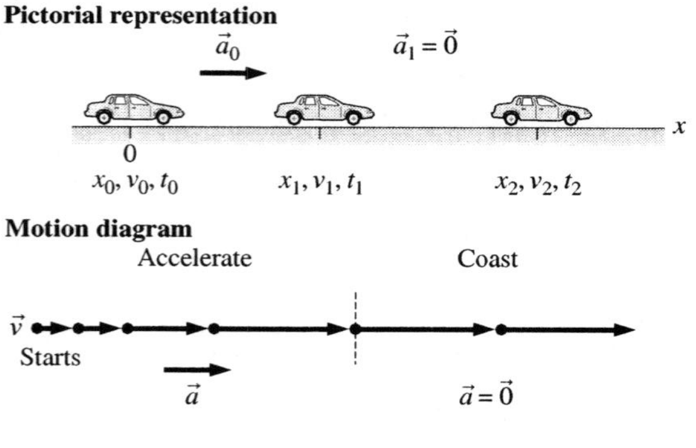

Known
$x_0 = 0$ $a_0 = 5$ m/s²
$v_0 = 0$ $t_1 = 5$ s
$t_0 = 0$ $t_2 = 8$ s
$v_2 = v_1$ $a_1 = 0$

Find
x_2

1.39. **Model:** Represent the wad as a particle for the motion diagram.

Visualize:

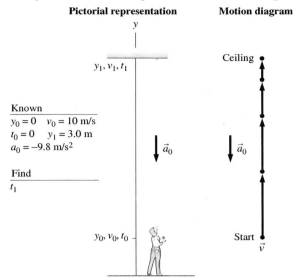

Pictorial representation   **Motion diagram**

Known
$y_0 = 0$ $v_0 = 10$ m/s
$t_0 = 0$ $y_1 = 3.0$ m
$a_0 = -9.8$ m/s^2

Find
t_1

1.43. **Model:** Represent Bruce and the puck as particles for the motion diagram.

Visualize:

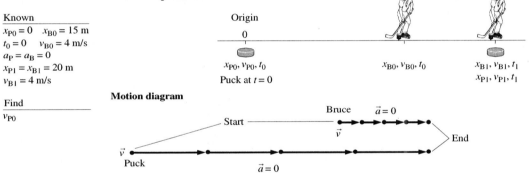

Pictorial representation

Known
$x_{P0} = 0$ $x_{B0} = 15$ m
$t_0 = 0$ $v_{B0} = 4$ m/s
$a_P = a_B = 0$
$x_{P1} = x_{B1} = 20$ m
$v_{B1} = 4$ m/s

Find
v_{P0}

Motion diagram

1.51. **Solve:** **(a)**

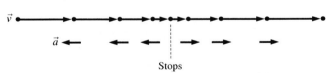

(b) Sue passes 3rd Street doing 40 mph, slows steadily to the stop sign at 4th Street, stops for 1 s, then speeds up and reaches her original speed as she passes 5th Street. If the blocks are 50 m long, how long does it take Sue to drive from 3rd Street to 5th Street?

(c)

Known
$x_0 = 0$ $t_0 = 0$
$v_0 = 40$ mph
$x_1 = x_2 = 50$ m
$v_1 = v_2 = 0$
$t_2 = t_1 + 1$ s
$x_3 = 100$ m $v_3 = 40$ mph

Find
t_3

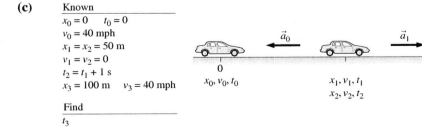

1.53.   Solve: (a)

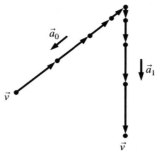

(b) Jeremy has perfected the art of steady acceleration and deceleration. From a speed of 60 mph he brakes his car to rest in 10 seconds with a constant deceleration. Then he turns into an adjoining street. Starting from rest, Jeremy accelerates with exactly the same magnitude as his earlier deceleration and reaches the same speed of 60 mph over the same distance in exactly the same time. Find the car's acceleration or deceleration.

(c)

Known
$v_0 = 60$ mph $t_0 = 0$
$x_0 = 0$ $v_1 = 0$ $t_1 = 10$ s
$v_2 = 60$ mph $t_2 = 20$ s
$x_2 = 2x_1$

Find
a_0 a_1

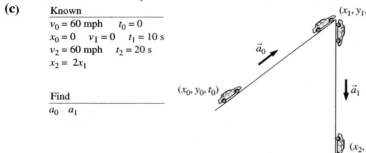

KINEMATICS: THE MATHEMATICS OF MOTION

2.5. Model: We will consider the car to be a particle that occupies a single point in space.
Visualize:

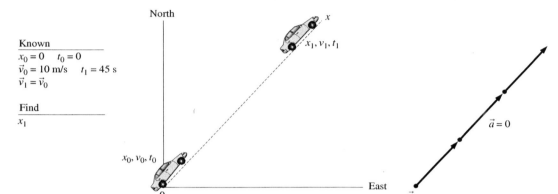

Pictorial representation   Physical representation

North

Known
$x_0 = 0$ $\quad t_0 = 0$
$\vec{v}_0 = 10$ m/s $\quad t_1 = 45$ s
$\vec{v}_1 = \vec{v}_0$

Find
x_1

x_0, v_0, t_0

x_1, v_1, t_1

$\vec{a} = 0$

East

$\vec{v}$

Solve: Since the velocity is constant, we have $x_f = x_i + v_x \Delta t$. Using the above values, we get

$$x_1 = 0 \text{ m} + (10 \text{ m/s})(45 \text{ s}) = 450 \text{ m}$$

Assess: 10 m/s $\approx$ 22 mph and implies a speed of 0.4 miles per minute. A displacement of 450 m in 45 s is reasonable and expected.

2.9. Solve: (a) The time for each of segment is $\Delta t_1 = 50 \text{ mi}/40 \text{ mph} = 5/4$ hr and $\Delta t_2 = 50 \text{ mi}/60 \text{ mph} = 5/6$ hr. The average speed to the house is

$$\frac{100 \text{ mi}}{5/6 \text{ hr} + 5/4 \text{ hr}} = 48 \text{ mph}$$

(b) Julie drives the distance Δx_1 in time Δt_1 at 40 mph. She then drives the distance Δx_2 in time Δt_2 at 60 mph. She spends the same amount of time at each speed, thus

$$\Delta t_1 = \Delta t_2 \Rightarrow \Delta x_1/40 \text{ mph} = \Delta x_2/60 \text{ mph} \Rightarrow \Delta x_1 = (2/3)\Delta x_2$$

But $\Delta x_1 + \Delta x_2 = 100$ miles, so $(2/3)\Delta x_2 + \Delta x_2 = 100$ miles. This means $\Delta x_2 = 60$ miles and $\Delta x_1 = 40$ miles. Thus, the times spent at each speed are $\Delta t_1 = 40 \text{ mi}/40 \text{ mph} = 1.00$ hr and $\Delta t_2 = 60 \text{ mi}/60 \text{ mph} = 1.00$ hr. The total time for her return trip is $\Delta t_1 + \Delta t_2 = 2.00$ hr. So, her average speed is 100 mi/2 hr = 50 mph.

2.11. Visualize: Please refer to Figure Ex2.11. The particle starts at $x_0 = 10$ m at $t_0 = 0$. Its velocity decreases as time increases, goes through zero at $t = 3$ s, and then reverses direction.
Solve: (a) Using the equation $x_f = x_0 +$ area of the velocity graph between t_i and t_f,

$$x_{2s} = 10 \text{ m} + \text{area of trapazoid between 0 s and 2 s}$$

$$= 10 \text{ m} + \frac{1}{2}(12 \text{ m/s} + 4 \text{ m/s})(2 \text{ s}) = 26 \text{ m}$$

$$x_{3s} = 10 \text{ m} + \text{area of triangle between 0 s and 3 s}$$

$$= 10 \text{ m} + \frac{1}{2}(12 \text{ m/s})(3 \text{ s}) = 28 \text{ m}$$

$$x_{4\,s} = x_{3\,s} + \text{area between 3 s and 4 s}$$

$$= 28 \text{ m} + \frac{1}{2}(-4 \text{ m/s})(1 \text{ s}) = 26 \text{ m}$$

(b) The particle reverses direction at $t = 3$ s.

2.17.   Model: We are using the particle model for the skater and the kinematics model of motion under constant acceleration.
Solve: Since we don't know the time of acceleration we will use

$$v_f^2 = v_i^2 + 2a(x_f - x_i)$$

$$\Rightarrow a = \frac{v_f^2 - v_i^2}{2(x_f - x_i)} = \frac{(6.0 \text{ m/s})^2 - (8.0 \text{ m/s})^2}{2(5.0 \text{ m})} = -2.8 \text{ m/s}^2$$

Assess: A deceleration of 2.8 m/s² is reasonable.

2.19.   Model: Represent the spherical drop of molten metal as a particle.
Visualize:

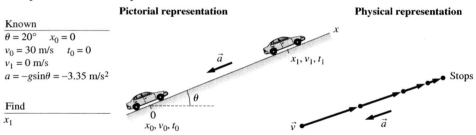

Known
$v_0 = 0 \quad t_0 = 0$
$y_1 = 0 \quad t_1 = 4$ s
$a = -g = -9.8$ m/s²

Find
$y_0 \quad v_1$

Solve: **(a)** The shot is in free fall, so we can use free fall kinematics with $a = -g$. The height must be such that the shot takes 4 s to fall, so we choose $t_1 = 4$ s. Then,

$$y_1 = y_0 + v_0(t_1 - t_0) - \frac{1}{2}g(t_1 - t_0)^2 \Rightarrow y_0 = \frac{1}{2}gt_1^2 = \frac{1}{2}(9.8 \text{ m/s}^2)(4 \text{ s})^2 = 78.4 \text{ m}$$

(b) The impact velocity is $v_1 = v_0 - g(t_1 - t_0) = -gt_1 = -39.2$ m/s.
Assess: Note the minus sign. The question asked for *velocity*, not speed, and the y-component of $\vec{v}$ is negative because the vector points downward.

2.23.   Model: Represent the car as a particle.
Visualize:

Known
$\theta = 20° \quad x_0 = 0$
$v_0 = 30$ m/s $\quad t_0 = 0$
$v_1 = 0$ m/s
$a = -g\sin\theta = -3.35$ m/s²

Find
x_1

Solve: Note that the problem "ends" at a turning point, where the car has an instantaneous speed of 0 m/s before rolling back down. The rolling back motion is *not* part of this problem. If we assume the car rolls without friction, then we have motion on a frictionless inclined plane with an accleration $a = -g\sin\theta = -g\sin 20° = -3.35$ m/s². Constant acceleration kinematics gives

$$v_1^2 = v_0^2 + 2a(x_1 - x_0) \Rightarrow 0 \text{ m}^2/\text{s}^2 = v_0^2 + 2ax_1 \Rightarrow x_1 = -\frac{v_0^2}{2a} = -\frac{(30 \text{ m/s})^2}{2(-3.35 \text{ m/s}^2)} = 134 \text{ m}$$

Notice how the two negatives canceled to give a positive value for x_1.
Assess: We must include the minus sign because the $\vec{a}$ vector points *down* the slope, which is in the negative x-direction.

2.27. **Solve:** The formula for the particle's velocity is given by

$$v_f = v_i + \text{area under the acceleration curve between } t_i \text{ and } t_f$$

For $t = 4$ s, we get

$$v_{4s} = 8 \text{ m/s} + \frac{1}{2}(4 \text{ m/s}^2)4 \text{ s} = 16 \text{ m/s}$$

Assess: The acceleration is positive but decreases as a function of time. The initial velocity of 8.0 m/s will therefore increase. A value of 16 m/s is reasonable.

2.29. **Solve:** **(a)**

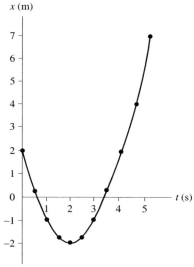

(b) To be completed by student.

(c) $\dfrac{dx}{dt} = v_x = 2t - 4 \Rightarrow v_x(\text{at } t = 1 \text{ s}) = [2 \text{ m/s}^2(1 \text{ s}) - 4 \text{ m/s}] = -2 \text{ m/s}$

(d) There is a turning point at $t = 2$ s.

(e) Using the equation in part (c),

$$v_x = 4 \text{ m/s} = (2t - 4) \text{ m/s} \Rightarrow t = 4$$

Since $x = (t^2 - 4t + 2)$ m, $x = 2$ m.

(f)

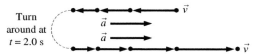

Turn around at $t = 2.0$ s

2.31. **Visualize:** Please refer to Figure P2.31.

Solve: The graph for particle A is a straight line from $t = 2$ s to $t = 8$ s. The slope of this line is -10 m/s, which is the velocity at $t = 7.0$ s. The negative sign indicates motion toward lower values on the x-axis. The velocity of particle B at $t = 7.0$ s can be read directly from its graph. The velocity of particle C can be obtained from the equation

$$v_f = v_i + \text{area under the acceleration curve between } t_i \text{ and } t_f$$

This area can be calculated by adding up three sections. The area between $t = 0$ s and $t = 2$ s is 40 m/s, the area between $t = 2$ s and $t = 5$ s is 45 m/s, and the area between $t = 5$ s and $t = 7$ s is -20 m/s. We get (10 m/s) + (40 m/s) + (45 m/s) − (20 m/s) = 75 m/s.

2.35. **Visualize:** Please refer to Figure P2.35.

Solve: **(a)** We can determine the velocity as follows:

$$v_x = v_x (\text{at } t = t_i) + \text{area under the acceleration-versus-time graph from } t = t_i \text{ to } t_f$$

$$v_x (\text{at } t = 2 \text{ s}) = (-1 \text{ m/s}^2)(2 \text{ s}) = -2 \text{ m/s} \qquad v_x (\text{at } t = 4 \text{ s}) = -2 \text{ m/s} + 0 \text{ m/s} = 2 \text{ m/s}$$

$$v_x (\text{at } t = 6 \text{ s}) = -2 \text{ m/s} + 6 \text{ m/s} = 4 \text{ m/s} \qquad v_x (\text{at } t = 8 \text{ s}) = 4 \text{ m/s} + 2 \text{ m/s} = 6 \text{ m/s}$$

$$v_x (\text{at } t = 10 \text{ s}) = 6 \text{ m/s} - 4 \text{ m/s} = 2 \text{ m/s}$$

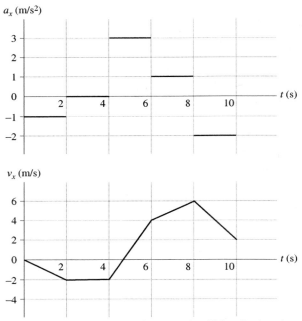

(b) If v_x (at $t = 0$ s) $= 2.0$ m/s, the entire velocity-versus-time graph will be displaced upward by 2.0 m/s.

2.41.   Model: Represent the ball as a particle.
Visualize: Please refer to Figure 2.41.
Solve: In the first and third segments the acceleration a_s is zero. In the second segment the acceleration is negative and constant. This means the velocity v_s will be constant in the first two segments and will decrease linearly in the third segment. Because the velocity is constant in the first and third segments, the position s will increase linearly. In the second segment, the position will increase parabolically rather than linearly because the velocity decreases linearly with time.

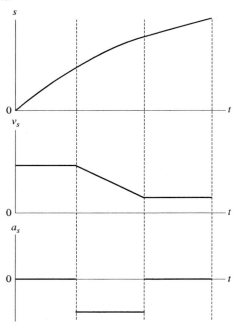

2.43.   Model: Represent the ball as a particle.
Visualize: Please refer to Figure P2.43. The ball moves to the right along the first track until it strikes the wall which causes it to move to the left on a second track. The ball then descends on a third track until it reaches the fourth track which is horizontal.

Solve:

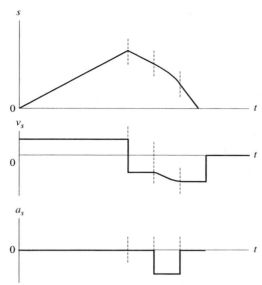

Assess: Note that the time derivative of the position graph yields the velocity graph, and the derivative of the velocity graph gives the acceleration graph.

2.47. **Model:** The plane is a particle and the constant-acceleration kinematic equations hold.
Solve: **(a)** To convert 80 m/s to mph, we calculate 80 m/s × 1 mi/1609 m × 3600 s/hr = 179 mph.
(b) Using $a_s = \Delta v / \Delta t$, we have,

$$a_s(t = 0 \text{ to } t = 10 \text{ s}) = \frac{23 \text{ m/s} - 0 \text{ m/s}}{10 \text{ s} - 0 \text{ s}} = 2.3 \text{ m/s}^2 \qquad a_s(t = 20 \text{ s to } t = 30 \text{ s}) = \frac{69 \text{ m/s} - 46 \text{ m/s}}{30 \text{ s} - 20 \text{ s}} = 2.3 \text{ m/s}^2$$

For all time intervals a is 2.3 m/s^2.
(c) Using kinematics as follows:

$$v_{fs} = v_{is} + a(t_f - t_i) \Rightarrow 80 \text{ m/s} = 0 \text{ m/s} + (2.3 \text{ m/s}^2)(t_f - 0 \text{ s}) \Rightarrow t_f = 35 \text{ s}$$

(d) Using the above values, we calculate the takeoff distance as follows:

$$s_f = s_i + v_{is}(t_f - t_i) + \frac{1}{2}a_s(t_f - t_i)^2 = 0 \text{ m} + (0 \text{ m/s})(35 \text{ s}) + \frac{1}{2}(2.3 \text{ m/s}^2)(35 \text{ s})^2 = 1410 \text{ m}$$

For safety, the runway should be 3 × 1410 m = 4230 m or 2.6 mi. This is longer than the 2.4 mi long runway, so the takeoff is not safe.

2.51. **Model:** The car is represented as a particle.
Visualize:

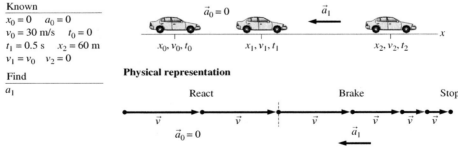

Solve: **(a)** This is a two-part problem. First, we need to use the information given to determine the acceleration during braking. Second, we need to use that acceleration to find the stopping distance for a different initial velocity. First, the car coasts at constant speed before braking:

$$x_1 = x_0 + v_0(t_1 - t_0) = v_0 t_1 = (30 \text{ m/s})(0.5 \text{ s}) = 15 \text{ m}$$

Then, the car brakes to a halt. Because we don't know the time interval, use

$$v_2^2 = 0 = v_1^2 + 2a_1(x_2 - x_1)$$

$$\Rightarrow a_1 = -\frac{v_1^2}{2(x_2 - x_1)} = -\frac{(30 \text{ m/s})^2}{2(60 \text{ m} - 15 \text{ m})} = -10 \text{ m/s}^2$$

We use $v_1 = v_0 = 30$ m/s. Note the minus sign, because $\vec{a}_1$ points to the left. We can repeat these steps now with $v_0 = 40$ m/s. The coasting distance before braking is

$$x_1 = v_0 t_1 = (40 \text{ m/s})(0.5 \text{ s}) = 20 \text{ m}$$

The braking distance is

$$v_2^2 = 0 = v_1^2 + 2a_1(x_2 - x_1)$$

$$\Rightarrow x_2 = x_1 - \frac{v_1^2}{2a_1} = 20 \text{ m} - \frac{(40 \text{ m/s})^2}{2(-10 \text{ m/s}^2)} = 100 \text{ m}$$

(b) The car coasts at a constant speed for 0.5 s, traveling 20 m. The graph will be a straight line with a slope of 40 m/s. For $t \geq 0.5$ the graph will be a parabola until the car stops at t_2. We can find t_2 from

$$v_2 = 0 = v_1 + a_1(t_2 - t_1) \Rightarrow t_2 = t_1 - \frac{v_1}{a_1} = 4.5 \text{ s}$$

The parabola will reach zero slope ($v = 0$ m/s) at $t = 4.5$ s. This is enough information to draw the graph shown in the figure.

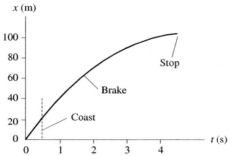

2.57.   Model: The car is a particle moving under constant-acceleration kinematic equations.

Visualize:

Pictorial representation

Known
$x_0 = 0$ $v_0 = 0$
$t_0 = 0$ $a_0 = 4.0$ m/s^2
$t_1 = 6$ s $t_2 = 8$ s
$v_2 = v_1$
$a_2 = -3.0$ m/s^2
$v_3 = 0$

Find
x_3

Physical representation

Solve: This is a three part problem. First the car accelerates, then it moves with a constant speed, and then it decelerates.
First, the car accelerates:

$$v_1 = v_0 + a_0(t_1 - t_0) = 0 \text{ m/s} + (4.0 \text{ m/s}^2)(6 \text{ s} - 0 \text{ s}) = 24 \text{ m/s}$$

$$x_1 = x_0 + v_0(t_1 - t_0) + \frac{1}{2}a_0(t_1 - t_0)^2 = 0 \text{ m} + \frac{1}{2}(4.0 \text{ m/s}^2)(6 \text{ s} - 0 \text{ s})^2 = 72 \text{ m}$$

Second, the car moves at v_1:

$$x_2 - x_1 = v_1(t_2 - t_1) + \frac{1}{2}a_1(t_2 - t_1)^2 = (24 \text{ m/s})(8 \text{ s} - 6 \text{ s}) + 0 \text{ m} = 48 \text{ m}$$

Third, the car decelerates:

$$v_3 = v_2 + a_2(t_3 - t_2) \Rightarrow 0 \text{ m/s} = 24 \text{ m/s} + (-3.0 \text{ m/s}^2)(t_3 - t_2) \Rightarrow (t_3 - t_2) = 8 \text{ s}$$

$$x_3 = x_2 + v_2(t_3 - t_2) + \frac{1}{2}a_2(t_3 - t_2)^2 \Rightarrow x_3 - x_2 = (24 \text{ m/s})(8 \text{ s}) + \frac{1}{2}(-3.0 \text{ m/s}^2)(8 \text{ s})^2 = 96 \text{ m}$$

Thus, the total distance between stop signs is:

$$x_3 - x_0 = (x_3 - x_2) + (x_2 - x_1) + (x_1 - x_0) = 96 \text{ m} + 48\text{m} + 72 \text{ m} = 216 \text{ m}$$

Assess: A distance of approximately 600 ft in a time of around 10 s with an acceleration/deceleration of the order of 7 mph/s is reasonable.

2.59. Model: Santa is a particle moving under constant-acceleration kinematic equations.
Visualize: Note that our *x*-axis is positioned along the incline.

Pictorial representation

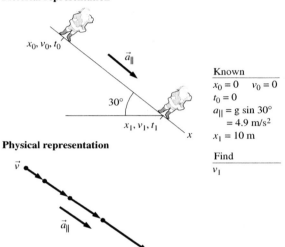

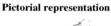

Known
$x_0 = 0$ $v_0 = 0$
$t_0 = 0$
$a_{\parallel} = g \sin 30°$
    $= 4.9 \text{ m/s}^2$
$x_1 = 10 \text{ m}$

Find
v_1

Physical representation

Solve: Using the following kinematic equation,

$$v_1^2 = v_0^2 + 2a_{\parallel}(x_1 - x_2) = (0 \text{ m/s})^2 + 2(4.9 \text{ m/s}^2)(10 \text{ m} - 0 \text{ m}) \Rightarrow v_1 = 9.9 \text{ m/s}$$

Assess: Santa's speed of 20 mph as he reaches the edge is reasonable.

2.61. Model: We will use the particle model for the ball.
Visualize:

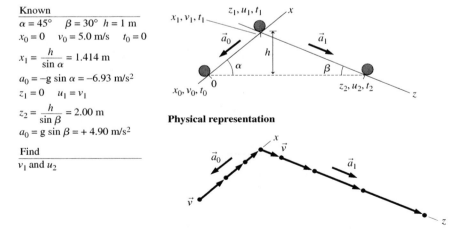

Pictorial representation

Known
$\alpha = 45°$ $\beta = 30°$ $h = 1 \text{ m}$
$x_0 = 0$ $v_0 = 5.0 \text{ m/s}$ $t_0 = 0$
$x_1 = \dfrac{h}{\sin \alpha} = 1.414 \text{ m}$
$a_0 = -g \sin \alpha = -6.93 \text{ m/s}^2$
$z_1 = 0$ $u_1 = v_1$
$z_2 = \dfrac{h}{\sin \beta} = 2.00 \text{ m}$
$a_0 = g \sin \beta = +4.90 \text{ m/s}^2$

Find
v_1 and u_2

Physical representation

We can view this problem as two one-dimensional motion problems. The horizontal segments do not affect the motion because the speed does not change. So, the problem "starts" at the bottom of the uphill ramp and "ends" at the bottom of the downhill ramp. The final speed from the uphill roll (first problem) becomes the initial speed of the downhill roll (second problem). Because the axes point in different directions, we can avoid possible confusion by calling the downhill axis the z-axis and the downhill velocities u. The uphill axis as usual will be denoted by x and the uphill velocities as v. Note that the height information, $h = 1$ m, has to be transformed into information about positions along the two axes.

Solve: (a) The uphill roll has $a_0 = -g\sin\alpha = -6.93$ m/s². The speed at the top is found from

$$v_1^2 = v_0^2 + 2a_0(x_1 - x_0)$$

$$\Rightarrow v_1 = \sqrt{v_0^2 + 2a_0 x_1} = \sqrt{(5 \text{ m/s})^2 + 2(-6.93 \text{ m/s}^2)(1.414 \text{ m})} = 2.32 \text{ m/s}$$

(b) The downward roll starts with velocity $u_1 = v_1 = 2.32$ m/s and $a_1 = +g\sin\beta = 4.90$ m/s². Then,

$$u_2^2 = u_1^2 + 2a_1(z_2 - z_1) = (2.32 \text{ m/s})^2 + 2(4.90 \text{ m/s}^2)(2.00 \text{ m} - 0 \text{ m}) \Rightarrow u_2 = 5.00 \text{ m/s}$$

(c) The final speed is equal to the initial speed, so the percentage change is zero! This result may seem surprising, but can be more easily understood after we introduce the concept of energy.

2.67.   Model: The ball is a particle that exhibits freely falling motion according to the constant-acceleration kinematic equations.

Visualize:

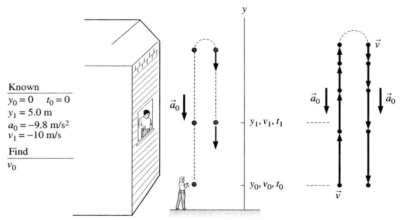

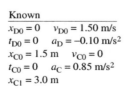

Pictorial representation   Physical representation

Known
$y_0 = 0$ $t_0 = 0$
$y_1 = 5.0$ m
$a_0 = -9.8$ m/s²
$v_1 = -10$ m/s

Find
v_0

Solve: Using the known values, we have

$$v_1^2 = v_0^2 + 2a_0(y_1 - y_0) \Rightarrow (-10 \text{ m/s})^2 = v_0^2 + 2(-9.8 \text{ m/s}^2)(5.0 \text{ m} - 0 \text{ m}) \Rightarrow v_0 = 14 \text{ m/s}$$

2.71.   Model: We will represent the dog and the cat in the particle model.

Visualize:

Pictorial representation   Window

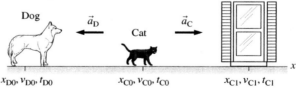

Known
$x_{D0} = 0$ $v_{D0} = 1.50$ m/s
$t_{D0} = 0$ $a_D = -0.10$ m/s²
$x_{C0} = 1.5$ m $v_{C0} = 0$
$t_{C0} = 0$ $a_C = 0.85$ m/s²
$x_{C1} = 3.0$ m

Find
x_{D1}

Physical representation

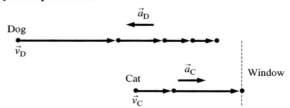

Solve: We will first calculate the time t_{C1} the cat takes to reach the window. The dog has exactly the same time to reach the cat (or the window). Let us therefore first calculate t_{C1} as follows:

$$x_{C1} = x_{C0} + v_{C0}(t_{C1} - t_{C0}) + \frac{1}{2}a_C(t_{C1} - t_{C0})^2$$

$$\Rightarrow 3.0\text{ m} = 1.5\text{ m} + 0\text{ m} + \frac{1}{2}(0.85\text{ m/s}^2)t_{C1}^2 \Rightarrow t_{C1} = 1.879\text{ s}$$

In the time $t_{D1} = 1.879$ s, the dog's position can be found as follows:

$$x_{D1} = x_{D0} + v_{D0}(t_{D1} - t_{D0}) + \frac{1}{2}a_D(t_{D1} - t_{D0})^2$$

$$= 0\text{ m} + (1.50\text{ m/s})(1.879\text{ s}) + \frac{1}{2}(-0.10\text{ m/s}^2)(1.879\text{ s})^2 = 2.6\text{ m}$$

That is, the dog is shy of reaching the cat by 0.4 m. The cat is safe.

2.77. Solve: (a) From the first equation, the particle starts from rest and accelerates for 5 s. The second equation gives a position consistent with the first equation. The third equation gives a subsequent position following the second equation with zero acceleration. A rocket sled accelerates from rest at 20 m/s^2 for 5 sec and then coasts at constant speed for an additional 5 sec. Draw a graph showing the velocity of the sled as a function of time up to $t = 10$ s. Also, how far does the sled move in 10 s?

(b)

Pictorial representation

Known
$x_0 = 0$ $v_0 = 0$
$t_0 = 0$ $a_0 = 20\text{ m/s}^2$
$t_1 = 5\text{ s}$ $t_2 = 10\text{ s}$
$v_2 = v_1$

Find
x_2

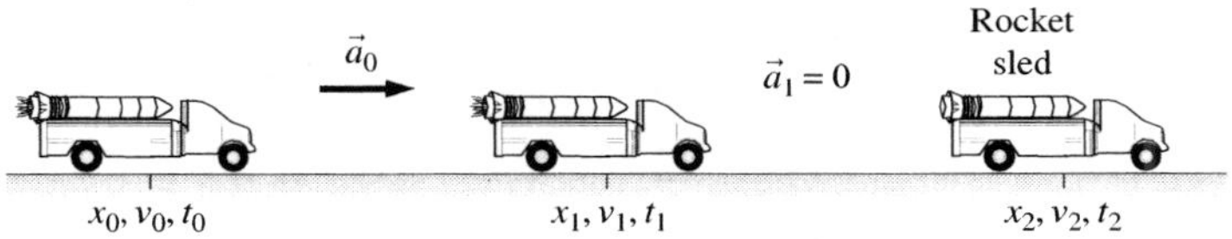

Physical representation

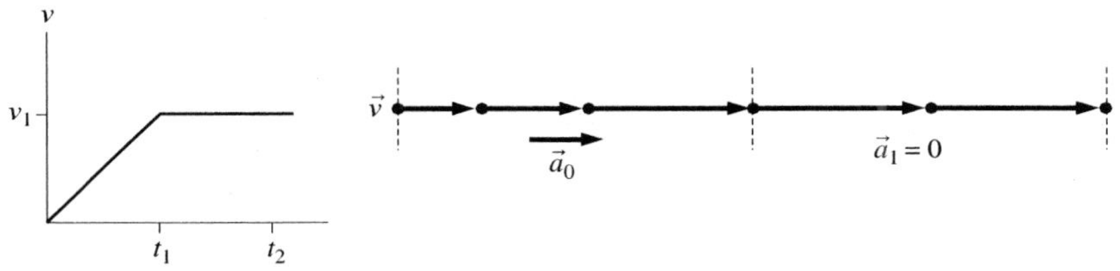

(c) $x_1 = \frac{1}{2}(20\text{ m/s}^2)(5\text{ s})^2 = 250\text{ m}$ $v_1 = 20\text{ m/s}^2(5\text{ s}) = 100\text{ m/s}$ $x_2 = 250\text{ m} + (100\text{ m/s})(5\text{ s}) = 750\text{ m}$

VECTORS AND COORDINATE SYSTEMS

3.3. Visualize:

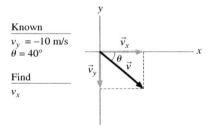

Solve: **(a)** $C = A - B$ if $\vec{B}$ is directed in the same direction as $\vec{A}$. Size does not matter, except that $A > B$ because C as a magnitude cannot be negative.

(b) $C = A + B$ if $\vec{B}$ is directed opposite to the direction of $\vec{A}$. Size does not matter.

3.7. Visualize: The figure shows the components v_x and v_y, and the angle θ.

Known
$v_y = -10$ m/s
$\theta = 40°$

Find
v_x

Solve: We have,

$$v_y = -v\sin 40°, \quad \text{or} \quad -10 \text{ m/s} = -v\sin 40°, \quad \text{or} \quad v = 15.6 \text{ m/s}.$$

Thus the x-component is $v_x = v\cos 40° = (15.6 \text{ m/s})\cos 40° = 11.9 \text{ m/s}$.

Assess: Note that we had to insert the minus sign manually with v_y since the vector is in the fourth quadrant.

3.13. Visualize:

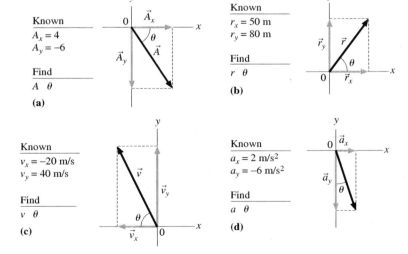

Known
$A_x = 4$
$A_y = -6$

Find
$A \quad \theta$

(a)

Known
$r_x = 50$ m
$r_y = 80$ m

Find
$r \quad \theta$

(b)

Known
$v_x = -20$ m/s
$v_y = 40$ m/s

Find
$v \quad \theta$

(c)

Known
$a_x = 2$ m/s^2
$a_y = -6$ m/s^2

Find
$a \quad \theta$

(d)

Solve: **(a)** Using the formulas for the magnitude and direction of a vector, we have:

$$A = \sqrt{(4)^2 + (-6)^2} = 7.21 \qquad \theta = \tan^{-1}\frac{6}{4} = \tan^{-1} 1.5 = 56.3°$$

(b) $\quad r = \sqrt{(50 \text{ m})^2 + (80 \text{ m})^2} = 94.3 \text{ m} \qquad \theta = \tan^{-1}\left(\frac{r_y}{r_x}\right) = \tan^{-1}\left(\frac{80 \text{ m}}{50 \text{ m}}\right) = 58.0°$

(c) $\quad v = \sqrt{(-20 \text{ m/s})^2 + (40 \text{ m/s})^2} = 44.7 \text{ m/s} \qquad \theta = \tan^{-1}\frac{40}{20} = \tan^{-1} 2 = 63.4°$

(d) $\quad a = \sqrt{(2 \text{ m/s}^2)^2 + (-6 \text{ m/s}^2)^2} = 6.3 \text{ m/s}^2 \qquad \theta = \tan^{-1}\frac{2}{6} = \tan^{-1} 0.33 = 18.4°$

Assess: Note that the angle θ made with the x-axis is smaller than 45° whenever $|E_y| < |E_x|$, $\theta = 45°$ for $|E_y| = |E_x|$, and $\theta > 45°$ for $|E_y| > |E_x|$. But, of course, θ in part (d) is with the y-axis, where the opposite of this rule applies.

3.21. **Visualize:**

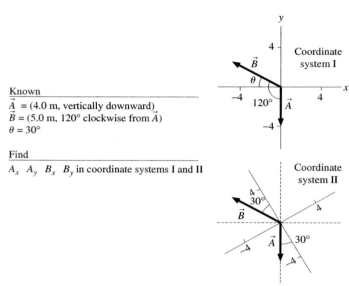

Known

$\vec{A}$ = (4.0 m, vertically downward)
$\vec{B}$ = (5.0 m, 120° clockwise from $\vec{A}$)
θ = 30°

Find

A_x A_y B_x B_y in coordinate systems I and II

Solve: In coordinate system I, $\vec{A} = -(4 \text{ m})\hat{j}$, so $A_x = 0$ m and $A_y = -4$ m. The vector $\vec{B}$ makes an angle of 120° clockwise from $\vec{A}$, or it makes an angle of $\theta = 30°$ with the –x-axis. Since $\vec{B}$ points to the left and up, it has a negative x-component and a positive y-component. That is, $B_x = -(5.0 \text{ m})\cos 30° = -4.33$ m and $B_y = +(5.0 \text{ m})\sin 30° = 2.50$ m. Thus, $\vec{B} = -(4.33 \text{ m})\hat{i} + (2.50 \text{ m})\hat{j}$.

In coordinate system II, $\vec{A}$ points to the left and down, and makes an angle of 30° with the –y-axis. Therefore, $A_x = -(4.0 \text{ m})\sin 30° = -2.00$ m and $A_y = -(4.0)\cos 30° = -3.46$ m. This implies $\vec{A} = -(2.00 \text{ m})\hat{i} - (3.46 \text{ m})\hat{j}$. The vector $\vec{B}$ makes an angle of 30° with the +y-axis and is to the left and up. This means, we have to manually insert a minus sign with the x-component. $B_x = -B\sin 30° = -(5.0 \text{ m})\sin 30° = -2.50$ m, and $B_y = +B\cos 30° = (5.0 \text{ m})\cos 30° = 4.33$ m. Thus $\vec{B} = -(2.50 \text{ m})\hat{i} + (4.33 \text{ m})\hat{j}$.

3.25. **Visualize:** Refer to Figure P3.25 in your textbook.
Solve: **(a)** We are given that $\vec{A} + \vec{B} + \vec{C} = -2\hat{i}$ with $\vec{A} = 4\hat{i}$, and $\vec{C} = -2\hat{j}$. This means $\vec{A} + \vec{C} = 4\hat{i} - 2\hat{j}$. Thus, $\vec{B} = (\vec{A} + \vec{B} + \vec{C}) - (\vec{A} + \vec{C}) = (-2\hat{i}) - (4\hat{i} - 2\hat{j}) = -6\hat{i} + 2\hat{j}$.
(b) We have $\vec{B} = B_x\hat{i} + B_y\hat{j}$ with $B_x = -6$ and $B_y = 2$. Hence, $B = \sqrt{(-6)^2 + (2)^2} = 6.32$

$$\theta = \tan^{-1}\frac{B_y}{|B_x|} = \tan^{-1}\frac{2}{6} = 18.4°$$

Since $\vec{B}$ has a negative x-component and a positive y-component, the angle θ made by $\vec{B}$ is with the –x-axis and it is above the –x-axis.
Assess: Since $|B_y| < |B_x|$, $\theta < 45°$ as is obtained above.

3.27. **Visualize:**

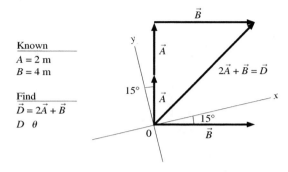

Known
$A = 2$ m
$B = 4$ m

Find
$\vec{D} = 2\vec{A} + \vec{B}$
D θ

Solve: In the tilted coordinate system, the vectors $\vec{A}$ and $\vec{B}$ are expressed as:

$$\vec{A} = (2\sin15°\ \text{m})\hat{i} + (2\cos15°\ \text{m})\hat{j} \quad \text{and} \quad \vec{B} = (4\cos15°\ \text{m})\hat{i} - (4\sin15°\ \text{m})\hat{j}.$$

Therefore, $\vec{D} = 2\vec{A} + \vec{B} = (4\ \text{m})[(\sin15° + \cos15°)\hat{i} + (\cos15° - \sin15°)\hat{j}] = (4.90\ \text{m})\hat{i} + (2.83\ \text{m})\hat{j}.$

The magnitude of this vector is $D = 5.66$ m, and it makes an angle of $\theta = \tan^{-1}(0.707\ \text{m}/1.225\ \text{m}) = 30°$ with the $+x$-axis.

Assess: The resultant vector can be obtained graphically by using the rule of tail-to-tip addition.

3.31. **Visualize:**

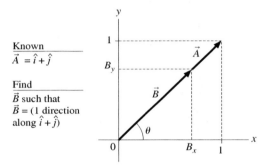

Known
$\vec{A} = \hat{i} + \hat{j}$

Find
$\vec{B}$ such that
$\vec{B} = (1$ direction
along $\hat{i} + \hat{j})$

The magnitude of the unknown vector is 1 and its direction is along $\hat{i} + \hat{j}$. Let $\vec{A} = \hat{i} + \hat{j}$ as shown in the diagram. That is, $\vec{A} = 1\hat{i} + 1\hat{j}$ and the x- and y-components of $\vec{A}$ are both unity. Since $\theta = \tan^{-1}(A_y/A_x) = 45°$, the unknown vector must make an angle of $45°$ with the $+x$-axis and have unit magnitude.

Solve: Let the unknown vector be $\vec{B} = B\hat{i} + B_y\hat{j}$ where

$$B_x = B\cos45° = \frac{1}{\sqrt{2}}B \quad \text{and} \quad B_y = B\sin45° = \frac{1}{\sqrt{2}}B$$

We want the magnitude of $\vec{B}$ to be 1, so we have

$$B = \sqrt{B_x^2 + B_y^2} = 1$$

$$\Rightarrow \sqrt{\left(\frac{1}{\sqrt{2}}B\right)^2 + \left(\frac{1}{\sqrt{2}}B\right)^2} = 1 \Rightarrow \sqrt{B^2} = 1 \Rightarrow B = 1$$

Hence,

$$B_x = \frac{1}{\sqrt{2}} \cdot 1 = \frac{1}{\sqrt{2}} \quad \text{and} \quad B_y = \frac{1}{\sqrt{2}} \cdot 1 = \frac{1}{\sqrt{2}}$$

Finally,

$$\vec{B} = B_x\hat{i} + B_y\hat{j} = \frac{1}{\sqrt{2}}\hat{i} + \frac{1}{\sqrt{2}}\hat{j}$$

3.35. Visualize: (a)

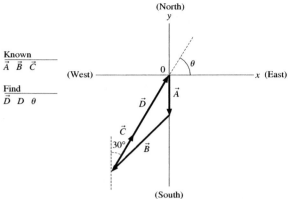

Note that +x is along the east and +y is along the north.

Solve: (b) We are given $\vec{A} = -(200 \text{ m})\hat{j}$, and can use trigonometry to obtain $\vec{B} = -(283 \text{ m})\hat{i} - (283 \text{ m})\hat{j}$ and $\vec{C} = (100 \text{ m})\hat{i} + (173 \text{ m})\hat{j}$. We want $\vec{A} + \vec{B} + \vec{C} + \vec{D} = 0$. This means

$$\vec{D} = -\vec{A} - \vec{B} - \vec{C}$$
$$= (200 \text{ m}\,\hat{j}) + (283 \text{ m}\,\hat{i} + 283 \text{ m}\,\hat{j}) + (-100 \text{ m}\,\hat{i} - 173 \text{ m}\,\hat{j}) = 183 \text{ m}\,\hat{i} + 310 \text{ m}\,\hat{j}$$

The magnitude and direction of $\vec{D}$ are

$$D = \sqrt{(183 \text{ m})^2 + (310 \text{ m})^2} = 360 \text{ m}, \quad \text{and} \quad \theta = \tan^{-1}\frac{D_y}{D_x} = \tan^{-1}\left(\frac{310 \text{ m}}{183 \text{ m}}\right) = 59.4°$$

This means $D = (360 \text{ m}, 59.4°$ north of east$)$.

(c) The measured length of the vector $\vec{D}$ on the graph (with a ruler) is approximately 1.75 times the measured length of vector $\vec{A}$. Since $A = 200$ m, this gives $D = 1.75 \times 200$ m $= 350$ m. Similarly, the angle θ measured with the protractor is close to 60°. These answers are in close agreement to part (b).

3.41. Visualize: Establish a coordinate system with origin at the tree and with the x-axis pointing east. Let $\vec{A}$ be a displacement vector directly from the tree to the treasure. Vector $\vec{A}$ is

$$\vec{A} = (100\hat{i} + 500\hat{j}) \text{ paces}.$$

This describes the displacement you would undergo by walking north 500 paces, then east 100 paces. Instead, you follow the road for 300 paces and undergo displacement

$$\vec{B} = (300\sin 60°\hat{i} + 300\cos 60°\hat{j}) \text{ paces}$$
$$= (260\hat{i} + 150\hat{j}) \text{ paces}.$$

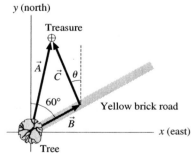

Solve: Now let $\vec{C}$ be the displacement vector from your position to the treasure. From the figure

$$\vec{A} = \vec{B} + \vec{C}.$$

So the displacement you need to reach the treasure is

$$\vec{C} = \vec{A} - \vec{B} = (-160\hat{i} + 350\hat{j}) \text{ paces}.$$

If θ is the angle measured between $\vec{C}$ and the *y*-axis,

$$\theta = \tan^{-1}\left(\frac{160}{350}\right) = 24.6°$$

You should head $24.6°$ west of north. You need to walk distance $C = \sqrt{C_x^2 + C_y^2} = 385$ paces to get to the treasure.

3.45. Visualize:

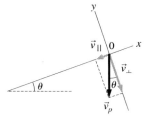
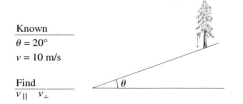

The coordinate system used here is tilted with *x*-axis along the slope.
Solve: The component of the velocity parallel to the *x*-axis is $v_\parallel = -v\cos 70° = -v\sin 20° = -10 \text{ m/s} (.34) = -3.4 \text{ m/s}$. This is the speed down the slope. The component of the velocity perpendicular $v_\perp = -v\sin 70° = -v\cos 20° = -10 \text{ m/s} (.94) = -9.4 \text{ m/s}$. This is the speed toward the ground.
Assess: A speed of approximately 10 m/s implies a fall time of approximately 1 second under free-fall. Note that $g = -9.8 \text{ m/s}^2$. This time is reasonable for a drop of approximately 5 m or 16 feet.

3.47. Model: We will treat the knot in the rope as a particle in static equilibrium.
Visualize:

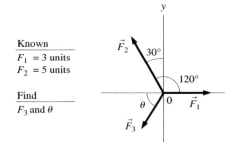

Pictorial representation

Solve: Expressing the vectors using unit vectors, we have $\vec{F}_1 = 3\hat{i}$ and $\vec{F}_2 = -5\sin 30°\hat{i} + 5\cos 30°\hat{j}$.
Since $\vec{F}_1 + \vec{F}_2 + \vec{F}_3 = \vec{0}$, we can write $\vec{F}_3 = -\vec{F}_1 - \vec{F}_2 = -0.5\hat{i} - 4.33\hat{j}$.
The magnitude of $\vec{F}_3$ is given by $F_3 = \sqrt{(-0.5)^2 + (-4.33)^2} = 4.36$ units. The angle $\vec{F}_3$ makes is $\theta = \tan^{-1}(4.33/0.5) = 83.4°$ and is below the negative *x*-axis.
Assess: The resultant vector has both components negative, and is therefore in quadrant III. Its magnitude and direction are reasonable. Note the minus sign that we have manually inserted with the force $\vec{F}_2$.

3.49. Visualize:

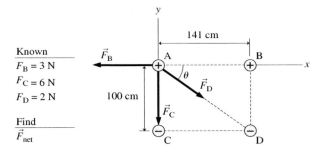

Solve: Using trigonometry to calculate θ, we get $\theta = \tan^{-1}(100 \text{ cm}/141 \text{ cm}) = 35.3°$.

Expressing the three forces in unit vectors, $\vec{F}_B = -(3 \text{ N})\hat{i}$, $\vec{F}_C = -(6 \text{ N})\hat{j}$, and $\vec{F}_D = +(2 \text{ N})\cos 35.3\hat{i} - (2 \text{ N})\sin 35.3\hat{j} = (1.63 \text{ N})\hat{i} - (1.16 \text{ N})\hat{j}$.

The total force is $\vec{F}_{net} = \vec{F}_B + \vec{F}_C + \vec{F}_D = -1.37 \text{ N}\hat{i} - 7.16 \text{ N}\hat{j}$. The magnitude of $\vec{F}_{net}$ is $F_{net} = \sqrt{(1.37 \text{ N})^2 + (7.16 \text{ N})^2} = 7.29 \text{ N}$.

$$\theta_{net} = \tan^{-1}\frac{|(F_{net})_y|}{|(F_{net})_x|} = \tan^{-1}\left(\frac{7.16 \text{ N}}{1.37 \text{ N}}\right) = 79.2°$$

$\vec{F}_{net} = (7.29 \text{ N}, 79.2°$ below $-x$ in quadrant III$)$.

FORCE AND MOTION

4.5. Visualize: Please refer to Figure Ex4.5.
Solve: Mass is defined to be

$$m = \frac{1}{\text{slope of the acceleration-versus-force graph}}$$

A larger slope implies a smaller mass. We know $m_2 = 0.20$ kg, and we can find the other masses relative to m_2 by comparing their slopes. Thus

$$\frac{m_1}{m_2} = \frac{1/\text{slope } 1}{1/\text{slope } 2} = \frac{\text{slope } 2}{\text{slope } 1} = \frac{1}{5/2} = \frac{2}{5} = 0.40$$

$$\Rightarrow m_1 = 0.40 m_2 = 0.40 \times 0.20 \text{ kg} = 0.08 \text{ kg}$$

Similarly,

$$\frac{m_3}{m_2} = \frac{1/\text{slope } 3}{1/\text{slope } 2} = \frac{\text{slope } 2}{\text{slope } 3} = \frac{1}{2/5} = \frac{5}{2} = 2.50$$

$$\Rightarrow m_3 = 2.50 m_2 = 2.50 \times 0.20 \text{ kg} = 0.50 \text{ kg}$$

Assess: From the initial analysis of the slopes we had expected $m_3 > m_2$ and $m_1 < m_2$. This is consistent with our numerical answers.

4.9. Visualize: Please refer to Figure Ex4.9.
Solve: Newton's second law is $F = ma$. We can read a force and an acceleration from the graph, and hence find the mass. Choosing the force $F = 1$ N gives us $a = 4$ m/s^2. Newton's second law yields $m = 0.25$ kg.

4.13. Visualize:

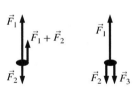

Solve: The object will be in equilibrium if $\vec{F}_3$ has the same magnitude as $\vec{F}_1 + \vec{F}_2$ but is in the opposite direction so that the sum of all three forces is zero.

4.19. Visualize:

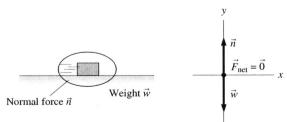

Force identification   Free-body diagram

Assess: The problem says that there is no friction and it tells you nothing about any drag; so we do not include either of these forces. The only remaining forces are the weight and the normal force.

4.21. Visualize:

Force identification
Free-body diagram
Weight $\vec{w}$
Normal force $\vec{n}$
Kinetic friction $\vec{f}_k$
y
x
$\vec{n}$
$\vec{f}_k$
$\vec{w}$
$\vec{F}_{net}$

Assess: The problem uses the word "sliding." Any real situation involves friction with the surface. Since we are not told to neglect it, we show that force.

4.23. Visualize:

Motion diagrams
$\vec{v}$
$\vec{a}$
$\vec{F}_{net}$
$\vec{a}$
$\vec{F}_{net}$
$\vec{v}$
(a)
(b)

The velocity vector in figure (a) is shown downward and to the left. So movement is downward and to the left. The velocity vectors get successively longer which means the speed is increasing. Therefore the acceleration is downward and to the left. By Newton's second law $\vec{F} = m\vec{a}$, the net force must be in the same direction as the acceleration. Thus, the net force is downward and to the left.

The velocity vector in (b) is shown to be upward and to the right. So movement is upward and to the right. The velocity vector gets successively shorter which means the speed is decreasing. Therefore the acceleration is downward and to the left. From Newton's second law, the net force must be in the direction of the acceleration and so it is directed downward and to the left.

4.25. Visualize:

F_x (N)
0.75
0.50
0.25
0
−0.25
1
2
3
4
t (s)

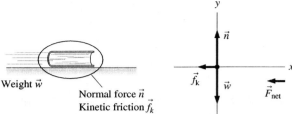

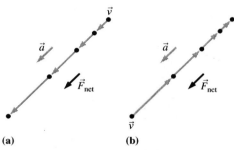

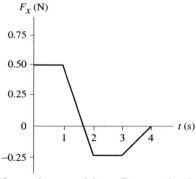

Solve: According to Newton's second law $F = ma$, the force at any time is found simply by multiplying the value of the acceleration by the mass of the object.

4.27. **Visualize:**

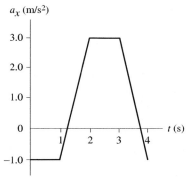

Solve: According to Newton's second law $F = ma$, the acceleration at any time is found simply by dividing the value of the force by the mass of the object.

4.37. **Visualize:**

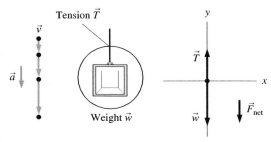

Tension is the only contact force. The downward acceleration implies that $w > T$.

4.39. **Visualize:**

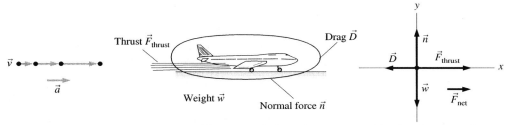

The normal force is perpendicular to the ground. The thrust force is parallel to the ground and in the direction of acceleration. The drag force is opposite to the direction of motion.

4.41. **Visualize:**

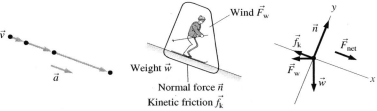

The normal force is perpendicular to the hill. The kinetic frictional force is parallel to the hill and directed upward opposite to the direction of motion. The wind force is given as *horizontal*. Since the skier stays on the slope (that is, there is no acceleration away from the slope) the net force must be parallel to the slope.

4.43. Visualize:

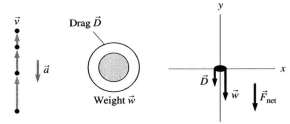

The drag force due to air is opposite the motion.

4.45. Visualize:

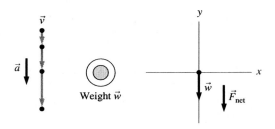

There are no contact forces on the rock. Weight is the only force acting on the rock.

DYNAMICS I: MOTION ALONG A LINE

5.1. **Model:** We can assume that the ring is a single massless particle in static equilibrium.
Visualize: **Physical representation**

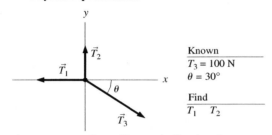

Known
$T_3 = 100$ N
$\theta = 30°$

Find
$T_1 \quad T_2$

Solve: Written in component form, Newton's first law is

$$\left(F_{\text{net}}\right)_x = \Sigma F_x = T_{1x} + T_{2x} + T_{3x} = 0 \text{ N} \qquad \left(F_{\text{net}}\right)_y = \Sigma F_y = T_{1y} + T_{2y} + T_{3y} = 0 \text{ N}$$

Evaluating the components of the force vectors from the free-body diagram:

$$T_{1x} = -T_1 \qquad T_{2x} = 0 \text{ N} \qquad T_{3x} = T_3 \cos 30°$$
$$T_{1y} = 0 \text{ N} \qquad T_{2y} = T_2 \qquad T_{3y} = -T_3 \sin 30°$$

Using Newton's first law:

$$-T_1 + T_3 \cos 30° = 0 \text{ N} \qquad T_2 - T_3 \sin 30° = 0 \text{ N}$$

Rearranging:

$$T_1 = T_3 \cos 30° = (100 \text{ N})(0.8666) = 86.7 \text{ N} \qquad T_2 = T_3 \sin 30° = (100 \text{ N})(0.5) = 50.0 \text{ N}$$

Assess: Since $\vec{T}_3$ acts closer to the x-axis than to the y-axis, it makes sense that $T_1 > T_2$.

5.5. **Visualize:** Please refer to the Figure Ex5.5.
Solve: Applying Newton's second law to the diagram on the left,

$$a_x = \frac{\left(F_{\text{net}}\right)_x}{m} = \frac{4 \text{ N} - 2 \text{ N}}{2 \text{ kg}} = 1.0 \text{ m/s}^2 \qquad a_y = \frac{\left(F_{\text{net}}\right)_y}{m} = \frac{3 \text{ N} - 3 \text{ N}}{2 \text{ kg}} = 0 \text{ m/s}^2$$

For the diagram on the right:

$$a_x = \frac{\left(F_{\text{net}}\right)_x}{m} = \frac{4 \text{ N} - 2 \text{ N}}{2 \text{ kg}} = 1.0 \text{ m/s}^2 \qquad a_y = \frac{\left(F_{\text{net}}\right)_y}{m} = \frac{3 \text{ N} - 1 \text{ N} - 2 \text{ N}}{2 \text{ kg}} = 0 \text{ m/s}^2$$

5.7. **Visualize:** Please refer to Figure Ex5.7.
Solve: We can use the constant slopes of the three segments of the graph to calculate the three accelerations. For t between 0 s and 3 s,

$$a_x = \frac{\Delta v_x}{\Delta t} = \frac{12 \text{ m/s} - 0 \text{ s}}{3 \text{ s}} = 4 \text{ m/s}^2$$

For t between 3 s and 6 s, $\Delta v_x = 0$ m/s, so $a_x = 0$ m/s^2. For t between 6 s and 8 s,

$$a_x = \frac{\Delta v_x}{\Delta t} = \frac{0 \text{ m/s} - 12 \text{ m/s}}{2 \text{ s}} = -6 \text{ m/s}^2$$

From Newton's second law, at $t = 1$ s we have

$$F_{net} = ma_x = (2.0 \text{ kg})(4 \text{ m/s}^2) = 8 \text{ N}$$

At $t = 4$ s, $a_x = 0$ m/s^2, so $F_{net} = 0$ N. At $t = 7$ s,

$$F_{net} = ma_x = (2.0 \text{ kg})(-6.0 \text{ m/s}^2) = -12 \text{ N}$$

Assess: The magnitudes of the forces look reasonable, given the small mass of the object. The positive and negative signs are appropriate for an object first speeding up, then slowing down.

5.9.   Model: We assume that the box is a particle being pulled in a straight line. Since the ice is frictionless, the tension in the rope is the only horizontal force.
Visualize: **Physical representation**

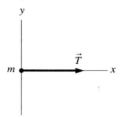

Solve: (a) Since the box is at rest, $a_x = 0$ m/s^2, and the net force on the box must be zero. Therefore, according to Newton's first law, the tension in the rope must be zero.
(b) For this situation again, $a_x = 0$ m/s^2, so $F_{net} = T = 0$ N.
(c) Here, the velocity of the box is irrelevant, since only a *change* in velocity requires a nonzero net force. Since $a_x = 5.0$ m/s^2,

$$F_{net} = T = ma_x = (50 \text{ kg})(5.0 \text{ m/s}^2) = 250 \text{ N}$$

Assess: For parts (a) and (b), the zero acceleration immediately implies that the rope is exerting no horizontal force on the box. For part (c), the 250 N force (the equivalent of about half the weight of a small person) seems reasonable to accelerate a box of this mass at 5.0 m/s^2.

5.13.   Model: We assume that the passenger is a particle subject to two vertical forces: the downward pull of gravity and the upward push of the elevator floor. We can use one-dimensional kinematics and Equation 5.10.
Visualize: **Pictorial representation**

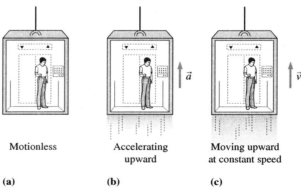

Motionless   Accelerating   Moving upward
                        upward   at constant speed

(a)   (b)   (c)

Solve: (a) The apparent weight is

$$w_{app} = w\left(1 + \frac{a_y}{g}\right) = w\left(1 + \frac{0}{g}\right) = mg = (60 \text{ kg})(9.8 \text{ m/s}^2) = 590 \text{ N}$$

(b) The elevator speeds up from $v_{0y} = 0$ m/s to its cruising speed at $v_y = 10$ m/s. We need its acceleration before we can find the apparent weight:

$$a_y = \frac{\Delta v}{\Delta t} = \frac{10 \text{ m/s} - 0 \text{ m/s}}{4.0 \text{ s}} = 2.5 \text{ m/s}^2$$

The passenger's apparent weight is

$$w_{app} = w\left(1 + \frac{a_y}{g}\right) = (590 \text{ N})\left(1 + \frac{2.5 \text{ m/s}^2}{9.8 \text{ m/s}^2}\right) = (590 \text{ N})(1.26) = 740 \text{ N}$$

(c) The passenger is no longer accelerating since the elevator has reached its cruising speed. Thus, $w_{app} = w = 590$ N as in part (a).

Assess: The passenger's apparent weight is his normal weight in parts (a) and (c), since there is no acceleration. In part (b), the elevator must not only support his weight but must also accelerate him upward, so it's reasonable that the floor will have to push up harder on him, increasing his apparent weight.

5.15. Model: We assume that the safe is a particle moving only in the *x*-direction. Since it is sliding during the entire problem, we can use the model of kinetic friction.

Visualize:

Pictorial and physical representations

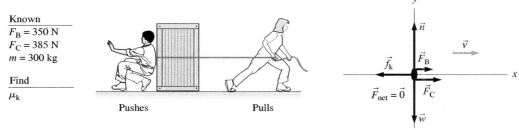

Solve: The safe is in equilibrium, since it's not accelerating. Thus we can apply Newton's first law in the vertical and horizontal directions:

$$\left(F_{net}\right)_x = \Sigma F_x = F_B + F_C - f_k = 0 \text{ N} \Rightarrow f_k = F_B + F_C = 350 \text{ N} + 385 \text{ N} = 735 \text{ N}$$

$$\left(F_{net}\right)_y = \Sigma F_y = n - w = 0 \text{ N} \Rightarrow n = w = mg = (300 \text{ kg})(9.8 \text{ m/s}^2) = 2940 \text{ N}$$

Then, for kinetic friction:

$$f_k = \mu_k n \Rightarrow \mu_k = \frac{f_k}{n} = \frac{735 \text{ N}}{2940 \text{ N}} = 0.25$$

Assess: The value of $\mu_k = 0.25$ is hard to evaluate without knowing the material the floor is made of, but it seems reasonable.

5.17. Model: We assume that the car is a particle undergoing skidding, so we will use the model of kinetic friction.

Visualize: **Pictorial representation**

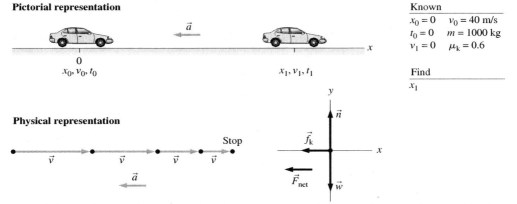

Solve: We begin with Newton's second law. Although the motion is one-dimensional, we need to consider forces in both the *x*- and *y*-directions. However, we know that $a_y = 0$ m/s^2. We have

$$a_x = \frac{\left(F_{net}\right)_x}{m} = \frac{-f_k}{m} \qquad a_y = 0 \text{ m/s}^2 = \frac{\left(F_{net}\right)_y}{m} = \frac{n - w}{m} = \frac{n - mg}{m}$$

We used $\left(f_k\right)_x = -f_k$ because the free-body diagram tells us that $\vec{f_k}$ points to the left. The friction model relates $\vec{f_k}$ to $\vec{n}$ with the equation $f_k = \mu_k n$. The *y*-equation is solved to give $n = mg$. Thus, the kinetic friction force is $f_k = \mu_k mg$. Substituting this into the *x*-equation yields:

$$a_x = \frac{-\mu_k mg}{m} = -\mu_k g = -(0.6)(9.8 \text{ m/s}^2) = -5.88 \text{ m/s}^2$$

The acceleration is negative because the acceleration vector points to the left as the car slows. Now we have a constant-acceleration kinematics problem. Δt isn't known, so use

$$v_1^2 = 0 \text{ m}^2/\text{s}^2 = v_0^2 + 2a_x\Delta x \Rightarrow \Delta x = -\frac{(40 \text{ m/s})^2}{2(-5.88 \text{ m/s}^2)} = 136 \text{ m}$$

Assess: The skid marks are 136 m long. This is $\approx$ 430 feet, reasonable for a car traveling at $\approx$80 mph. It is worth noting that an algebraic solution led to the m canceling out.

5.21.   Model: We assume that the skydiver is shaped like a box and is a particle.
Visualize: **Pictorial and physical representations**

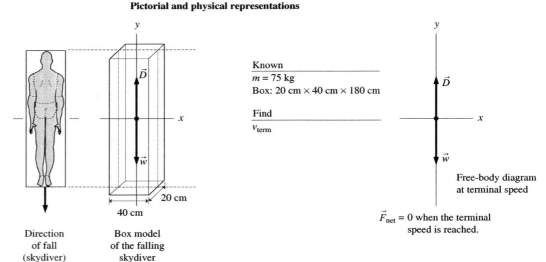

Known
$m = 75$ kg
Box: 20 cm × 40 cm × 180 cm

Find
v_{term}

Free-body diagram
at terminal speed

$\vec{F}_{\text{net}} = 0$ when the terminal
speed is reached.

Direction of fall (skydiver)   Box model of the falling skydiver

The skydiver falls straight down toward the earth's surface, that is, the direction of fall is vertical. Since the skydiver falls feet first, the surface perpendicular to the drag has the cross-sectional area $A = 20$ cm × 40 cm. The physical conditions needed to use Equation 5.16 for the drag force are satisfied. The terminal speed corresponds to the situation when the net force acting on the skydiver becomes zero.
Solve: The expression for the magnitude of the drag with v in m/s is

$$D \approx \frac{1}{4}Av^2 = 0.25(0.20 \times 0.40)v^2 \text{ N} = 0.020v^2 \text{ N}$$

The skydiver's weight is $w = mg = (75 \text{ kg})(9.8 \text{ m/s}^2) = 735$ N. The mathematical form of the condition defining dynamical equilibrium for the skydiver and the terminal speed is

$$\vec{F}_{\text{net}} = \vec{w} + \vec{D} = 0 \text{ N}$$

$$\Rightarrow 0.02v_{\text{term}}^2 \text{ N} - 735 \text{ N} = 0 \text{ N} \Rightarrow v_{\text{term}} = \sqrt{\frac{735}{0.02}} \approx 192 \text{ m/s}$$

Assess: The result of the above simplified physical modeling approach and subsequent calculation, even if approximate, shows that the terminal velocity is very high. This result implies that the skydiver will be very badly hurt at landing if the parachute does not open in time.

5.25.   Visualize:

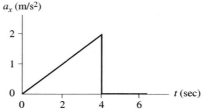

We used the force-versus-time graph to draw the acceleration-versus-time graph. The peak acceleration was calculated as follows:

$$a_{\text{max}} = \frac{F_{\text{max}}}{m} = \frac{10 \text{ N}}{5 \text{ kg}} = 2 \text{ m/s}^2$$

Solve: The acceleration is not constant, so we cannot use constant acceleration kinematics. Instead, we use the more general result that

$$v_x(t) = v_{0x} + \text{area under the acceleration curve from 0 s to } t$$

The object starts from rest, so $v_{0x} = 0$ m/s. The area under the acceleration curve between 0 s and 6 s is $\frac{1}{2}$(4 s) $(2 \text{ m/s}^2) = 4.0$ m/s. We've used the fact that the area between 4 s and 6 s is zero. Thus, at $t = 6$ s, $v_x = 4.0$ m/s.

5.31. **Model:** We'll assume Zach is a particle moving under the effect of two forces acting in a single vertical line: gravity and the supporting force of the elevator.
Visualize: **Pictorial and physical representations**

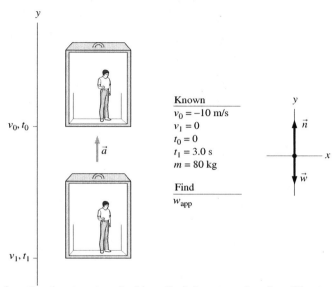

Known
$v_0 = -10$ m/s
$v_1 = 0$
$t_0 = 0$
$t_1 = 3.0$ s
$m = 80$ kg

Find
w_{app}

Solve: **(a)** Before the elevator starts braking, Zach is not accelerating. His apparent weight (see Equation 5.10) is

$$w_{app} = w\left(1 + \frac{a}{g}\right) = w\left(1 + \frac{0 \text{ m/s}^2}{g}\right) = mg = (80 \text{ kg})(9.8 \text{ m/s}^2) = 784 \text{ N}$$

(b) Using the definition of acceleration,

$$a = \frac{\Delta v}{\Delta t} = \frac{v_1 - v_0}{t_1 - t_0} = \frac{0 - (-10) \text{ m/s}}{3.0 \text{ s}} = 3.33 \text{ m/s}^2$$

$$\Rightarrow w_{app} = w\left(1 + \frac{a}{g}\right) = (80 \text{ kg})(9.8 \text{ m/s}^2)\left(1 + \frac{3.33 \text{ m/s}^2}{9.8 \text{ m/s}^2}\right) = (784 \text{ N})(1 + 0.340) = 1050 \text{ N}$$

Assess: While the elevator is braking, it not only must support Zach's weight but must also push upward on him to decelerate him, so the apparent weight is greater than his normal weight.

5.35. **Model:** We will represent the bullet as a particle.
Visualize:

Pictorial representation

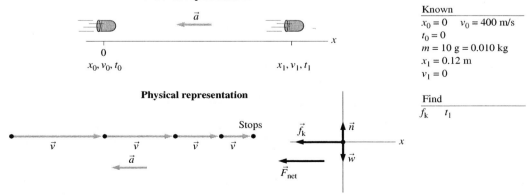

Known
$x_0 = 0$ $v_0 = 400$ m/s
$t_0 = 0$
$m = 10$ g $= 0.010$ kg
$x_1 = 0.12$ m
$v_1 = 0$

Find
f_k t_1

Solve: **(a)** We have enough information to use kinematics to find the acceleration of the bullet as it stops. Then we can relate the acceleration to the force with Newton's second law. (Note that the barrel length is not relevant to the problem.) The kinematic equation is

$$v_1^2 = v_0^2 + 2a\Delta x \Rightarrow a = -\frac{v_0^2}{2\Delta x} = -\frac{(400 \text{ m/s})^2}{2(0.12 \text{ m})} = -6.67 \times 10^5 \text{ m/s}^2$$

Notice that a is negative, in agreement with the vector $\vec{a}$ in the motion diagram. Turning to forces, the wood exerts two forces on the bullet. First, an upward normal force that keeps the bullet from "falling" through the wood. Second, a retarding friction force $\vec{f}_k$ that stops the bullet. The only horizontal force is $\vec{f}_k$, which points to the left and thus has a negative x-component. The x-component of Newton's second law is

$$\left(F_{\text{net}}\right)_x = -f_k = ma \Rightarrow f_k = -ma = -(0.01 \text{ kg})(-6.67 \times 10^5 \text{ m/s}^2) = 6670 \text{ N}$$

Notice how the signs worked together to give a positive value of the magnitude of the force.
(b) The time to stop is found from $v_1 = v_0 + a\Delta t$ as follows:

$$\Delta t = -\frac{v_0}{a} = 6.00 \times 10^{-4} \text{ s } = 600 \text{ μs}$$

(c)

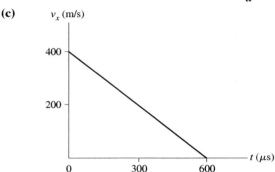

Using the above kinematic equation, we can find the velocity as a function of t. For example at $t = 60$ μs,

$$v_x = 400 \text{ m/s} + (-6.667 \times 10^5 \text{ m/s}^2)(60 \times 10^{-6} \text{ s}) = 360 \text{ m/s}$$

5.39. **Model:** The steel block will be represented by a particle. Steel-on-steel has a static coefficient of friction $\mu_s = 0.80$ and a kinetic coefficient of friction $\mu_k = 0.60$.
Visualize: **Pictorial representation**   **Physical representation**

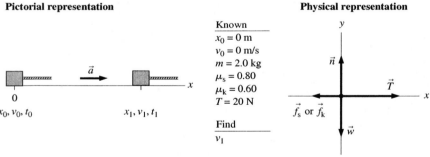

Solve: **(a)** While the block is at rest, Newton's second law is

$$\left(F_{\text{net}}\right)_x = T - f_s = 0 \text{ N} \Rightarrow T = f_s \qquad \left(F_{\text{net}}\right)_y = n - w \Rightarrow n = mg$$

The static friction force has a maximum value $\left(f_s\right)_{\text{max}} = \mu_s mg$. The string tension that will cause the block to slip and start to move is

$$T = \mu_s mg = (0.80)(2 \text{ kg})(9.8 \text{ m/s}^2) = 15.7 \text{ N}$$

Any tension less than this will not be sufficient to cause the block to move, so this is the minimum tension for motion.
(b) As the block is moving with a tension of 20 N in the string, we can find its acceleration from the x-component of Newton's second law as follows:

$$\left(F_{\text{net}}\right)_x = T - f_k = ma_x \Rightarrow a_x = \frac{T - f_k}{m}$$

The kinetic friction force $f_k = \mu_k mg$. The acceleration of the block is

$$a_x = \frac{20 \text{ N} - (0.60)(2 \text{ kg})(9.8 \text{ m/s}^2)}{2 \text{ kg}} = 4.12 \text{ m/s}^2$$

Using kinematics, the block's speed after moving 1.0 m will be

$$v_1^2 = 0 \text{ m}^2/\text{s}^2 + 2(4.12 \text{ m/s}^2)(1.0 \text{ m}) \Rightarrow v = 2.87 \text{ m/s}$$

(c) The only difference in this case is the coefficient of kinetic friction whose value is 0.05 instead of 0.60. The acceleration of the block is

$$a_x = \frac{20 \text{ N} - (0.05)(2 \text{ kg})(9.8 \text{ m/s}^2)}{2 \text{ kg}} = 9.51 \text{ m/s}^2$$

The block's speed after moving 1.0 m will be

$$v_1^2 = 0 \text{ m}^2/\text{s}^2 + 2(9.51 \text{ m/s}^2)(1.0 \text{ m}) \Rightarrow v = 4.36 \text{ m/s}$$

5.45. Model: We will represent the wood block as a particle, and use the model of kinetic friction and kinematics. Assume $w \sin \theta > f_s$, so it does not hang up at the top.
Visualize:

Pictorial representation

Known
$\theta = 30°$ $m = 2 \text{ kg}$
$x_0 = 0$ $v_0 = 10 \text{ m/s}$
$t_0 = 0$ $v_1 = 0$
$x_2 = 0$

Find
$h = x_1 \sin\theta$ and v_2

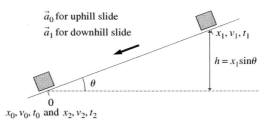

$\vec{a}_0$ for uphill slide
$\vec{a}_1$ for downhill slide
x_1, v_1, t_1
$h = x_1 \sin\theta$
θ
0
x_0, v_0, t_0 and x_2, v_2, t_2

Physical representation

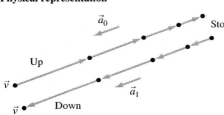

$\vec{a}_0$
Stops
Up
$\vec{v}$
$\vec{a}_1$
$\vec{v}$ Down

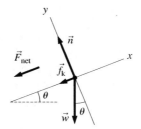

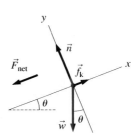

The block ends where it starts, so $x_2 = x_0 = 0$ m. We expect v_2 to be negative, because the block will be moving in the $-x$-direction, so we'll want to take $|v_2|$ as the final speed. Because of friction, we expect to find $|v_2| < v_0$.

Solve: **(a)** The friction force is opposite to $\vec{v}$, so $\vec{f}_k$ points down the slope during the first half of the motion and up the slope during the second half. $\vec{w}$ and $\vec{n}$ are the only other forces. Newton's second law for the upward motion is

$$a_x = a_0 = \frac{(F_{\text{net}})_x}{m} = \frac{-w\sin\theta - f_k}{m} = \frac{-mg\sin\theta - f_k}{m}$$

$$a_y = 0 \text{ m/s}^2 = \frac{(F_{\text{net}})_y}{m} = \frac{n - w\cos\theta}{m} = \frac{n - mg\cos\theta}{m}$$

The friction model is $f_k = \mu_k n$. First solve the y-equation to give $n = mg\cos\theta$. Use this in the friction model to get $f_k = \mu_k mg\cos\theta$. Now substitute this result for f_k into the x-equation:

$$a_0 = \frac{-mg\sin\theta - \mu_k mg\cos\theta}{m} = -g(\sin\theta + \mu_k \cos\theta) = -(9.8 \text{ m/s}^2)(\sin 30° + 0.20\cos 30°) = -6.60 \text{ m/s}^2$$

Kinematics now gives

$$v_1^2 = v_0^2 + 2a_0(x_1 - x_0) \Rightarrow x_1 = \frac{v_1^2 - v_0^2}{2a_0} = \frac{0 \text{ m}^2/\text{s}^2 - (10 \text{ m/s})^2}{2(-6.60 \text{ m/s}^2)} = 7.58 \text{ m}$$

The block's height is then $h = x_1\sin\theta = (7.58 \text{ m})\sin 30° = 3.79 \text{ m}$.

(b) For the return trip, $\vec{f}_k$ points up the slope, so the *x*-component of the second law is

$$a_x = a_1 = \frac{(F_{net})_x}{m} = \frac{-w\sin\theta + f_k}{m} = \frac{-mg\sin\theta + f_k}{m}$$

Note the sign change. The *y*-equation and the friction model are unchanged, so we have

$$a_1 = -g(\sin\theta - \mu_k \cos\theta) = -3.20 \text{ m} / \text{s}^2$$

The kinematics for the return trip are

$$v_2^2 = v_1^2 + 2a_1(x_2 - x_1) \Rightarrow v_2 = \sqrt{-2a_1 x_1} = \sqrt{-2(-3.20 \text{ m/s}^2)(7.58 \text{ m})} = -6.97 \text{ m/s}$$

Notice that we used the *negative* square root because v_2 is a *velocity* with the vector pointing in the *–x*-direction. The final *speed* is $|v_2| = 6.97$ m/s.

5.51.   Model: The box will be treated as a particle. Because the box slides down a vertical wood wall, we will also use the model of kinetic friction.
Visualize: **Physical representation**

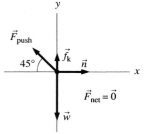

Solve: The normal force due to the wall, which is perpendicular to the wall, is here to the right. The box slides down the wall at constant speed, so $\vec{a} = \vec{0}$ and the box is in dynamic equilibrium. Thus, $\vec{F}_{net} = \vec{0}$. Newton's second law for this equilibrium situation is

$$(F_{net})_x = 0 \text{ N} = n - F_{push} \cos45°$$
$$(F_{net})_y = 0 \text{ N} = f_k + F_{push} \sin45° - w = f_k + F_{push} \sin45° - mg$$

The friction force is $f_k = \mu_k n$. Using the *x*-equation to get an expression for *n*, we see that $f_k = \mu_k F_{push} \cos45°$. Substituting this into the *y*-equation and using Table 5.1 to find $\mu_k = 0.20$ gives,

$$\mu_k F_{push} \cos45° + F_{push} \sin45° - mg = 0 \text{ N}$$

$$\Rightarrow F_{push} = \frac{mg}{\mu_k \cos45° + \sin45°} = \frac{(2 \text{ kg})(9.8 \text{ m/s}^2)}{0.20\cos45° + \sin45°} = 23.1 \text{ N}$$

5.53.   Model: We will model the skier along with the wooden skis as a particle of mass *m*. The snow exerts a contact force and the wind exerts a drag force on the skier. We will therefore use the models of kinetic friction and drag.
Visualize: **Pictorial and physical representations**

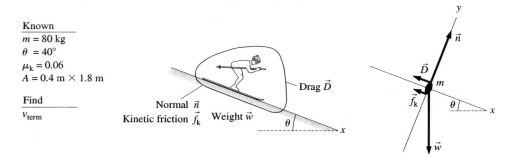

We choose a coordinate system such that the skier's motion is along the +x-direction. While the forces of kinetic friction $\vec{f}_k$ and drag $\vec{D}$ act along the –x-direction opposing the motion of the skier, the weight of the skier has a component in the +x-direction. At the terminal speed, the net force on the skier is zero as the forces along the +x-direction cancel out the forces along the –x-direction.

Solve: Newton's second law and the models of kinetic friction and drag are

$$(F_{net})_x = \Sigma F_x = n_x + w_x + (f_k)_x + (D)_x = 0\text{ N} + mg\sin\theta - f_k - \frac{1}{4}Av^2 = ma_x = 0\text{ N}$$

$$(F_{net})_y = \Sigma F_y = n_y + w_y + (f_k)_y + (D)_y = n - mg\cos\theta + 0\text{ N} + 0\text{ N} = 0\text{ N}$$

$$f_k = \mu_k n$$

These three equations can be combined together as follows:

$$(1/4)Av^2 = mg\sin\theta - f_k = mg\sin\theta - \mu_k n = mg\sin\theta - \mu_k\, mg\cos\theta$$

$$\Rightarrow v_{term} = \left(mg\frac{\sin\theta - \mu_k\cos\theta}{\frac{1}{4}A}\right)^{1/2}$$

Using $\mu_k = 0.06$ and $A = 1.8\text{ m} \times 0.40\text{ m} = 0.72\text{ m}^2$, we find

$$v_{term} = \left[(80\text{ kg})(9.8\text{ m/s}^2)\left(\frac{\sin 40° - 0.06\cos 40°}{\left(\frac{1}{4}\text{ kg/m}^3\right)(0.72\text{ m}^2)}\right)\right]^{1/2} = 51\text{ m/s}$$

Assess: A terminal speed of 51 m/s corresponds to a speed of $\approx$110 mph. This speed is reasonable but high due to the steep slope angle of 40° and a small coefficient of friction.

5.55. **Model:** Take the coin to be a particle held against the palm of your hand (which is like a vertical wall) by friction. The friction needs to be vertical and equal to the weight of the coin to hold the coin in place.

Visualize: **Pictorial and physical representations**

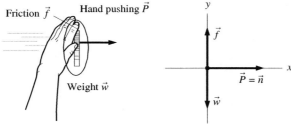

The hand pushes on the coin giving a normal force to the coin and causing a friction force.

Solve: **(a)** We need a force (push) to create a normal force. Since the force accelerates the coin, a minimum acceleration a_{min} is needed.

(b) Newton's second law and the model of friction are

$$\Sigma F_y = (f_{min})_y - (w)_y = f_{min} - mg = 0\text{ N} \qquad \Sigma F_x = n_{min} = ma_{min} \qquad f_{min} = \mu n_{min}$$

Since you do not want the coin to slip down the hand you need μ_s. Combining the above three equations yields

$$f_{min} = mg \Rightarrow \mu_s n_{min} = mg \Rightarrow \mu_s ma_{min} = mg \Rightarrow a_{min} = \frac{g}{\mu_s} = \frac{9.8\text{ m/s}^2}{0.8} = 12.3\text{ m/s}^2$$

5.67. **Solve:** **(a)** A 20.0 kg wooden crate is being pulled up a 20° wooden incline by a rope that is connected to an electric motor. The crate's acceleration is measured to be 2 m/s². The coefficient of kinetic friction between the crate and the incline is 0.2. Find the tension T in the rope.

(b)

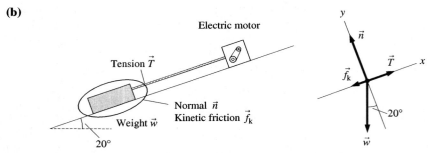

(c) Newton's second law for this problem in the component form is

$$(F_{net})_x = \Sigma F_x = T - 0.2n - (20 \text{ kg})(9.80 \text{ m/s}^2) \sin 20° = (20 \text{ kg})(2 \text{ m/s}^2)$$
$$(F_{net})_y = \Sigma F_y = n - (20 \text{ kg})(9.80 \text{ m/s}^2) \cos 20° = 0 \text{ N}$$

Solving the y-component equation, $n = 184.18$ N. Substituting this value for n in the x-component equation yields $T = 144$ N.

6

DYNAMICS II: MOTION IN A PLANE

6.1. **Model:** We will assume motion under constant-acceleration kinematics in a plane.
Visualize: **Pictorial representation**

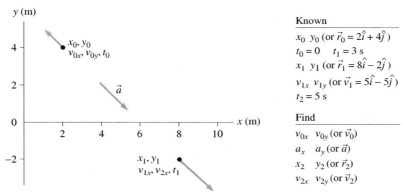

Known
x_0 y_0 (or $\vec{r}_0 = 2\hat{i} + 4\hat{j}$)
$t_0 = 0$ $t_1 = 3$ s
x_1 y_1 (or $\vec{r}_1 = 8\hat{i} - 2\hat{j}$)
v_{1x} v_{1y} (or $\vec{v}_1 = 5\hat{i} - 5\hat{j}$)
$t_2 = 5$ s

Find
v_{0x} v_{0y} (or $\vec{v}_0$)
a_x a_y (or $\vec{a}$)
x_2 y_2 (or $\vec{r}_2$)
v_{2x} v_{2y} (or $\vec{v}_2$)

Instead of working with the components of position, velocity, and acceleration in the x and y directions, we will use the kinematic equations in vector form.
Solve: **(a)** From the kinematic equation for position, after some manipulation:

$$\vec{r}_1 = \vec{r}_0 + \vec{v}_0(t_1 - t_0) + \tfrac{1}{2}\vec{a}(t_1 - t_0)^2 \Rightarrow (2 \text{ s})\vec{v}_0 + (3 \text{ s}^2)\vec{a} = (4\hat{i} - 4\hat{j}) \text{ m}$$

From the kinematic equation for velocity:

$$\vec{v}_1 = \vec{v}_0 + \vec{a}(t_1 - t_0) \Rightarrow (5\hat{i} - 5\hat{j}) \text{ m/s} = \vec{v}_0 + \vec{a}(3 \text{ s} - 0 \text{ s}) \Rightarrow \vec{v}_0 = -(3 \text{ s})\vec{a} + (5\hat{i} - 5\hat{j}) \text{ m/s}$$

Substituting this form of $\vec{v}_0$ into the position equation, we find

$$(2 \text{ s})\left[-(3 \text{ s})\vec{a} + (5\hat{i} - 5\hat{j}) \text{ m/s}\right] + (3 \text{ s}^2)\vec{a} = (4\hat{i} - 4\hat{j}) \text{ m} \Rightarrow \vec{a} = (2\hat{i} - 2\hat{j}) \text{ m/s}^2$$

Substituting $\vec{a}$ back into either the velocity equation or the position equation gives $\vec{v}_0 = (-\hat{i} + \hat{j}) \text{ m/s}$.
(b) Using the kinematic equation $\vec{r}_2 = \vec{r}_1 + \vec{v}_1(t_2 - t_1) + \tfrac{1}{2}\vec{a}(t_2 - t_1)^2$,

$$(8\hat{i} - 2\hat{j}) \text{ m} + \left[(5\hat{i} - 5\hat{j}) \text{ m/s}\right](5 \text{ s} - 3 \text{ s}) + \tfrac{1}{2}\left[(2\hat{i} - 2\hat{j}) \text{ m/s}^2\right](5 \text{ s} - 3 \text{ s})^2 = (22\hat{i} - 16\hat{j}) \text{ m}$$

$$\vec{v}_2 = \vec{v}_1 + \vec{a}(t_2 - t_1) = (5\hat{i} - 5\hat{j}) \text{ m/s} + \left[(2\hat{i} - 2\hat{j}) \text{ m/s}^2\right](5 \text{ s} - 3 \text{ s}) = (9\hat{i} - 9\hat{j}) \text{ m/s}$$

Thus, the speed at t = 5 s is $v_2 = \sqrt{(v_{2x})^2 + (v_{2y})^2} = \sqrt{(9)^2 + (-9)^2} \text{ m/s} = 12.7 \text{ m/s}$.

6.3. Solve: (a)

t (s)	x (m)	y (m)
−2	−12	6
−1	−2.5	2.5
0	0	0
1	−1.5	−1.5
2	−4	−2
3	−4.5	−1.5
4	0	0
5	12.5	2.5

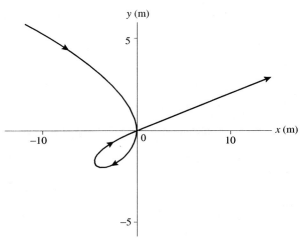

(b) At $t = 0$ s, $x = 0$ m and $y = 0$ m, or $\vec{r} = \left(0\hat{i} + 0\hat{j}\right)$ m. At $t = 4$ s, $x = 0$ m and $y = 0$ m, or $\vec{r} = \left(0\hat{i} + 0\hat{j}\right)$ m. In other words, the particle is at the origin at both $t = 0$ s and at $t = 4$ s. From the expressions for x and y,

$$\vec{v} = \frac{dx}{dt}\hat{i} + \frac{dy}{dt}\hat{j} = \left[\left(\frac{3}{2}t^2 - 4t\right)\hat{i} + (t - 2)\hat{j}\right] \text{m/s}$$

At $t = 0$ s, $\vec{v} = -2\hat{j}$ m/s, $v = 2$ m/s. At $t = 4$ s, $\vec{v} = \left(8\hat{i} + 2\hat{j}\right)$ m/s, $v = 8.3$ m/s.

(c) At $t = 0$ s, $\vec{v}$ is along $-\hat{j}$, or 90° south of +x. At $t = 4$ s,

$$\theta = \tan^{-1}\left(\frac{2 \text{ m/s}}{8 \text{ m/s}}\right) = 14° \text{ north of } +x$$

6.5. Model: The model rocket and the target will be treated as particles. Kinematic equations in two dimensions apply.

Visualize: **Pictorial representation**

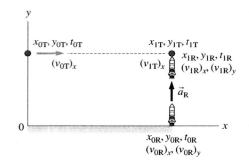

Known
$y_{0T} = y_{1T} = 30$ m
$t_{1T} = t_{1R}$ $t_{0T} = t_{0R} = 0$
$x_{0R} = y_{0R} = 0$
$y_{1R} = 30$ m
$F_R = 15.0$ N $m = 0.8$ kg
$(v_{0T})_x = (v_{1T})_x = 15$ m/s

Find
x_{1T}

Physical representation

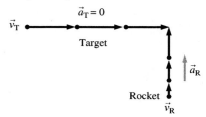

Solve: For the rocket, Newton's second law along the y-direction is

$$\vec{F}_{net} = \vec{F}_R - m\vec{g} = m\vec{a}_R$$

$$\Rightarrow \vec{a}_R = \frac{1}{m}\left(\vec{F}_R - mg\right) = \frac{1}{0.8 \text{ kg}}\left[15 \text{ N} - (0.8 \text{ kg})(9.8 \text{ m/s}^2)\right] = 8.95 \text{ m/s}^2$$

Using the kinematic equation $y_{1R} = y_{0R} + (v_{0R})_y(t_{1R} - t_{0R}) + \frac{1}{2}a_R(t_{1R} - t_{0R})^2$,

$$30 \text{ m} = 0 \text{ m} + 0 \text{ m} + \tfrac{1}{2}(8.95 \text{ m/s}^2)(t_{1R} - 0 \text{ s})^2 \Rightarrow t_{1R} = 2.589 \text{ s}$$

For the target (noting $t_{1T} = t_{1R}$),

$$x_{1T} = x_{0T} + (v_{0T})_x(t_{1T} - t_{0T}) + \tfrac{1}{2}a_T(t_{1T} - t_{0T})^2 = 0 \text{ m} + (15 \text{ m/s})(2.589 \text{ s} - 0 \text{ s}) + 0 \text{ m} = 38.8 \text{ m}$$

You should launch when the target is 38.8 m away.

Assess: The rocket is to be fired when the target is at x_{0T}. For a net acceleration of approximately 9 m/s² in the vertical direction and a time of 2.6 s to cover a vertical distance of 30 m, a horizontal distance of 38.8 m is reasonable.

6.9. Model: Assume the particle model for the object.
Visualize: The object is undergoing projectile motion as illustrated in Figure 6.15.
Solve: (a) The components of v_0 are

$$v_{0x} = v_0\cos\theta = (50 \text{ m/s})\cos 36.9° = 40.0 \text{ m/s}$$
$$v_{0y} = v_0\sin\theta = (50 \text{ m/s})\sin 36.9° = 30.0 \text{ m/s}$$

Since v_{0x} is constant, the position x increases by 40.0 m every second. The y-velocity and the y-position are obtained from the following equations:

$$v_{fy} = v_{iy} + a_y(t_f - t_i) \qquad\qquad y_f = y_i + v_{iy}(t_f - t_i) + \tfrac{1}{2}a_y(t_f - t_i)^2$$

Thus,

$$v_{1y} = v_{0y} + a_y(t_1 - t_0) = (30.0 \text{ m/s}) + (-9.8 \text{ m/s}^2)(1 \text{ s} - 0 \text{ s}) = 20.2 \text{ m/s}$$

$$y_1 = y_0 + v_{0y}(t_1 - t_0) + \tfrac{1}{2}a_y(t_1 - t_0)^2 = 0 \text{ m} + (30.0 \text{ m/s})(1 \text{ s} - 0 \text{ s}) + \tfrac{1}{2}(-9.8 \text{ m/s}^2)(1 \text{ s} - 0 \text{ s})^2 = 25.1 \text{ m}$$

$$v_{2y} = v_{0y} + a_y(t_2 - t_0) = (30.0 \text{ m/s}) + (-9.8 \text{ m/s}^2)(2 \text{ s} - 0 \text{ s}) = 10.4 \text{ m/s}$$

$$y_2 = y_0 + v_{0y}(t_2 - t_0) + \tfrac{1}{2}a_y(t_2 - t_0)^2 = 0 + (30.0 \text{ m/s})(2 \text{ s} - 0 \text{ s}) + \tfrac{1}{2}(-9.8 \text{ m/s}^2)(2 \text{ s} - 0 \text{ s})^2 = 40.4 \text{ m}$$

and so on.
The table showing x, y, v_x, v_y and v (from t = 0 s to t = 6 s) is given below.

t (s)	x (m)	y (m)	v_x (m/s)	v_y (m/s)	v (m/s)
0	0	0	40	30.0	50.0
1	40	25.1	40	20.2	44.8
2	80	40.4	40	10.4	41.3
3	120	45.9	40	0.6	40.0
4	160	41.6	40	−9.2	41.0
5	200	27.5	40	−19.0	44.3
6	240	3.6	40	−28.8	49.3

(b)   y (m)

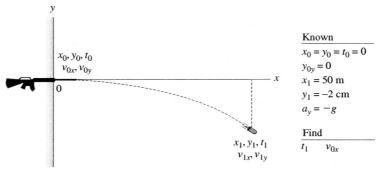

Assess: As expected the trajectory is a parabola. Given an initial velocity of 50 m/s, a value of $x = 240$ m for $x = 6$ s is reasonable.

6.11.   Model: The bullet is treated as a particle and the effect of air resistance on the motion of the bullet is neglected.
Visualize: **Pictorial representation**

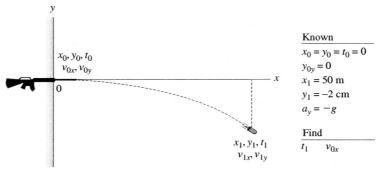

Known
$x_0 = y_0 = t_0 = 0$
$y_{0y} = 0$
$x_1 = 50$ m
$y_1 = -2$ cm
$a_y = -g$

Find
t_1 v_{0x}

Solve: **(a)** Using $y_1 = y_0 + v_{0y}(t_1 - t_0) + \frac{1}{2}a_y(t_1 - t_0)^2$, we obtain

$$(-2.0 \times 10^{-2} \text{ m}) = 0 \text{ m} + 0 \text{ m} + \frac{1}{2}(-9.8 \text{ m/s}^2)(t_1 - 0 \text{ s})^2 \Rightarrow t_1 = 0.0639 \text{ s}$$

(b) Using $x_1 = x_0 + v_{0x}(t_1 - t_0) + \frac{1}{2}a_x(t_1 - t_0)^2$,

$$(50 \text{ m}) = 0 \text{ m} + v_{0x}(0.0639 \text{ s} - 0 \text{ s}) + 0 \text{ m} \Rightarrow v_{0x} = 782 \text{ m/s}$$

Assess: The bullet falls 2 cm during a horizontal displacement of 50 m. This implies a large initial velocity, and a value of 782 m/s is understandable.

6.13.   Model: Assume motion along the x-direction. Let the earth frame be S and a frame attached to the water be S′. Frame S′ moves relative to S with a velocity V_x.
Visualize: **Pictorial representation**

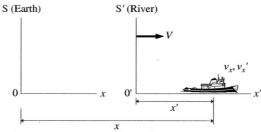

Solve: Let v_x be the velocity of the boat in frame S, and v'_x be the velocity of the boat in S'. Then for travel down the river,

$$v_x = v'_x + V_x = \frac{30 \text{ km}}{3.0 \text{ hr}} = 10.0 \text{ km/hr}$$

For travel up the river,

$$-v'_x + V_x = -\left(\frac{30\text{ km}}{5.0\text{ hr}}\right) = -6.0\text{ km/hr}$$

Adding these two equations yields $V_x = 2.0$ km/hr. That is, the velocity of the flowing river relative to the earth is 2.0 km/hr.

6.17. Model: If a frame S′ is in motion with velocity $\vec{V}$ relative to another frame S and has a displacement $\vec{R}$ relative to S, the positions and velocities ($\vec{r}$ and $\vec{v}$) in S are related to the positions and velocities ($\vec{r}'$ and $\vec{v}'$) in S′ as $\vec{r} = \vec{r}' + \vec{R}$ and $\vec{v} = \vec{v}' + \vec{V}$. In the present case, ship A is frame S and ship B is frame S′. Both ships have a common origin at $t = 0$ s. The position and velocity measurements are made in S and S′ relative to their origins.
Solve: **(a)** The velocity vectors of the two ships are:

$$\vec{v}_A = (20\text{ mph})\left[\cos 30°\hat{i} - \sin 30°\hat{j}\right] = (17.32\text{ mph})\hat{i} - (10.0\text{ mph})\hat{j}$$

$$\vec{v}_B = (25\text{ mph})\left[\cos 20°\hat{i} + \sin 20°\hat{j}\right] = (23.49\text{ mph})\hat{i} + (8.55\text{ mph})\hat{j}$$

Since $\vec{r} = \vec{v}\Delta t$,

$$\vec{r}_A = \vec{v}_A(2\text{ hr}) = (34.64\text{ miles})\hat{i} - (20.0\text{ miles})\hat{j}$$

$$\vec{r}_B = \vec{v}_B(2\text{ hr}) = (46.98\text{ miles})\hat{i} + (17.10\text{ miles})\hat{j}$$

As $\vec{r}_A = \vec{r}_B + \vec{R}$,

$$\vec{R} = \vec{r}_A - \vec{r}_B = (-12.34\text{ miles})\hat{i} - (37.10\text{ miles})\hat{j} \Rightarrow R = 39.1\text{ miles}$$

(b) Because $\vec{v}_A = \vec{v}_B + \vec{V}$,

$$\vec{V} = \vec{v}_A - \vec{v}_B = -(6.17\text{ mph})\hat{i} - (18.55\text{ mph})\hat{j} \Rightarrow V = 19.5\text{ mph}$$

Assess: The value of the speed is reasonable.

6.21. Model: The ions are particles that move in a plane. They have vertical acceleration while between the acceleration plates, and they move with constant velocity from the plates to the tumor. The flight time will be so small, because of the large speeds, that we'll ignore any deflection due to gravity.
Visualize:

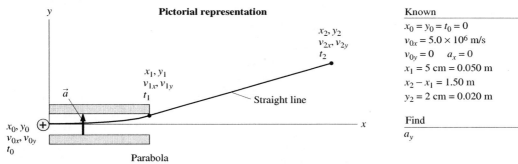

Solve: There's never a horizontal acceleration, so the horizontal motion is constant velocity motion at $v_x = 5.0 \times 10^6$ m/s. The times to pass between the 5.0-cm-long acceleration plates and from the plates to the tumor are

$$t_1 - t_0 = t_1 = \frac{0.050\text{ m}}{5.0 \times 10^6\text{ m/s}} = 1.00 \times 10^{-8}\text{ s}$$

$$t_2 - t_1 = \frac{1.50\text{ m}}{5.0 \times 10^6\text{ m/s}} = 3.00 \times 10^{-7}\text{ s}$$

Upon leaving the acceleration plates, the ion has been deflected sideways to position y_1 and has velocity v_{1y}. These are

$$y_1 = y_0 + v_{0y}t_1 + \tfrac{1}{2}a_y t_1^2 = \tfrac{1}{2}a_y t_1^2$$
$$v_{1y} = v_{0y} + a_y t_1 = a_y t_1$$

In traveling from the plates to the tumor, with no vertical acceleration, the ion reaches position

$$y_2 = y_1 + v_{1y}(t_2 - t_1) = \tfrac{1}{2}a_y t_1^2 + (a_y t_1)(t_2 - t_1) = \left(\tfrac{1}{2}t_1^2 + t_1(t_2 - t_1)\right)a_y$$

We know $y_2 = 2.0$ cm $= 0.020$ m, so we can solve for the acceleration a_y that the ion had while between the plates:

$$a_y = \frac{y_2}{\tfrac{1}{2}t_1^2 + t_1(t_2 - t_1)} = \frac{0.020 \text{ m}}{\tfrac{1}{2}(1.00 \times 10^{-8} \text{ s})^2 + (1.00 \times 10^{-8} \text{ s})(3.00 \times 10^{-7} \text{ s})} = 6.56 \times 10^{12} \text{ m/s}^2$$

Assess: This acceleration is roughly 10^{12} times larger than the acceleration due to gravity. This justifies our assumption that the acceleration due to gravity can be neglected.

6.23.   Model: Assume particle motion in a plane and constant-acceleration kinematics for the projectile.
Visualize: **Pictorial representation**

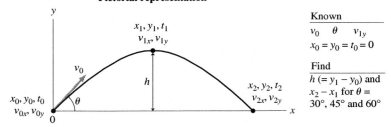

Solve: (a) We know that $v_{0y} = v_0 \sin\theta$, $a_y = -g$, and $v_{1y} = 0$ m/s. Using $v_{1y}^2 = v_{0y}^2 + 2a_y(y_1 - y_0)$,

$$0 \text{ m}^2/\text{s}^2 = v_0^2 \sin^2\theta + 2(-g)h \Rightarrow h = \frac{v_0^2 \sin^2\theta}{2g}$$

(b) Using Equation 6.19 and the above expression for $\theta = 30°$:

$$h = \frac{(33.6 \text{ m/s})^2 \sin^2 30°}{2(9.8 \text{ m/s}^2)} = 14.4 \text{ m}$$

$$(x_2 - x_0) = \frac{v_0^2 \sin 2\theta}{g} = \frac{(33.6 \text{ m/s})^2 \sin(2 \times 30°)}{(9.8 \text{ m/s}^2)} = 99.8 \text{ m}$$

For $\theta = 45°$:

$$h = \frac{(33.6 \text{ m/s})^2 \sin^2 45°}{2(9.8 \text{ m/s}^2)} = 28.8 \text{ m}$$

$$(x_2 - x_0) = \frac{(33.6 \text{ m/s})^2 \sin(2 \times 45°)}{(9.8 \text{ m/s}^2)} = 115.2 \text{ m}$$

For $\theta = 60°$:

$$h = \frac{(33.6 \text{ m/s})^2 \sin^2 60°}{2(9.8 \text{ m/s}^2)} = 43.2 \text{ m}$$

$$(x_2 - x_0) = \frac{(33.6 \text{ m/s})^2 \sin(2 \times 60°)}{2(9.8 \text{ m/s}^2)} = 99.8 \text{ m}$$

Assess: The projectile's range, being proportional to $\sin(2\theta)$, is maximum at a launch angle of 45°, but the maximum height reached is proportional to $\sin^2(\theta)$. These dependencies are seen in this problem.

6.25. Model: Assume the particle model for the projectile and motion in a plane.
Visualize: **Pictorial representation**

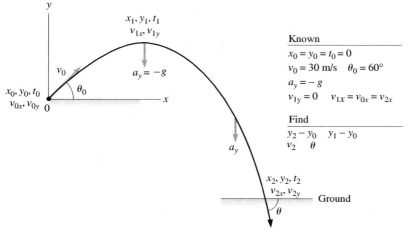

Solve: **(a)** Using $y_2 = y_0 + v_{0y}(t_2 - t_0) + \frac{1}{2}a_y(t_2 - t_0)^2$,

$$y_2 = 0\text{ m} + (30\text{ m/s})\sin 60°(7.5\text{ s} - 0\text{ s}) + \frac{1}{2}(-9.8\text{ m/s}^2)(7.5\text{ s} - 0\text{ s})^2 = -80.8\text{ m}$$

Thus the launch point is 80.8 m higher than where the projectile hits the ground.
(b) Using $v_{1y}^2 = v_{0y}^2 + 2a_y(y_1 - y_0)$,

$$0\text{ m}^2/\text{s}^2 = (30\sin 60°\text{ m/s})^2 + 2(-9.8\text{ m/s}^2)(y_1 - 0\text{ m}) \Rightarrow y_1 = 34.4\text{ m}$$

(c) The x-component is $v_{2x} = v_{0x} = v_0\cos 60° = (30\text{ m/s})\cos 60° = 15\text{ m/s}$. The y-component is

$$v_{2y} = v_{0y} + a_y(t_2 - t_0) = v_0\sin 60° - g(t_2 - t_1) = (30\text{ m/s})\sin 60° - (9.8\text{ m/s}^2)(7.5\text{ s} - 0\text{ s}) = -47.52\text{ m/s}$$

$$\Rightarrow v = \sqrt{(15\text{ m/s})^2 + (-47.52\text{ m/s})^2} = 49.8\text{ m/s}$$

$$\theta = \tan^{-1}\frac{|v_{2y}|}{v_{2x}} = \tan^{-1}\frac{47.52}{15} = 72.5° \text{ below } +x$$

Assess: An angle of 72.5° made with the ground, as the projectile hits the ground 80.8 m below its launch point, is reasonable in view of the fact that the projectile was launched at an angle of 60°.

6.31. Model: We will use the particle model and the constant-acceleration kinematic equations in a plane.
Visualize: **Pictorial representation**

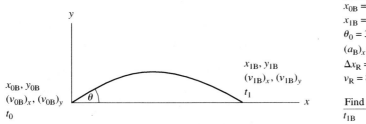

Solve: The x- and y-equations of the ball are

$$x_{1B} = x_{0B} + (v_{0B})_x(t_{1B} - t_{0B}) + \frac{1}{2}(a_B)_x(t_{1B} - t_{0B})^2 \Rightarrow 65\text{ m} = 0\text{ m} + (v_{0B}\cos 30°)t_{1B} + 0\text{ m}$$

$$y_{1B} = y_{0B} + (v_{0B})_y(t_{1B} - t_{0B}) + \frac{1}{2}(a_B)_y(t_{1B} - t_{0B})^2 \Rightarrow 0\text{ m} = 0\text{ m} + (v_{0B}\sin 30°)t_{1B} + \frac{1}{2}(-g)t_{1B}^2$$

From the *y*-equation,

$$v_{0B} = \frac{gt_{1B}}{(2\sin 30°)}$$

Substituting this into the *x*-equation yields

$$65 \text{ m} = \frac{g \ \cos 30° \ t_{1B}^2}{2 \sin 30°}$$

$$\Rightarrow t_{1B} = 2.77 \text{ s}$$

For the runner:

$$t_{1R} = \frac{20 \text{ m}}{8.0 \text{ m/s}} = 2.50 \text{ s}$$

Thus, the throw is too late by 0.27 s.

Assess: The times involved in running the bases are small, and a time of 2.5 s is reasonable.

6.33.   Model: We will use the particle model for the ball's motion under constant-acceleration kinematic equations. Note that the ball's motion on the smooth, flat board is $a_y = -g\sin 20° = -3.352 \text{ m/s}^2$.

Visualize: **Pictorial representation**

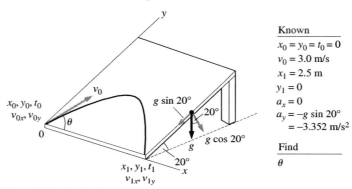

Known
$x_0 = y_0 = t_0 = 0$
$v_0 = 3.0$ m/s
$x_1 = 2.5$ m
$y_1 = 0$
$a_x = 0$
$a_y = -g \sin 20°$
   $= -3.352$ m/s^2

Find
θ

Solve: The ball's initial velocity is

$$v_{0x} = v_0\cos\theta = (3.0 \text{ m / s})\cos\theta \qquad v_{0y} = v_0\sin\theta = (3.0 \text{ m/s})\sin\theta$$

Using $x_1 = x_0 + v_{0x}(t_1 - t_0) + \frac{1}{2}a_x(t_1 - t_0)^2$,

$$2.5 \text{ m} = 0 \text{ m} + (3.0 \text{ m/s})\cos\theta(t_1 - 0 \text{ s}) + 0 \text{ m} \Rightarrow t_1 = \frac{(2.5 \text{ m})}{(3.0 \text{ m/s})\cos\theta} = \frac{0.833 \text{ s}}{\cos\theta}$$

Using $y_1 = y_0 + v_{0y}(t_1 - t_0) + \frac{1}{2}a_y(t_1 - t_0)^2$ and the above equation for t_1,

$$0 \text{ m} = 0 \text{ m} + (3.0 \text{ m/s})\sin\theta\left(\frac{0.833 \text{ s}}{\cos\theta}\right) - \frac{1}{2}(3.352 \text{ m/s}^2)\frac{(0.833 \text{ s})^2}{\cos^2\theta}$$

$$\Rightarrow (2.5 \text{ m})\frac{\sin\theta}{\cos\theta} = \frac{1.164}{\cos^2\theta} \Rightarrow 2.5\sin\theta\cos\theta = 1.164 \Rightarrow 2\theta = 68.6° \Rightarrow \theta = 34.3°$$

6.37. **Model:** We will assume a particle model for the cannonball, and apply the constant-acceleration kinematic equations.

Visualize:

Pictorial representation

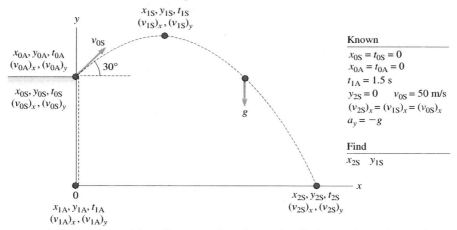

Known

$x_{0S} = t_{0S} = 0$
$x_{0A} = t_{0A} = 0$
$t_{1A} = 1.5$ s
$y_{2S} = 0$ $v_{0S} = 50$ m/s
$(v_{2S})_x = (v_{1S})_x = (v_{0S})_x$
$a_y = -g$

Find
x_{2S} y_{1S}

Solve: **(a)** The cannonball that was accidentally dropped can be used to find the height of the wall:

$$y_{1A} = y_{0A} + (v_{0A})_y (t_{1A} - t_{0A}) + \tfrac{1}{2}(a_A)_y (t_{1A} - t_{0A})^2 \Rightarrow 0 \text{ m} = y_{0A} + 0 \text{ m} - \tfrac{1}{2}g t_{1A}^2$$

$$\Rightarrow y_{0A} = \tfrac{1}{2}(9.8 \text{ m/s}^2)(1.5 \text{ s})^2 = 11.03 \text{ m}$$

For the cannonball that was shot:

$$(v_{0S})_x = v_{0S}\cos 30° = (50 \text{ m/s})\cos 30° = 43.30 \text{ m/s}$$

$$(v_{0S})_y = v_{0s}\sin 30° = (50 \text{ m/s})\sin 30° = 25.0 \text{ m/s}$$

We can now find the time it takes the cannonball to hit the ground:

$$y_{2S} = y_{0S} + (v_{0S})_y (t_{2S} - t_{0S}) + \tfrac{1}{2}(a_S)_y (t_{2S} - t_{0S})^2$$

$$\Rightarrow 0 \text{ m} = (11.03 \text{ m}) + (25.0 \text{ m/s})t_{2S} - \frac{(9.8 \text{ m/s}^2)}{2} t_{2S}^2$$

$$\Rightarrow (4.9 \text{ m/s}^2)t_{2S}^2 - (25.0 \text{ m/s})t_{2S} - (11.03 \text{ m}) = 0 \Rightarrow t_{2S} = 5.51 \text{ s}$$

There is also an unphysical root $t_{2S} = -0.41$ s. Using this time t_{2S}, we can now find the horizontal distance from the wall as follows:

$$x_{2s} = x_{0s} + (v_{0s})_x (t_{2s} - t_{0s}) = 0 \text{ m} + (43.30 \text{ m/s})(5.51 \text{ s}) = 239 \text{ m}$$

(b) At the top of the trajectory $(v_{1S})_y = 0$ m/s. Using $(v_{1S})_y^2 = (v_{0S})_y^2 - 2g(y_{1S} - y_{0S})$,

$$0 \text{ m}^2/\text{s}^2 = (25.0 \text{ m/s})^2 - 2(9.8 \text{ m/s}^2)(y_{1s} - 11.03 \text{ m}) \Rightarrow y_{1s} = 42.9 \text{ m}$$

Assess: In view of the fact that the cannon ball has a speed of approximately 110 mph, a distance of 239 m for the cannonball to hit the ground is reasonable.

6.41. **Model:** The object is treated as a particle in the model of kinetic friction with its motion governed by constant-acceleration kinematics.

Visualize:

Pictorial representation	Physical representation

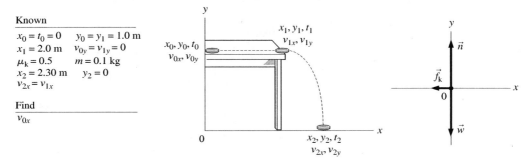

Known

$x_0 = t_0 = 0$ $y_0 = y_1 = 1.0$ m
$x_1 = 2.0$ m $v_{0y} = v_{1y} = 0$
$\mu_k = 0.5$ $m = 0.1$ kg
$x_2 = 2.30$ m $y_2 = 0$
$v_{2x} = v_{1x}$

Find
v_{0x}

Solve: The velocity v_{1x} as the object sails off the edge is related to the initial velocity v_{0x} by $v_{1x}^2 = v_{0x}^2 + 2a_x(x_1 - x_0)$. Using Newton's second law to determine a_x gives

$$\sum F_x = -f_k = ma_x \Rightarrow \sum F_y = n - mg = 0 \text{ N} \Rightarrow n = mg$$

Using this result and the model of kinetic friction $(f_k = \mu_k n)$, the x-component equation can be written as $-\mu_k mg = ma_x$. This implies

$$a_x = -\mu_k g = -(0.5)(9.8 \text{ m/s}^2) = -4.9 \text{ m/s}^2$$

Kinematic equations for the object's free fall can be used to determine v_{1x}:

$$y_2 = y_1 + v_{1y}(t_2 - t_1) + \tfrac{1}{2}(-g)(t_2 - t_1)^2 \Rightarrow 0 \text{ m} = 1.0 \text{ m} + 0 \text{ m} - \frac{g}{2}(t_2 - t_1)^2 \Rightarrow (t_2 - t_1) = 0.4518 \text{ s}$$

$$x_2 = x_1 + v_{1x}(t_2 - t_1) = 2.3 \text{ m} = 2.0 \text{ m} + v_{1x}(0.4518 \text{ s}) \Rightarrow v_{1x} = 0.664 \text{ m/s}$$

Having determined v_{1x} and a_x, we can go back to the velocity equation $v_{1x}^2 = v_{0x}^2 + 2a_x(x_1 - x_0)$:

$$(0.664 \text{ m/s})^2 = v_{0x}^2 + 2(-4.9 \text{ m/s}^2)(2.0 \text{ m}) \Rightarrow v_{0x} = 4.48 \text{ m/s}$$

Assess: $v_{0x} = 4.48$ m/s is about 10 mph and is a reasonable speed.

6.43. Model: Treat Sam as a particle.
Visualize: This is a two-part problem. Use an s-axis parallel to the slope for the first part, regular xy-coordinates for the second. Sam's final velocity at the top of the slope is his initial velocity as he becomes airborne.

Pictorial representation

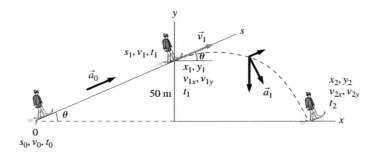

Known
$m = 75$ kg $\theta = 10°$
$s_0 = v_0 = 0$
$s_1 = 50$ m/sin $\theta = 288$ m
$x_1 = 0$ $y_1 = 50$ m $t_1 = 0$
$y_2 = 0$ $F = 200$ N

Find
x_2

Physical representation

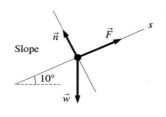 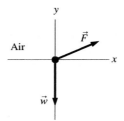

Solve: Sam's acceleration up the slope is given by Newton's second law:

$$(F_{net})_s = F - mg\sin 10° = ma_0$$

$$a_0 = \frac{F}{m} - g\sin 10° = \frac{200 \text{ N}}{75 \text{ kg}} - (9.8 \text{ m/s}^2)\sin 10° = 0.965 \text{ m/s}^2$$

The length of the slope is $s_1 = (50 \text{ m})/\sin 10° = 288$ m. His velocity at the top of the slope is

$$v_1^2 = v_0^2 + 2a_0(s_1 - s_0) = 2a_0 s_1 \Rightarrow v_1 = \sqrt{2(0.965 \text{ m/s}^2)(288 \text{ m})} = 23.6 \text{ m/s}$$

This is Sam's initial speed into the air, giving him velocity components $v_{1x} = v_1 \cos 10° = 23.2$ m/s and $v_{1y} = v_1 \sin 10° = 4.10$ m/s. This is not projectile motion because Sam experiences both the force of gravity *and* the thrust of his skis. Newton's second law for Sam's acceleration is

$$a_{1x} = \frac{(F_{net})_x}{m} = \frac{(200\ \text{N})\cos 10°}{75\ \text{kg}} = 2.63\ \text{m/s}^2$$

$$a_{1y} = \frac{(F_{net})_y}{m} = \frac{(200\ \text{N})\sin 10° - (75\ \text{kg})(9.80\ \text{m/s}^2)}{75\ \text{kg}} = -9.34\ \text{m/s}^2$$

The *y*-equation of motion allows us to find out how long it takes Sam to reach the ground:

$$y_2 = 0\ \text{m} = y_1 + v_{1y}t_2 + \tfrac{1}{2}a_{1y}t_2^2 = 50\ \text{m} + (4.10\ \text{m/s})\,t_2 - (4.67\ \text{m/s}^2)\,t_2^2$$

This quadratic equation has roots $t_2 = -2.86$ s (unphysical) and $t_2 = 3.74$ s. The *x*-equation of motion—this time with an acceleration—is

$$x_2 = x_1 + v_{1x}t_2 + \tfrac{1}{2}a_{1x}t_2^2 = 0\ \text{m} + (23.2\ \text{m/s})\,t_2 - \tfrac{1}{2}(2.63\ \text{m/s}^2)\,t_2^2 = 105\ \text{m}$$

Sam lands 105 m from the base of the cliff.

6.51. Solve: **(a)** A submarine moving east at 3.0 m/s sees an enemy ship 100 m north of its path. The submarine's torpedo tube happens to be stuck in a position pointing 45° west of north. The tube fires a torpedo with a speed of 6.0 m/s relative to the submarine. How far east or west of the ship should the sub be when it fires?
(b) Relative to the water, the torpedo will have velocity components

$$v_x = -6.0\cos 45°\ \text{m/s} + 3.0\ \text{m/s} = -4.24\ \text{m/s} + 3\ \text{m/s} = -1.24\ \text{m/s}$$

$$v_y = +6.0\cos 45°\ \text{m/s} = +4.24\ \text{m/s}$$

The time to travel north to the ship is

$$100\ \text{m} = (4.24\ \text{m/s})\,t_1 \Rightarrow t_1 = 25.6\ \text{s}$$

Thus, $x = (1.24\ \text{m/s})(23.6\ \text{s}) = -29.2\ \text{m}$. That is, the ship should be 29.2 m west of the submarine.

6.53. Model: Let the earth frame be S and a frame attached to the water be S′. Frame S′ moves relative to S with velocity V. We define the *x*-axis along the direction of east and the *y*-axis along the direction of north for both frames. The frames S and S′ have their origins coincident at $t = 0$ s.
Solve: **(a)** According to the Galilean transformation of position: $\vec{r} = \vec{r}' + \vec{R} = \vec{r}' + t\vec{V}$. We need to find Mary's position vector $\vec{r}$ from the earth frame S. The observer in frame S′ will observe the boat move straight north and will find its position as $\vec{r}' = (2.0t)\hat{j}$ m/s. We also know that $\vec{V} = (3.0)\hat{i}$ m/s. Since $r' = 100\ \text{m} = (2.0\ \text{m/s})t$ and $t = 50$ s, we have

$$\vec{r} = (2.0\ \text{m/s})(50\ \text{s})\hat{j} + (50\ \text{s})(3.0\ \text{m/s})t\,\hat{i} = (150\ \text{m})\hat{i} + (100\ \text{m})\hat{j}$$

Thus she lands 150 m east of the point that was straight across the river from her when she started.
(b)

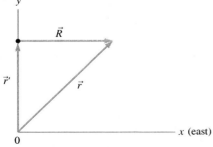

Note that $\vec{r}'$ is the displacement due to rowing, $\vec{R}$ is the displacement due to the river's motion, and $\vec{r}$ is the net displacement.

6.59. **Model:** Let the ground be frame S and the pickup be frame S′. S′ moves relative to S with velocity V along the *y*-direction. *x* is the direction perpendicular to the pickup's motion.

Visualize:

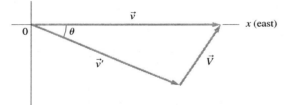

y (north)   **Pictorial representation**

Known
$\vec{V} = 10$ mph $\hat{j}$
$v' = 20$ mph

Find
v and θ

x (east)

Solve: **(a)** The Galilean transformation of velocity is $\vec{v} = \vec{v}' + \vec{V}$, where $\vec{V} = (10 \text{ mph})\hat{j}$ and $\vec{v}' = (20 \text{ mph})\cos\theta\hat{i} - (20 \text{ mph})\sin\theta\hat{j}$ Thus,

$$\vec{v} = (20 \text{ mph})\cos\theta\hat{i} + \left[(10 \text{ mph}) - (20 \text{ mph})\sin\theta\right]\hat{j}$$

Since the paper is thrown just as the pickup passes the driveway, the observer in the driveway will find the paper to have no *y*-component of the velocity. That is,

$$v_y = 0 \text{ mph} = (10 \text{ mph}) - (20 \text{ mph})\sin\theta \Rightarrow \theta = \sin^{-1}\left(\frac{1}{2}\right) = 30°$$

He must throw the paper 30° to the side of the driveway opposite the motion.

(b) Since $\vec{v} = (20 \text{ mph})\cos 30°\hat{i} + (0 \text{ mph})\hat{j} = (17.3 \text{ mph})\hat{i}$, the speed is 17.3 mph.

6.61. **Model:** Let the ground be frame S and the wind be frame S′. S′ moves relative to S. The ground frame S has the *x*-axis along the direction of east and the *y*-axis along the direction of north.

Visualize: y (north)

x (east)

Known
$\vec{V}$ (50 mph, 30° N of E)
$\vec{v}'$ (200 mph, θ S of E)

Find
θ v

Solve: **(a)** The Galilean velocity transformation is $\vec{v} = \vec{v}' + \vec{V}$, where

$$\vec{V} = (50 \text{ mph})\cos 30°\hat{i} + (50 \text{ mph})\sin 30°\hat{j}$$

$$\vec{v}' = (200 \text{ mph})\cos\theta\hat{i} - (200 \text{ mph})\sin\theta\hat{j}$$

Thus, $\vec{v} = \left[(50\cos 30° + 200\cos\theta)\hat{i} + (50\sin 30° - 200\sin\theta)\hat{j}\right]$ mph . Because $\vec{v}$ should have no j-component,

$$50\sin 30° - 200\sin\theta = 0 \Rightarrow \theta = 7.18°$$

(b) The pilot must head 7.18° south of east. Substituting this value of θ in the $\vec{v}$ equation gives $\vec{v} = (242)\hat{i}$ mph, along the direction of east. At a speed of 242 mph, the trip takes $t = \dfrac{600 \text{ mi}}{242 \text{ mph}} = 2.48$ hours.

DYNAMICS III: MOTION IN A CIRCLE

7.1. Solve: (a) From $t = 0$ s to $t = 1$ s the particle rotates clockwise from the angular position $+4\pi$ rad to -2π rad. Therefore, $\Delta\theta = -2\pi - (+4\pi) = -6\pi$ rad in one sec, or $\omega = -6\pi$ rad/s. From $t = 1$ s to $t = 2$ s, $\omega = 0$ rad/s. From $t = 2$ s to $t = 4$ s the particle rotates counterclockwise from the angular position -2π rad to 0 rad. Thus $\Delta\theta = 0 - (-2\pi) = 2\pi$ rad and $\omega = +\pi$ rad/s.

(b)

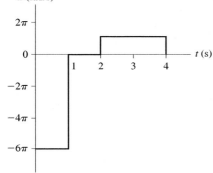

7.5. Model: The earth is a particle orbiting around the sun.
Solve: (a) The magnitude of the earth's velocity is displacement divided by time:

$$v = \frac{2\pi r}{T} = \frac{2\pi\left(1.5\times10^{11}\text{ m}\right)}{365\text{ days}\times\dfrac{24\text{ hr}}{1\text{ day}}\times\dfrac{3600\text{ s}}{1\text{ hr}}} = 3.0\times10^{4}\text{ m/s}$$

(b) Since $v = r\omega$, the angular acceleration is

$$\omega = \frac{v}{r} = \frac{3.0\times10^{4}\text{ m / s}}{1.5\times10^{11}\text{ m}} = 2.0\times10^{-7}\text{ rad / s}$$

(c) The centripetal acceleration is

$$a_r = \frac{v^2}{r} = \frac{\left(3.0\times10^{4}\text{ m / s}\right)^2}{1.5\times10^{11}\text{ m}} = 6.0\times10^{-3}\text{ m / s}^2$$

Assess: A tangential velocity of 3.0×10^4 m/s or 30 km/s is large, but needed for the earth to go through a displacement of $2\pi(1.5\times10^{11}$ m$) \approx 9.4 \times 10^8$ km in 1 year.

7.11. Model: Treat the block as a particle attached to a massless string that is swinging in a circle on a frictionless table.
Visualize: **Pictorial representation**   **Physical representation**

Known
$m = 0.20$ kg
$r = 0.50$ m
$\omega = 75$ rpm

Find
v, T

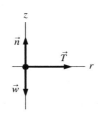

Solve: **(a)** The angular velocity and speed are

$$\omega = 75\frac{\text{rev}}{\text{min}} \times \frac{2\pi\,\text{rad}}{1\,\text{rev}} = 471.2\ \text{rad / min} \qquad v_t = r\omega = (0.5\ \text{m})(471.2\ \text{rad/min}) \times \frac{1\text{min}}{60\ \text{s}} = 3.93\ \text{m / s}$$

(b) The radial component of Newton's second law is

$$\sum F_r = T = \frac{mv^2}{r}$$

Thus

$$T = (0.2\ \text{kg})\frac{(3.93\ \text{m / s})^2}{0.5\ \text{m}} = 6.18\ \text{N}$$

7.13. **Model:** The vehicle is to be treated as a particle in uniform circular motion.
Visualize: **Physical representation**   **Pictorial representation**
(r-z plane)

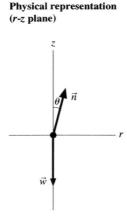 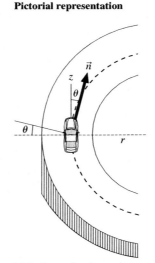

Known
r = 500 m
v = 90 km/hr

Find
θ

On a banked road, the normal force on a vehicle has a horizontal component that provides the necessary centripetal acceleration. The vertical component of the normal force balances the weight.
Solve: From the physical representation of the forces in the r-z plane, Newton's second law can be written

$$\sum F_r = n\sin\theta = \frac{mv^2}{r} \qquad\qquad \sum F_z = n\cos\theta - mg = 0 \Rightarrow n\cos\theta = mg$$

Dividing the two equations and making the conversion 90 km/hr = 25 m / s yields:

$$\tan\theta = \frac{v^2}{rg} = \frac{(25\ \text{m / s})^2}{(9.8\ \text{m / s}^2)500\ \text{m}} = 0.128 \Rightarrow \theta = 7.27°$$

Assess: Such a banking angle for a speed of approximately 55 mph is clearly reasonable and within our experience as well.

7.17. **Model:** The satellite is considered to be a particle in uniform circular motion around the moon.
Visualize:

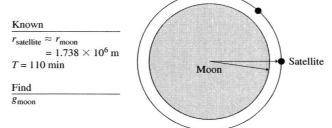

Known

$r_{\text{satellite}} \approx r_{\text{moon}}$
$= 1.738 \times 10^6$ m
T = 110 min

Find
g_{moon}

Moon
Satellite

Solve: The radius of moon is 1.738×10^6 m and the satellite's distance from the center of the moon is the same quantity. The angular velocity of the satellite is

$$\omega = \frac{2\pi}{T} = \frac{2\pi\ \text{rad}}{110\ \text{min}} \times \frac{1\text{min}}{60\ \text{s}} = 9.52 \times 10^{-4}\ \text{rad / s}$$

and the centripetal acceleration is

$$a_r = r\omega^2 = (1.738 \times 10^6 \text{ m})(9.52 \times 10^{-4} \text{ rad / s})^2 = 1.58 \text{ m / s}^2$$

The acceleration of a body in orbit is the local "g" experienced by that body.

7.19.   Model: Model the passenger in a roller coaster car as a particle in uniform circular motion.
Visualize:

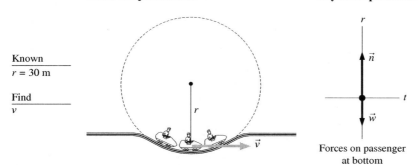

Pictorial representation   **Physical representation**

Known
r = 30 m

Find
v

Forces on passenger
at bottom

Note that the normal force $\vec{n}$ of the seat pushing on the passenger is the passenger's apparent weight.
Solve: Since the passengers feel 50% heavier than their true weight, $n = 1.50w$. Thus, from Newton's second law:

$$\sum F_r = n - w = 1.50w - w = \frac{mv^2}{r} \Rightarrow 0.50mg = \frac{mv^2}{r}$$

$$\Rightarrow v = \sqrt{0.50gr} = \sqrt{(0.50)(30 \text{ m})(9.8 \text{ m / s}^2)} = 12.1 \text{ m / s}$$

7.21.   Model: Model the roller coaster car as a particle undergoing uniform circular motion along a loop.
Visualize: **Pictorial representation**   **Physical representation**

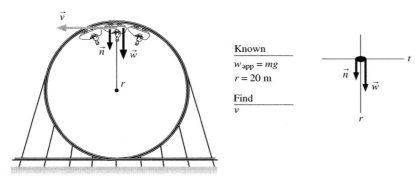

Known
$w_{\text{app}} = mg$
r = 20 m

Find
v

Notice that the *r*-axis points downward, toward the center of the circle.
Solve: In this problem the apparent weight is equal to the weight: $w_{\text{app}} = n = mg$. We have

$$\sum F_r = n + w = \frac{mv^2}{r} = mg + mg \Rightarrow v = \sqrt{2rg} = \sqrt{2(20 \text{ m})(9.8 \text{ m / s}^2)} = 19.8 \text{ m / s}$$

7.23.   Model: Model the car as a particle in nonuniform circular motion.
Visualize: **Pictorial representation**

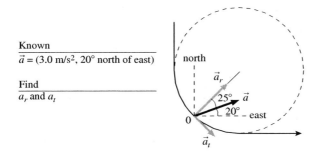

Known
$\vec{a} = (3.0 \text{ m/s}^2, 20° \text{ north of east})$

Find
a_r and a_t

Note that halfway around the curve, the tangent is 45° south of east. The perpendicular component of the acceleration is 45° north of east.

Solve: The radial and tangential components of the acceleration are

$$a_r = a\cos 25° = (3.0 \text{ m/s}^2)\cos 25° = 2.72 \text{ m/s}^2$$

$$a_t = a\sin 25° = (3.0 \text{ m/s}^2)\sin 25° = 1.27 \text{ m/s}^2$$

7.27. Model: Model the car as a particle in nonuniform circular motion.

Visualize: **Pictorial representation**

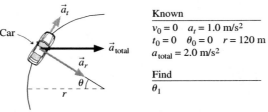

Known
$v_0 = 0$ $a_t = 1.0$ m/s²
$t_0 = 0$ $\theta_0 = 0$ $r = 120$ m
$a_{total} = 2.0$ m/s²

Find
θ_1

Note that the tangential acceleration stays the same at 1.0 m/s². As the tangential velocity increases, the radial acceleration increases as well. After a time t_1, as the car goes through an angle $\theta_1 - \theta_0$, the total acceleration will increase to 2.0 m/s². Our objective is to find this angle.

Solve: Using $v_1 = v_0 + a_t(t_1 - t_0)$, we get

$$v_1 = 0 \text{ m/s} + (1.0 \text{ m/s}^2)(t_1 - 0 \text{ s}) = (1.0 \text{ m/s}^2)t_1$$

$$\Rightarrow a_r = \frac{rv_1^2}{r^2} = \frac{(1.0 \text{ m/s}^2)^2 t_1^2}{120 \text{ m}} = \frac{t_1^2}{120}(\text{m/s}^4)$$

$$\Rightarrow a_{total} = 2.0 \text{ m/s}^2 = \sqrt{a_t^2 + a_r^2} = \sqrt{(1.0 \text{ m/s}^2)^2 + \left[\frac{t_1^2}{120}(\text{m/s}^4)\right]^2} \Rightarrow t_1 = 14.4 \text{ s}$$

We can now determine the angle θ_1 using

$$\theta_1 = \theta_0 + \omega_0(t_1 - t_0) + \tfrac{1}{2}\left(\frac{a_t}{r}\right)(t_1 - t_0)^2$$

$$= 0 \text{ rad} + 0 \text{ rad} + \frac{1}{2}\frac{(1.0 \text{ m/s}^2)}{(120 \text{ m})}(14.4 \text{ s})^2 = 0.864 \text{ rad} = 49.5°$$

7.33. Model: Use the particle model for the (cart+child) system which is in uniform circular motion.

Visualize: **Pictorial representation**

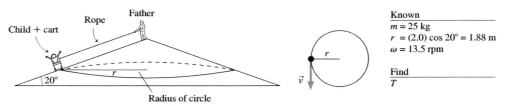

Known
$m = 25$ kg
$r = (2.0)\cos 20° = 1.88$ m
$\omega = 13.5$ rpm

Find
T

Physical representation

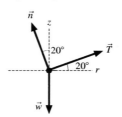

Forces in the r-z plane

Solve: Newton's second law along r and z directions can be written:

$$\sum F_r = T\cos 20° - n\sin 20° = ma_r \qquad \sum F_z = T\sin 20° + n\cos 20° - mg = 0$$

The cart's centripetal acceleration is

$$a_r = r\omega^2 = (2.0\cos 20° \text{ m})\left(13.5 \ \frac{\text{rev}}{\text{min}} \times \frac{1 \text{ min}}{60 \text{ s}} \times \frac{2\pi \text{ rad}}{1 \text{ rev}}\right)^2 = 3.756 \text{ m / s}^2$$

The above force equations can be rewritten as

$$0.94T - 0.342n = (25 \text{ kg})(3.756 \text{ m / s}^2) = 93.9 \text{ N}$$

$$0.342T + 0.94n = (25 \text{ kg})(9.8 \text{ m / s}^2) = 245 \text{ N}$$

Solving these two equations yields $T = 172$ N for the tension in the rope.
Assess: In view of the child+cart weight of 245 N, a tension of 172 N is reasonable.

7.35. Model: We will use the particle model for the car, which is undergoing uniform circular motion on a banked highway, and the model of static friction.
Visualize:

Pictorial representation   **Physical representation**

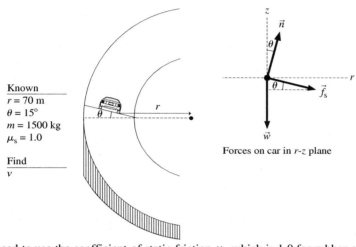

Known
r = 70 m
θ = 15°
m = 1500 kg
μ_s = 1.0

Find
v

Forces on car in *r-z* plane

Note that we need to use the coefficient of static friction μ_s, which is 1.0 for rubber on concrete.
Solve: Newton's second law for the car is

$$\sum F_r = f_s\cos\theta + n\sin\theta = \frac{mv^2}{r} \qquad \sum F_z = n\cos\theta - f_s\sin\theta - w = 0 \text{ N}$$

Maximum speed is when the static friction force reaches its maximum value $f_{s\,max} = \mu_s n$. Then

$$n(\mu_s\cos 15° + \sin 15°) = \frac{mv^2}{r} \qquad n(\cos 15° - \mu_s\sin 15°) = mg$$

Dividing these two equations and simplifying, we get

$$\frac{\mu_s + \tan 15°}{1 - \mu_s\tan 15°} = \frac{v^2}{gr} \Rightarrow v = \sqrt{gr\frac{\mu_s + \tan 15°}{1 - \mu_s\tan 15°}}$$

$$= \sqrt{(9.80 \text{ m / s}^2)(70 \text{ m})\frac{(1.0 + 0.268)}{(1 - 0.268)}} = 34.5 \text{ m / s}$$

Assess: The above value of 34.5 m/s $\approx$ 70 mph is reasonable.

7.41.   Model: Consider the passenger to be a particle and use the model of static friction.
Visualize:

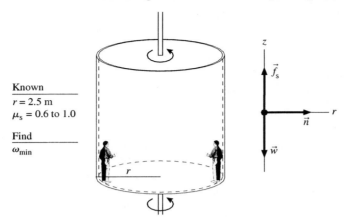

Pictorial representation   Physical representation

Known
$r = 2.5$ m
$\mu_s = 0.6$ to 1.0

Find
ω_{min}

Solve: The passengers stick to the wall if the static friction force is sufficient to support their weight: $f_s = w$. The minimum angular velocity occurs when static friction reaches its maximum possible value $f_{s\,max} = \mu_s n$. Although clothing has a range of coefficients of friction, it is the clothing with the smallest coefficient ($\mu_s = 0.6$) that will slip first, so this is the case we need to examine. Assuming that the person is stuck to the wall, Newton's second law is

$$\sum F_r = n = m\omega^2 r \qquad \sum F_z = f_s - w = 0 \Rightarrow f_s = mg$$

The minimum frequency occurs when

$$f_s = f_{s\,max} = \mu_s n = \mu_s m r \omega_{min}^2$$

Using this expression for f_s in the z-equation gives

$$f_s = \mu_s m r \omega_{min}^2 = mg$$

$$\Rightarrow \omega_{min} = \sqrt{\frac{g}{\mu_s r}} = \sqrt{\frac{9.80 \text{ m/s}^2}{0.60(2.5 \text{ m})}} = 2.56 \text{ rad/s} = 2.56 \text{ rad/s} \times \frac{1 \text{ rev}}{2\pi \text{ rad}} \times \frac{60 \text{ s}}{1 \text{ min}} = 24.4 \text{ rpm}$$

Assess: Note the velocity does not depend on the mass of the individual. Therefore, the minimum mass sign is not necessary.

7.43.   Model: Use the particle model for the car and the model of kinetic friction.
Visualize: Physical representation

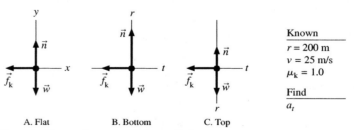

A. Flat   B. Bottom   C. Top

Known
$r = 200$ m
$v = 25$ m/s
$\mu_k = 1.0$

Find
a_t

Solve: We will apply Newton's second law to all three cars.
Car A:

$$\sum F_x = n_x + (f_k)_x + w_x = 0 \text{ N} - f_k + 0 \text{ N} = ma_x$$

$$\sum F_y = n_y + (f_k)_y + y_y = n + 0 \text{ N} - mg = 0 \text{ N}$$

The y-component equation means $n = mg$. Since $f_k = \mu_k n$, we have $f_k = \mu_k mg$. From the x-component equation,

$$a_x = \frac{-f_k}{m} = \frac{-\mu_k mg}{m} = -\mu_k g = -9.8 \text{ m / s}^2$$

Car B: Car B is in circular motion with the center of the circle above the car.

$$\sum F_r = n_r + (f_k)_r + w_r = n + 0 \text{ N} - mg = ma_r = \frac{mv^2}{r}$$

$$\sum F_t = n_t + (f_k)_t + w_t = 0 \text{ N} - f_k + 0 \text{ N} = +ma_t$$

From the *r*-equation

$$n = mg + \frac{mv^2}{r} \Rightarrow f_k = \mu_k n = \mu_k m\left(g + \frac{v^2}{r}\right)$$

Substituting back into the *t*-equation,

$$a_t = -\frac{f_k}{m} = -\frac{\mu_k m}{m}\left(g + \frac{v^2}{r}\right) = -\mu_k\left(9.8 \text{ m/s}^2 + \frac{(25 \text{ m/s})^2}{200 \text{ m}}\right) = -12.9 \text{ m/s}^2$$

Car C: Car C is in circular motion with the center of the circle below the car.

$$\sum F_r = n_r + (f_k)_r + w_r = -n + 0 \text{ N} + mg = ma_r = \frac{mv^2}{r}$$

$$\sum F_t = n_t + (f_k)_t + w_t = 0 \text{ N} - f_k + 0 \text{ N} = ma_t$$

From the *r*-equation $n = m(g - v^2/r)$. Substituting this into the *t*-equation yields

$$a_t = \frac{-f_k}{m} = \frac{-\mu_k n}{m} = -\mu_k(g - v^2/r) = -6.68 \text{ m/s}^2$$

7.49.   Model: Model the ball as a particle in motion in a vertical circle.
Visualize: **Pictorial representation**   **Physical representation**

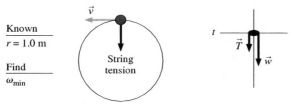

Solve: *If* the ball moves in a complete circle, then there is a tension force $\vec{T}$ when the ball is at the top of the circle. The tension force adds to the weight to cause the centripetal acceleration. The forces are along the *r*-axis, and the center of the circle is below the ball. Newton's second law at the top is

$$(F_{\text{net}})_r = T + w = T + mg = \frac{mv^2}{r}$$

$$\Rightarrow v_{\text{top}} = \sqrt{rg + \frac{rT}{m}}$$

The tension *T* can't become negative, so $T = 0$ N gives the minimum speed v_{min} at which the ball moves in a circle. If the speed is less than v_{min}, then the string will go slack and the ball will fall out of the circle before it reaches the top. Thus,

$$v_{\text{min}} = \sqrt{rg} \Rightarrow \omega_{\text{min}} = \frac{v_{\text{min}}}{r} = \frac{\sqrt{rg}}{r} = \sqrt{\frac{g}{r}} = \sqrt{\frac{(9.8 \text{ m/s}^2)}{(1.0 \text{ m})}} = 3.13 \text{ rad/s} = 29.9 \text{ rpm}$$

7.51. Model: Model the ball as a particle swinging in a vertical circle.
Visualize:

Pictorial representation   **Physical representation**

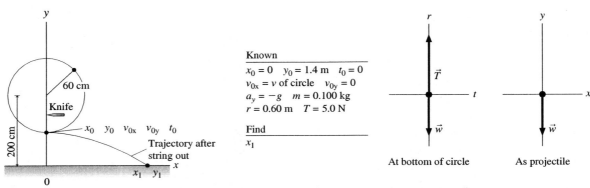

Known
$x_0 = 0$ $y_0 = 1.4$ m $t_0 = 0$
$v_{0x} = v$ of circle $v_{0y} = 0$
$a_y = -g$ $m = 0.100$ kg
$r = 0.60$ m $T = 5.0$ N

Find
x_1

At bottom of circle   As projectile

Solve: Initially, the ball is moving in a circle. Once the string is cut, it becomes a projectile. The final circular-motion velocity is the initial velocity for the projectile. The free body diagram for circular motion is shown at the bottom of the circle. Since $T > w$, there is a net force toward the center of the circle that causes the centripetal acceleration. The r-equation of Newton's second law is

$$(F_{net})_r = T - w = T - mg = \frac{mv^2}{r}$$

$$\Rightarrow v_{bottom} = \sqrt{\frac{r}{m}(T - mg)} = \sqrt{\frac{0.60 \text{ m}}{0.100 \text{ kg}}\left[5.0 \text{ N } - (0.10 \text{ kg})(9.8 \text{ m / s}^2)\right]} = 4.91 \text{ m / s}$$

As a projectile the ball starts at $y_0 = 1.4$ m with $\vec{v}_0 = 4.91\hat{i}$ m / s. The equation for the y-motion is

$$y_1 = 0 \text{ m} = y_0 + v_{0y}\Delta t - \tfrac{1}{2}g(\Delta t)^2 = y_0 - \tfrac{1}{2}gt_1^2$$

This is easily solved to find that the ball hits the ground at time

$$t_1 = \sqrt{\frac{2y_0}{g}} = 0.535 \text{ s}$$

During this time interval it travels a horizontal distance

$$x_1 = x_0 + v_{0x}t_1 = (4.91 \text{ m / s})(0.535 \text{ s}) = 2.63 \text{ m}$$

So the ball hits the floor 2.63 m to the right of the point where the string was cut.

7.59. Solve: (a) A 1000 kg race car enters a 50 m radius curve and accelerates around the curve for 10.0 s. The forward force provided by the car's wheels is 1500 N. After 10.0 s the car has moved 125 m around the track. Find the initial and final angular velocities.
(b) From Newton's second law,

$$F_t = ma_t \Rightarrow 1500 \text{ N} = (1000 \text{ kg})a_t \Rightarrow a_t = 1.5 \text{ m / s}^2 \qquad \Delta\theta = \frac{\Delta s}{r} = \frac{125 \text{ m}}{50 \text{ m}} = 2.5 \text{ radians}$$

$$\theta_f = \theta_i + \omega_i t + \frac{a_t}{2r}t^2 \Rightarrow 2.5 \text{ rad} = 0 \text{ rad} + \omega_i(10 \text{ s}) + \frac{1.5 \text{ m / s}^2}{2(50 \text{ m})}(10 \text{ s})^2 \Rightarrow \omega_i = 0.10 \text{ rad / s}$$

$$\omega_f = \omega_i + \frac{a_t}{r}t = 0.1 \text{ rad / s} + \frac{1.5 \text{ m / s}^2}{50 \text{ m}}(10 \text{ s}) = 0.40 \text{ rad / s}$$

NEWTON'S THIRD LAW

8.1. **Visualize:**

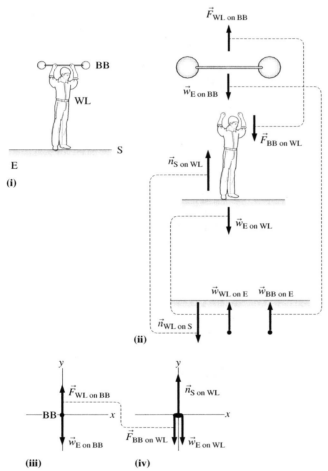

Solve: Figure (i) shows a weightlifter (WL) holding a heavy barbell (BB) across his shoulders. He is standing on a rough surface (S) that is a part of the earth (E). We distinguish between the surface (S), which exerts a contact force, and the earth, which exerts the long range force of gravity. Figure (ii) shows the barbell, the weightlifter, and the earth separated from one another. This separation helps to indicate the forces acting on each object. Figures (iii) and (iv) are free body diagrams for the barbell and the weightlifter, respectively.

Altogether there are four interactions. There is the interaction between the barbell and the weightlifter, the weightlifter and the surface of the earth (contact force), the barbell and the earth, and the weightlifter and the earth. The interaction between the barbell and the weightlifter leads to two forces: $\vec{F}_{\text{WL on BB}}$ and $\vec{F}_{\text{BB on WL}}$. These are an action/reaction pair. The interaction between the weightlifter and the surface of the earth is a contact interaction leading to $\vec{n}_{\text{S on WL}}$ and $\vec{n}_{\text{WL on S}}$. These two forces also constitute an action/reaction pair. The weight force $\vec{w}_{\text{E on BB}}$ has its action/reaction force $\vec{w}_{\text{BB on E}}$, and the weight force $\vec{w}_{\text{E on WL}}$ has its action/reaction force $\vec{w}_{\text{WL on E}}$.

8.3.   Visualize:

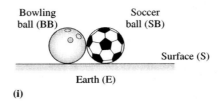

(i)

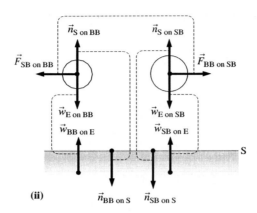

(ii)

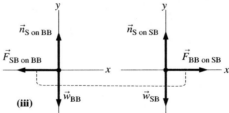

(iii)

Solve: Figure (i) shows the head-on collision of a bowling ball (BB) and a soccer ball (SB) on a hard surface (S) of the earth (E). There are 3 types of interactions in the present case: between the bowling ball and the soccer ball, between the earth and the balls (long-range force of gravity), and between the balls and the surface (contact force). Figure (ii) shows the bowling ball, the soccer ball, and the surface separated from one another. The force on the bowling ball due to the soccer ball $\vec{F}_{SB\ on\ BB}$ and the force on the soccer ball due to the bowling ball $\vec{F}_{BB\ on\ SB}$ make an action/reaction pair. The weights $\vec{w}_{E\ on\ SB}$ and $\vec{w}_{SB\ on\ E}$ are an action/reaction pair, and so are the weights $\vec{w}_{E\ on\ BB}$ and $\vec{w}_{BB\ on\ E}$. The contact forces $\vec{n}_{S\ on\ BB}$ and $\vec{n}_{S\ on\ SB}$ have action/reaction forces in $\vec{n}_{BB\ on\ S}$ and $\vec{n}_{SB\ on\ S}$, respectively. All the action/reaction pairs are indicated by dotted lines. Figure (iii) shows the free-body diagrams for the bowling ball and the soccer ball.

8.5.   Visualize:

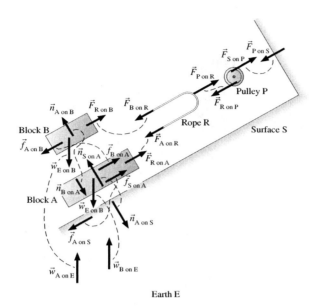

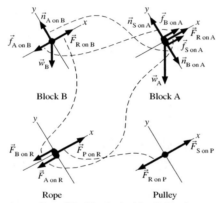

Solve: The top figure shows the pulley (P), block A, block B, the surface S of the incline, the rope (R), and the earth (E). In indicating the various forces, we have denoted the normal (contact) forces by $\vec{n}$, the kinetic frictional (contact) forces by $\vec{f}$, and the weights by $\vec{w}$. All the action/reaction forces have been identified with dotted lines. The bottom figure shows the free body diagrams of each block, the rope, and the pulley.

8.9.   Model: The blocks are to be modeled as particles and denoted as 1, 2, and 3. The surface is frictionless and along with the earth it is a part of the environment. The three blocks are our three systems of interest.

Visualize: **Pictorial representation**

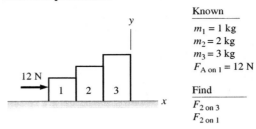

Known

$m_1 = 1$ kg
$m_2 = 2$ kg
$m_3 = 3$ kg
$F_{A \text{ on } 1} = 12$ N

Find

$F_{2 \text{ on } 3}$
$F_{2 \text{ on } 1}$

Physical representation

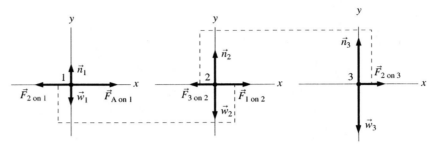

The force applied on block 1 is $F_{A \text{ on } 1} = 12$ N. The acceleration for all the blocks is the same and is denoted by a.
Solve: Newton's second law for the three blocks along the x-direction is

$$\sum \left(F_{\text{on }1} \right)_x = F_{A \text{ on } 1} - F_{2 \text{ on } 1} = m_1 a \qquad \sum \left(F_{\text{on }2} \right)_x = F_{1 \text{ on } 2} - F_{3 \text{ on } 2} = m_2 a \qquad \sum \left(F_{\text{on }3} \right)_x = F_{2 \text{ on } 3} = m_3 a$$

Adding these three equations and using Newton's third law ($F_{2 \text{ on } 1} = F_{1 \text{ on } 2}$ and $F_{3 \text{ on } 2} = F_{2 \text{ on } 3}$), we get

$$F_{A \text{ on } 1} = (m_1 + m_2 + m_3)a \Rightarrow (12 \text{ N}) = (1 \text{ kg} + 2 \text{ kg} + 3 \text{ kg})a \Rightarrow a = 2 \text{ m/s}^2$$

Using this value of a, the force equation on block 3 gives

$$F_{2 \text{ on } 3} = m_3 a = (3 \text{ kg})(2 \text{ m/s}^2) = 6 \text{ N}$$

Substituting into the force equation on block 1,

$$12 \text{ N} - F_{2 \text{ on } 1} = (1 \text{ kg})(2 \text{ m/s}^2) \Rightarrow F_{2 \text{ on } 1} = 10 \text{ N}$$

Assess: Because all three blocks are pushed forward by a force of 12 N, the value of 10 N for the force that the 2 kg block exerts on the 1 kg block is reasonable.

8.13.   Model: The block of ice (I) is a particle and so is the rope (R) because it is not massless. We must therefore consider both the block of ice and the rope as systems.
Visualize: **Pictorial representation**

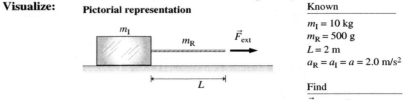

Known

$m_I = 10$ kg
$m_R = 500$ g
$L = 2$ m
$a_R = a_I = a = 2.0 \text{ m/s}^2$

Find

$\vec{F}_{R \text{ on } I}$ F_{ext}

Physical representation

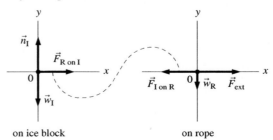

on ice block   on rope

Solve: The force $\vec{F}_{ext}$ acts only on the rope. Since the rope and the ice block move together, they have the same acceleration. Also because the rope has mass, F_{ext} on the front end of the rope is not the same as $F_{I\,on\,R}$ that acts on the rear end of the rope.

Newton's second law along the *x*-axis for the ice block and the rope is

$$\sum \left(F_{on\,I}\right)_x = F_{R\,on\,I} = m_I a = \left(10\ \text{kg}\right)\left(2.0\ \text{m/s}^2\right) = 20\ \text{N}$$

$$\sum \left(F_{on\,R}\right)_x = F_{ext} - F_{I\,on\,R} = m_R a \Rightarrow F_{ext} - F_{R\,on\,I} = m_R a$$

$$\Rightarrow F_{ext} = F_{R\,on\,I} + m_R a = 20\ \text{N} + \left(0.5\ \text{kg}\right)\left(2.0\ \text{m/s}^2\right) = 21\ \text{N}$$

8.15.   **Model:**   The two hanging blocks, which can be modeled as particles, form two systems. The other two systems are the two knots where rope 1 meets with rope 2 and rope 2 meets with rope 3. All the four systems are in static equilibrium. The ropes are assumed to be massless.

Visualize: **Pictorial representation**

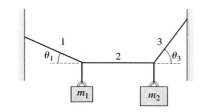

Known
$m_1 = 2.0$ kg
$m_2 = 4.0$ kg
$\theta_1 = 20°$

Find
θ_3 T_3

Physical representation

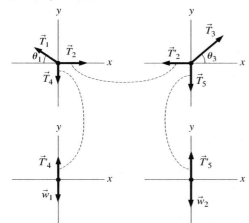

Solve: **(a)** We will consider both the two hanging blocks *and* the two knots. The blocks are in static equilibrium with $\vec{F}_{net} = 0$ N. Note that there are three action/reaction pairs. For Block 1 and Block 2, $\vec{F}_{net} = 0$ N and we have

$$T_4' = w_1 = m_1 g \qquad\qquad T_5' = w_2 = m_2 g$$

Then, by Newton's third law:

$$T_4 = T_4' = m_1 g \qquad\qquad T_5 = T_5' = m_2 g$$

The knots are also in equilibrium. Newton's law applied to the left knot is

$$\left(F_{net}\right)_x = T_2 - T_1 \cos\theta_1 = 0\ \text{N} \qquad \left(F_{net}\right)_y = T_1 \sin\theta_1 - T_4 = T_1 \sin\theta_1 - m_1 g = 0\ \text{N}$$

The *y*-equation gives $T_1 = m_1 g / \sin\theta_1$. Substitute this into the *x*-equation to find

$$T_2 = \frac{m_1 g \cos\theta_1}{\sin\theta_1} = \frac{m_1 g}{\tan\theta_1}$$

Newton's law applied to the right knot is

$$\left(F_{net}\right)_x = T_3 \cos\theta_3 - T_2' = 0\ \text{N} \qquad \left(F_{net}\right)_y = T_3 \sin\theta_3 - T_5 = T_3 \sin\theta_3 - m_2 g = 0\ \text{N}$$

These can be combined just like the equations for the left knot to give

$$T_2' = \frac{m_2 g \cos\theta_3}{\sin\theta_3} = \frac{m_2 g}{\tan\theta_3}$$

But the forces $\vec{T}_2$ and $\vec{T}_2'$ are an action/reaction pair, so $T_2 = T_2'$. Therefore,

$$\frac{m_1 g}{\tan\theta_1} = \frac{m_2 g}{\tan\theta_3} \Rightarrow \tan\theta_3 = \frac{m_2}{m_1}\tan\theta_1 \Rightarrow \theta_3 = \tan^{-1}(2\tan 20°) = 36°$$

We can now use the y-equation for the right knot to find $T_3 = m_2 g/\sin\theta_3 = 66.6\ \text{N}$.

8.23. **Model:** The starship and the shuttlecraft will be denoted as M and m, respectively, and both will be treated as particles. We will also use the constant-acceleration kinematic equations.
Visualize:

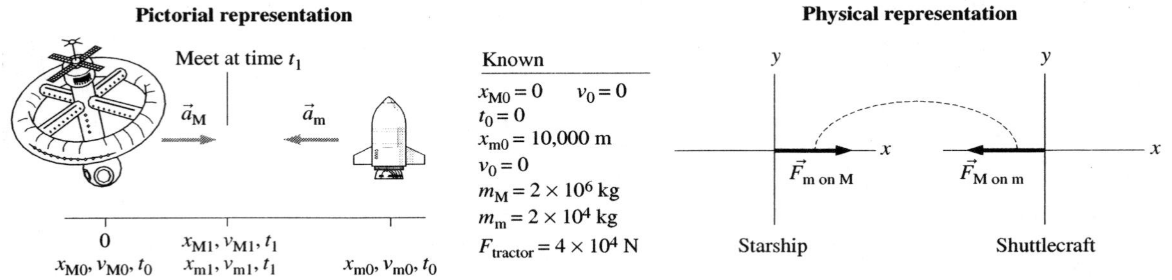

Pictorial representation

Meet at time t_1

$\vec{a}_M$ $\vec{a}_m$

0
x_{M0}, v_{M0}, t_0 x_{M1}, v_{M1}, t_1 x_{m0}, v_{m0}, t_0
x_{m1}, v_{m1}, t_1

Known
$x_{M0} = 0$ $v_0 = 0$
$t_0 = 0$
$x_{m0} = 10{,}000$ m
$v_0 = 0$
$m_M = 2 \times 10^6$ kg
$m_m = 2 \times 10^4$ kg
$F_{tractor} = 4 \times 10^4$ N

Physical representation

y y

$\vec{F}_{m\ on\ M}$ $\vec{F}_{M\ on\ m}$

Starship   Shuttlecraft

Solve: **(a)** The tractor beam is some kind of long-range force $\vec{F}_{M\ on\ m}$. Regardless of what kind of force it is, by Newton's third law there *must* be a reaction force $\vec{F}_{m\ on\ M}$ on the starship. As a result, both the shuttlecraft *and* the starship move toward each other (rather than the starship remaining at rest as it pulls the shuttlecraft in). However, the very different masses of the two craft means that the distances they each move will also be very different. The pictorial representation shows that they meet at time t_1 when $x_{M1} = x_{m1}$. There's only one force on each craft, so Newton's second law is very simple. Furthermore, because the forces are an action/reaction pair,

$$F_{M\ on\ m} = F_{m\ on\ M} = F_{tractor\ beam} = 4 \times 10^4\ \text{N}$$

The accelerations of the two craft are

$$a_M = \frac{F_{m\ on\ M}}{M} = \frac{4 \times 10^4\ \text{N}}{2 \times 10^6\ \text{kg}} = 0.020\ \text{m/s}^2 \qquad a_m = \frac{\vec{F}_{M\ on\ m}}{m} = \frac{-4 \times 10^4\ \text{N}}{2 \times 10^4\ \text{kg}} = -2.0\ \text{m/s}^2$$

Acceleration a_m is negative because the force and acceleration vectors point in the negative x-direction. The accelerations are very different even though the forces are the same. Now we have a constant-acceleration problem in kinematics. At a later time t_1 the positions of the crafts are

$$x_{M1} = x_{M0} + v_{M0}(t_1 - t_0) + \tfrac{1}{2}a_M(t_1 - t_0)^2 = \tfrac{1}{2}a_M t_1^2$$

$$x_{m1} = x_{m0} + v_{m0}(t_1 - t_0) + \tfrac{1}{2}a_m(t_1 - t_0)^2 = x_{m0} + \tfrac{1}{2}a_m t_1^2$$

The craft meet when $x_{M1} = x_{m1}$, so

$$\tfrac{1}{2}a_M t_1^2 = x_{m0} + \tfrac{1}{2}a_m t_1^2 \Rightarrow t_1 = \sqrt{\frac{2x_{m0}}{a_M - a_m}} = \sqrt{\frac{2x_{m0}}{a_M + |a_m|}} = \sqrt{\frac{2(10{,}000\ \text{m})}{2.02\ \text{m/s}^2}} = 99.5\ \text{s}$$

Knowing t_1, we can now find the starship's position as it meets the shuttlecraft:

$$x_{M1} = \tfrac{1}{2}a_M t_1^2 = 99.0\ \text{m}$$

The starship moves 99.0 m as it pulls in the shuttlecraft from 10 km away.

8.25. **Model:** Assume package A and package B are particles. Use the model of kinetic friction and the constant-acceleration kinematic equations.

Visualize: **Pictorial representation**

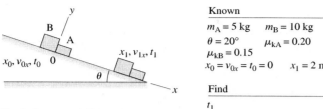

Known

$m_A = 5$ kg $m_B = 10$ kg

$\theta = 20°$ $\mu_{kA} = 0.20$

$\mu_{kB} = 0.15$

$x_0 = v_{0x} = t_0 = 0$ $x_1 = 2$ m

Find

t_1

Physical representation

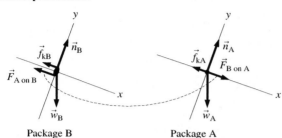

Package B   Package A

Solve: Package B has a smaller coefficient of friction. It will try to overtake package A and push against it. Package A will push back on B. The acceleration constraint is $(a_A)_x = (a_B)_x = a$.

Newton's second law for each package is

$$\sum \left(F_{\text{on A}} \right)_x = F_{\text{B on A}} + w_A \sin\theta - f_{kA} = m_A a$$

$$\Rightarrow F_{\text{B on A}} + m_A g \sin\theta - \mu_{kA}\left(m_A g \cos\theta \right) = m_A a$$

$$\sum \left(F_{\text{on B}} \right)_x = -F_{\text{A on B}} - f_{kB} + w_B \sin\theta = m_B a$$

$$\Rightarrow -F_{\text{A on B}} - \mu_{kB}\left(m_B g \cos\theta \right) + m_B g \sin\theta = m_B a$$

where we have used $n_A = m_A \cos\theta\, g$ and $n_B = m_B \cos\theta\, g$. Adding the two force equations, and using $F_{\text{A on B}} = F_{\text{B on A}}$ because they are an action/reaction pair, we get

$$a = g\sin\theta - \frac{\left(\mu_{kA} m_A + \mu_{kB} m_B \right)\left(g\cos\theta \right)}{m_A + m_B} = 1.817 \text{ m/s}^2$$

Finally, using $x_1 = x_0 + v_{0x}\left(t_1 - t_0 \right) + \frac{1}{2} a \left(t_1 - t_0 \right)^2$,

$$2 \text{ m} = 0 \text{ m} + 0 \text{ m} + \tfrac{1}{2}\left(1.817 \text{ m/s}^2 \right)\left(t_1 - 0 \text{ s} \right)^2 \Rightarrow t_1 = 1.48 \text{ s}$$

8.29.   Model: The sled (S) and the box (B) will be treated in the particle model, and the model of friction will be used.

Visualize: **Pictorial representation**   **Physical representation**

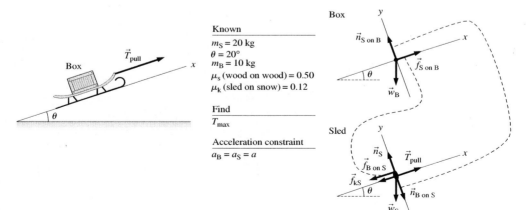

Known

$m_S = 20$ kg

$\theta = 20°$

$m_B = 10$ kg

μ_s (wood on wood) = 0.50

μ_k (sled on snow) = 0.12

Find

T_{max}

Acceleration constraint

$a_B = a_S = a$

In the sled's physical representation n_S is the normal (contact) force on the sled due to the snow. Similarly f_{kS} is the force of kinetic friction on the sled due to snow.

Solve: Newton's second law on the box in the y-direction is

$$n_{\text{S on B}} - w_B \cos 20° = 0 \text{ N} \Rightarrow n_{\text{S on B}} = (10 \text{ kg})(9.8 \text{ m/s}^2)\cos 20° = 92.09 \text{ N}$$

The static friction force $\vec{f}_{\text{S on B}}$ accelerates the box. The maximum acceleration occurs when static friction reaches its maximum possible value.

$$f_{s\,\text{max}} = \mu_s n_{\text{S on B}} = (0.50)(92.09 \text{ N}) = 46.05 \text{ N}$$

Newton's second law along the x-direction thus gives the maximum acceleration

$$f_{\text{S on B}} - w_B \sin 20° = m_B a \Rightarrow 46.05 \text{ N} - (10 \text{ kg})(9.8 \text{ m/s}^2)\sin 20° = (10 \text{ kg})a \Rightarrow a = 1.25 \text{ m/s}^2$$

Newton's second law for the sled along the y-direction is

$$n_S - n_{\text{B on S}} - w_S \cos 20° = 0 \text{ N}$$

$$\Rightarrow n_S = n_{\text{B on S}} + m_S g \cos 20° = (92.09 \text{ N}) + (20 \text{ kg})(9.8 \text{ m/s}^2)\cos 20° = 276.27 \text{ N}$$

Therefore, the force of friction on the sled by the snow is

$$f_{kS} = (\mu_k)n_S = (0.12)(276.27 \text{ N}) = 33.15 \text{ N}$$

Newton's second law along the x-direction is

$$T_{\text{pull}} - w_S \sin 20° - f_{kS} - f_{\text{B on S}} = m_S a$$

The friction force $f_{\text{B on S}} = f_{\text{S on B}}$ because these are an action/reaction pair. We're using the maximum acceleration, so the maximum tension is

$$T_{\text{max}} - (20 \text{ kg})(9.8 \text{ m/s}^2)\sin 20° - 33.15 \text{ N} - 46.05 \text{ N} = (20 \text{ kg})(1.25 \text{ m/s}^2)$$

$$\Rightarrow T_{\text{max}} = 171.2 \text{ N}$$

Assess: T_{max} of 171.2 N corresponds to a mass of 171.2 N/9.8 m/s² = 17.5 kg. For the masses and the angle in this problem, a maximum tension of 171.2 N is physically understandable.

8.35.   Model: Assume the particle model for m_1, m_2, and m_3, and the model of kinetic friction. Assume the ropes to be massless, and the pulleys to be frictionless and massless.

Visualize: **Pictorial representation**

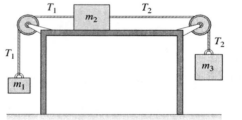

Known
m_1 = 1.0 kg
m_2 = 2.0 kg
m_3 = 3.0 kg
μ_k (block and table) = 0.30

Find
a_2

Physical representation

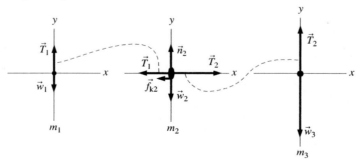

Solve: Newton's second law for m_1 is $T_1 - w_1 = m_1 a_1$. Newton's second law for m_2 is

$$\sum \left(F_{\text{on } m_2} \right)_y = n_2 - w_2 = 0 \text{ N} \Rightarrow n_2 = (2 \text{ kg})(9.8 \text{ m/s}^2) = 19.6 \text{ N}$$

$$\sum \left(F_{\text{on } m_2} \right)_x = T_2 - f_{k2} - T_1 = m_2 a_2 \Rightarrow T_2 - \mu_k n_2 - T_1 = (2 \text{ kg}) a_2$$

Newton's second law for m_3 is

$$\sum \left(F_{\text{on } m_3} \right)_y = T_2 - w_3 = m_3 a_3$$

Since m_1, m_2, and m_3 move together, $a_1 = a_2 = -a_3 = a$. The equations for the three masses thus become

$$T_1 - w_1 = m_1 a = (1 \text{ kg}) a \qquad T_2 - \mu_k n_2 - T_1 = m_2 a = (2 \text{ kg}) a \qquad T_2 - w_3 = -m_3 a = -(3 \text{ kg}) a$$

Subtracting the third equation from the sum of the first two equations yields:

$$-w_1 - \mu_k n_2 + w_3 = (6 \text{ kg}) a$$

$$\Rightarrow -(1 \text{ kg})(9.8 \text{ m/s}^2) - (0.300)(19.6 \text{ N}) + (3 \text{ kg})(9.8 \text{ m/s}^2) = (6 \text{ kg}) a \Rightarrow a = 2.29 \text{ m/s}^2$$

8.37. Model: Assume the particle model for the two blocks.
Visualize:

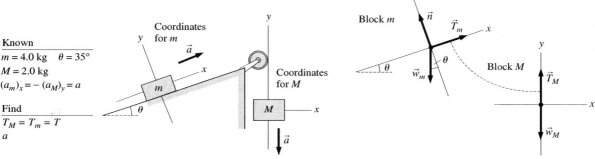

Pictorial representation

Known
$m = 4.0$ kg $\theta = 35°$
$M = 2.0$ kg
$(a_m)_x = -(a_M)_y = a$

Find
$T_M = T_m = T$
a

Coordinates for m

Coordinates for M

Physical representation

Block m

Block M

Solve: **(a)** The slope is frictionless, so the blocks stay in place *only* if held. Once m is released, the blocks will move one way or the other. As long as m is held, the blocks are in static equilibrium with $\vec{F}_{\text{net}} = 0$ N. Newton's second law for the hanging block M is

$$\left(F_{\text{net on } M} \right)_y = T_M - Mg = 0 \text{ N} \Rightarrow T_M = Mg = 19.6 \text{ N}$$

By Newton's third law, $T_M = T_m = T = 19.6$ N is the tension in the string.
(b) The free-body diagram shows box m after it is released. Whether it moves up or down the slope depends on whether the acceleration a is positive or negative. The acceleration constraint is $(a_m)_x = a = -(a_M)_y$. Newton's second law for each system gives

$$\left(F_{\text{net on } m} \right)_x = T - mg \sin 35° = m(a_m)_x = ma \qquad \left(F_{\text{net on } M} \right)_y = T - Mg = M(a_M)_y = -Ma$$

We have two equations in two unknowns. Subtract the second from the first to eliminate T:

$$-mg \sin 35° + Mg = (m + M) a \Rightarrow a = \frac{M - m \sin 35°}{M + m} g = -0.481 \text{ m/s}^2$$

Since $a < 0$ m/s^2, the box accelerates *down* the slope.
(c) It is now straightforward to compute $T = Mg - Ma = 20.6$ N. Notice how the tension is *larger* than when the blocks were motionless.

8.43. Model: Use the particle model for the tightrope walker and the rope. The rope is assumed to be massless, so the tension in the rope is uniform.

Visualize:

Pictorial representation

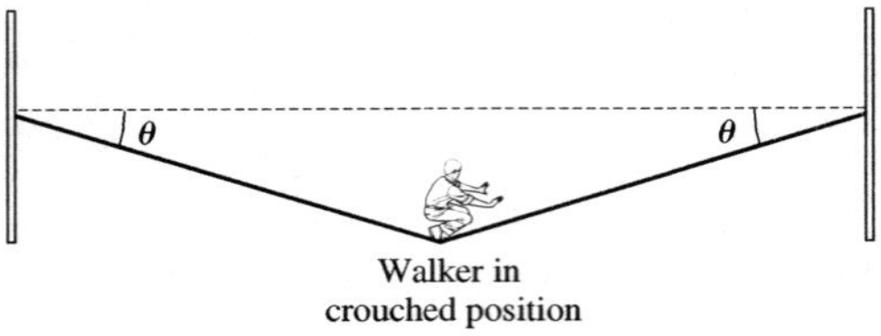

Walker in
crouched position

Known
$\theta = 10°$
$a = 8.0 \text{ m/s}^2$
$m = 70 \text{ kg}$

Physical representation

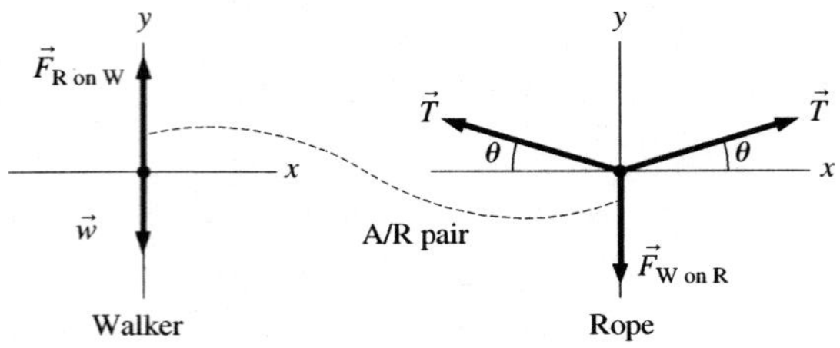

Solve: Newton's second law for the tightrope walker is

$$F_{\text{R on W}} - w = ma \Rightarrow F_{\text{R on W}} = m(a + g) = (70 \text{ kg})(8.0 \text{ m/s}^2 + 9.8 \text{ m/s}^2) = 1246 \text{ N}$$

Now, Newton's second law for the rope gives

$$\sum \left(F_{\text{on R}}\right)_y = T\sin\theta + T\sin\theta - F_{\text{W on R}} = 0 \text{ N} \Rightarrow T = \frac{F_{\text{W on R}}}{2\sin 10°} = \frac{F_{\text{R on W}}}{2\sin 10°} = \frac{1246}{2\sin 10°} = 3590 \text{ N}$$

We used $F_{\text{W on R}} = F_{\text{R on W}}$ because they are an action/reaction pair.

IMPULSE AND MOMENTUM

9.3. **Visualize:** Please refer to Figure Ex9.3.
Solve: The impulse is defined in Equation 9.6 as

$$J_x = \int_{t_i}^{t_f} F_x(t)\,dt = \text{area under the } F_x(t) \text{ curve between } t_i \text{ and } t_f$$

$$\Rightarrow 6.0 \text{ N s} = \tfrac{1}{2}(F_{max})(8 \text{ ms}) \Rightarrow F_{max} = 1500 \text{ N}$$

9.7. **Model:** Model the object as a particle and the interaction with the force as a collision.
Visualize: Please refer to Figure Ex9.7.
Solve: **(a)** Using the equations

$$p_{fx} = p_{ix} + J_x \qquad J_x = \int_{t_i}^{t_f} F_x(t)\,dt$$

$$\Rightarrow v_{fx} = (1.0 \text{ m/s}) + \frac{1}{2.0 \text{ kg}} \text{ (area under the positive } F_x(t) \text{ curve)}$$

$$= (1.0 \text{ m/s}) + \frac{1}{2.0 \text{ kg}}(1.0 \text{ Ns}) = 1.5 \text{ m/s}$$

(b) Likewise,

$$v_{fx} = (1.0 \text{ m/s}) + \left(\frac{1}{2.0 \text{ kg}}\right) \text{ (area under the negative } F_x(t) \text{ curve)}$$

$$= (1.0 \text{ m/s}) + \left(\frac{1}{2.0 \text{ kg}}\right)(-1.0 \text{ Ns}) = 0.5 \text{ m/s}$$

Assess: For an object with positive velocity, a negative impulse of the force slows an object, whereas a positive impulse increases an object's speed. The opposite is true for an object with negative velocity.

9.9. **Model:** Use the particle model for the falling object and the impulse-momentum theorem.
Visualize: **Pictorial representation**

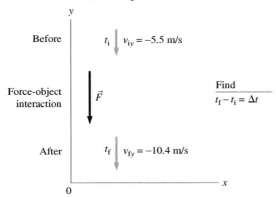

Note that the object is interacting with the gravitational force, whose magnitude is *mg* and which is practically a constant near the earth's surface.

Solve: Using the impulse-momentum theorem,

$$p_{fy} - p_{iy} = J_y = \int_{t_i}^{t_f} F(t)\,dt \Rightarrow mv_{fy} - mv_{iy} = -mg(t_f - t_i)$$

$$\Rightarrow (t_f - t_i) = \Delta t = \frac{v_{iy} - v_{fy}}{g} = \frac{-5.5 \text{ m/s} - (-10.4 \text{ m/s})}{9.8 \text{ m/s}^2} = 0.5 \text{ s}$$

Assess: Since $F = -mg$ is independent of time, we have taken it out of the impulse integral.

9.13. Model: Model the railroad car and the load of gravel as particles.

Visualize:

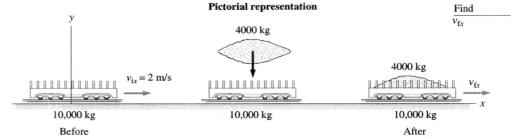

Solve: The impulse of any force on the car along the horizontal or *x*-direction is zero. Therefore, $J_x = 0$ Ns, which means $p_{fx} = p_{ix}$. Hence,

$$(10{,}000 \text{ kg} + 4{,}000 \text{ kg})v_{fx} = (10{,}000 \text{ kg})(2.0 \text{ m/s}) \Rightarrow v_{fx} = 1.43 \text{ m/s}$$

9.15. Model: We will define our system to be archer+arrow. The force of the archer (A) on the arrow (a) is equal to the force of the arrow on the archer. These are internal forces within the system. The archer is standing on frictionless ice, and the normal force by ice on the system balances the weight force. Thus $\vec{F}_{ext} = \vec{0}$ on the system, and momentum is conserved.

Visualize:

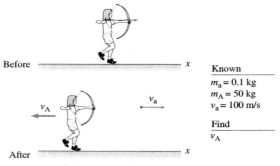

The initial momentum p_{ix} of the system is zero, because the archer and the arrow are at rest. The final moment p_{fx} must also be zero.

Solve: We have $M_A v_A + m_a v_a = 0$ kg m/s. Therefore,

$$v_A = \frac{-m_a v_a}{m_A} = \frac{-(0.1 \text{ kg})(100 \text{ m/s})}{50 \text{ kg}} = -0.2 \text{ m/s}$$

Assess: It is the total final momentum that is zero, although the individual momenta are nonzero. Since the arrow has forward momentum, the archer will have backward momentum.

9.19. Model: The two cars are not an isolated system because of external frictional forces. But during the collision friction is not going to be significant. Within the impulse approximation, the momentum of the Cadillac+Volkswagen system will be conserved in the collision.

Visualize:

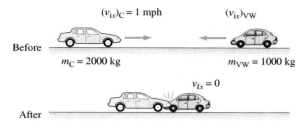

Pictorial representation

Solve: The momentum conservation equation $p_{fx} = p_{ix}$ is

$$\left(m_{\text{C}} + m_{\text{VW}}\right)v_{fx} = m_{\text{C}}\left(v_{ix}\right)_{\text{C}} + m_{\text{VW}}\left(v_{ix}\right)_{\text{VW}} \Rightarrow 0 \text{ kg mph} = \left(2000 \text{ kg}\right)\left(1 \text{ mph}\right) + \left(1000 \text{ kg}\right)\left(v_{ix}\right)_{\text{VW}} \Rightarrow \left(v_{ix}\right)_{\text{VW}} = -2 \text{ mph}$$

9.21.   Model: This problem deals with the conservation of momentum in two dimensions. The balls of clay will be treated as particles.

Visualize: Pictorial representation

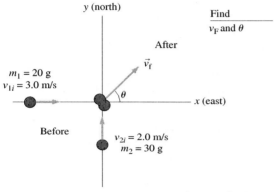

Solve: The conservation of momentum equation $\vec{p}_{\text{before}} = \vec{p}_{\text{after}}$ is

$$m_1 v_{1x} + m_2 v_{2x} = \left(m_1 + m_2\right)v_{fx} \qquad\qquad m_1 v_{1y} + m_2 v_{2y} = \left(m_1 + m_2\right)v_{fy}$$

Substituting in the given values,

$$\left(.02 \text{ kg}\right)\left(3.0 \text{ m/s}\right) + 0 \text{ kg m/s} = \left(.02 \text{ kg} + .03 \text{ kg}\right)v_f \cos\theta$$

$$0 \text{ kg m/s} + \left(.03 \text{ kg}\right)\left(2.0 \text{ m/s}\right) = \left(.02 \text{ kg} + .03 \text{ kg}\right)v_f \sin\theta$$

$$\Rightarrow v_f \cos\theta = 1.2 \text{ m/s} \qquad v_f \sin\theta = 1.2 \text{ m/s}$$

$$\Rightarrow v_f = \sqrt{\left(1.2 \text{ m/s}\right)^2 + \left(1.2 \text{ m/s}\right)^2} = 1.7 \text{ m/s} \qquad \theta = \tan^{-1}\frac{v_y}{v_x} = \tan^{-1}(1) = 45°$$

9.23.   Model: The moon is treated as a particle.

Solve: A particle moving in a circular orbit of radius r with velocity v has an angular momentum $L = mvr$. The sidereal period of the moon is $T = 27.32$ days $= 2.36 \times 10^6$ s. The radius of the orbit $r = 3.8 \times 10^8$ m. The mass of the moon $m = 7.34 \times 10^{22}$ kg. Using $v = 2\pi r/T$, we can write

$$L = m\frac{2\pi}{T}r^2 = 7.34 \times 10^{22} \text{ kg}\frac{2\pi}{2.36 \times 10^6 \text{ sec}}\left(3.8 \times 10^8 \text{ m}\right)^2 = 2.82 \times 10^{34} \text{ kg }\frac{\text{m}^2}{\text{s}}$$

9.27.   Model: Model the racket and the ball as particles. The two objects constitute our system. During the collision of the ball and racket, momentum is conserved because all external interactions are insignificantly small.

Visualize: **Pictorial representation**

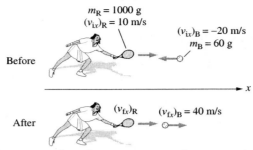

$m_R = 1000$ g
$(v_{ix})_R = 10$ m/s

$(v_{ix})_B = -20$ m/s
$m_B = 60$ g

Before

$\longrightarrow x$

$(v_{fx})_R$ $(v_{fx})_B = 40$ m/s

After

Solve: **(a)** The conservation of momentum equation $p_{fx} = p_{ix}$ is

$$m_R(v_{fx})_R + m_B(v_{fx})_B = m_R(v_{ix})_R + m_B(v_{ix})_B$$

$$(1.0 \text{ kg})(v_{fx})_R + (0.06 \text{ kg})(40 \text{ m/s}) = (1.0 \text{ kg})(10 \text{ m/s}) + (0.06 \text{ kg})(-20 \text{ m/s}) \Rightarrow (v_{fx})_R = 6.4 \text{ m/s}$$

(b) The impulse on the ball is calculated from $(p_{fx})_B = (p_{ix})_B + J_x$ as follows:

$$(0.06 \text{ kg})(40 \text{ m/s}) = (0.06 \text{ kg})(-20 \text{ m/s}) + J_x \Rightarrow J_x = 3.6 \text{ N s} = \int F dt = F_{avg} \Delta t$$

$$\Rightarrow F_{avg} = \frac{3.6 \text{ Ns}}{10 \text{ ms}} = 360 \text{ N}$$

Let us now compare this force with the ball's weight $w_B = m_B g = (0.06 \text{ kg})(9.8 \text{ m/s}^2) = 0.588 \text{ N}$. Thus, $F_{avg} = 612 \, w_B$.

Assess: This is a significant force and is reasonable because the impulse due to this force changes the direction as well as the speed of the ball from approximately 45 mph to 90 mph.

9.31. **Model:** Use the particle model for the ball of clay (C) and the 1.0 kg block (B). The two objects are a system and it is a case of a perfectly inelastic collision. Since no significant external forces act on the system in the x-direction during the collision, momentum is conserved along the x-direction.

Visualize: **Pictorial representation**

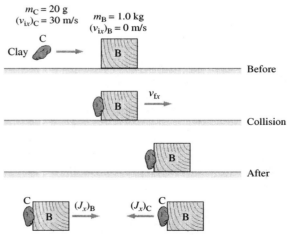

$m_C = 20$ g
$(v_{ix})_C = 30$ m/s

$m_B = 1.0$ kg
$(v_{ix})_B = 0$ m/s

C

Clay

B

Before

v_{fx}

B

Collision

B

After

C

B $(J_x)_B$ $(J_x)_C$ C

B

Solve: **(a)** The conservation of momentum equation $p_{fx} = p_{ix}$ is

$$(1.0 \text{ kg} + 0.02 \text{ kg})v_{fx} = (0.02 \text{ kg})(30 \text{ m/s}) + (1.0 \text{ kg})(0 \text{ m/s}) \Rightarrow v_{fx} = 0.588 \text{ m/s}$$

The impulse of the ball of clay on the block is calculated as follows:

$$(p_{fx})_B = (p_{ix})_B + (J_x)_B \Rightarrow (J_x)_B = m_B(v_{fx})_B - m_B(v_{ix})_B = (1.0 \text{ kg})(v_{fx}) - 0 \text{ Ns} = 0.588 \text{ Ns}$$

(b) The impulse of the block on the ball of clay is calculated as follows:

$$(p_{fx})_C = (p_{ix})_C + (J_x)_C \Rightarrow (J_x)_C = m_C v_{fx} - m_C(v_{ix})_C = (0.02 \text{ kg})(0.588 \text{ m/s}) - (0.02 \text{ kg})(30 \text{ m/s}) = -0.588 \text{ Ns}$$

(c) Yes, $(J_x)_B = -(J_x)_C$.

Assess: During the collision, the ball of clay and the block exert equal and opposite forces on each other for the same time. Impulse is therefore also equal in magnitude but opposite in direction.

9.37. Model: The billiard balls will be modeled as particles. The two balls, m_1 (moving east) and m_2 (moving west), together are our system. This is an isolated system because any frictional force during the brief collision period is going to be insignificant. Within the impulse approximation, the momentum of our system will be conserved in the collision.

Visualize: Pictorial representation

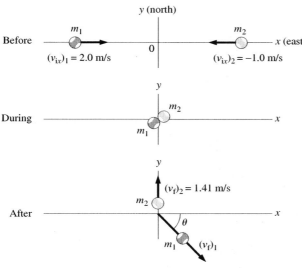

Note that $m_1 = m_2 = m$.

Solve: The equation $p_{fx} = p_{ix}$ yields:

$$m_1(v_{fx})_1 + m_2(v_{fx})_2 = m_1(v_{ix})_1 + m_2(v_{ix})_2 \Rightarrow m_1(v_f)_1 \cos\theta + 0 \text{ kg m / s} = m_1(v_{ix})_1 + m_2(v_{ix})_2$$

$$\Rightarrow (v_f)_1 \cos\theta = (v_{ix})_1 + (v_{ix})_2 = 2.0 \text{ m / s} - 1.0 \text{ m / s} = 1.0 \text{ m / s}$$

The equation $p_{fy} = p_{iy}$ yields:

$$+m_1(v_f)_1 \sin\theta + m_2(v_f)_2 = 0 \text{ kg / s} \Rightarrow (v_f)_1 \sin\theta = -(v_f)_2 = -1.41 \text{ m / s}$$

$$\Rightarrow (v_f)_1 = \sqrt{(1.0 \text{ m / s})^2 + (-1.41 \text{ m / s})^2} = 1.73 \text{ m / s}$$

$$\theta = \tan^{-1}\left(\frac{1.41 \text{ m / s}}{1.0 \text{ m / s}}\right) = 54.7°$$

The angle is below $+x$ axis.

9.39. Model: This is a two-part problem. First, we have an inelastic collision between Fred (F) and Brutus (B). Fred and Brutus are an isolated system. The momentum of the system during collision is conserved since no significant external force acts on the system. The second part involves the dynamics of the Fred+Brutus system sliding on the ground.

Visualize: Pictorial representation

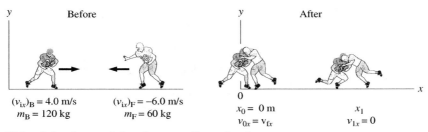

Note that the collision is head-on and therefore one-dimensional.

Solve: The equation $p_{fx} = p_{ix}$ is

$$(m_F + m_B)v_{fx} = m_F(v_{ix})_F + m_B(v_{ix})_B \Rightarrow (60 \text{ kg} + 120 \text{ kg})v_{fx} = (60 \text{ kg})(-6.0 \text{ m / s}) + (120 \text{ kg})(4.0 \text{ m / s})$$
$$\Rightarrow v_{fx} = 0.667 \text{ m / s}$$

The model of kinetic friction yields:

$$f_k = \mu_k n = \mu_k (m_F + m_B)g = -(m_F + m_B)a_x \Rightarrow a_x = -\mu_k g$$

Using the kinematic equation $v_{1x}^2 = v_{0x}^2 + 2a_x(x_1 - x_0)$, we get

$$v_{1x}^2 = v_{0x}^2 - 2\mu_k g\, x_1 \Rightarrow 0 \text{ m}^2/\text{s}^2 = v_{fx}^2 - 2(0.30)(9.8 \text{ m / s}^2)x_1$$
$$\Rightarrow 0 \text{ m}^2/\text{s}^2 = (0.667 \text{ m / s})^2 - (5.88 \text{ m / s}^2)x_1 \Rightarrow x_1 = 7.57 \text{ cm}$$

Assess: After the collision, Fred and Brutus slide with a small speed but with a good amount of kinetic friction. A stopping distance of 7.57 cm is reasonable.

9.45.   Model: Model Brian (B) along with his wooden skis as a particle. The "collision" between Brian and Ashley lasts for a short time, and during this time no significant external forces act on the Brian+Ashley system. Within the impulse approximation, we can then assume momentum conservation for our system. After finding the velocity of the system immediately after the collision, we will apply constant-acceleration kinematic equations and the model of kinetic friction to find the final speed at the bottom of the slope.
Visualize:

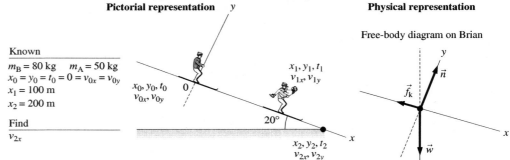

Solve: Brian skiing down for 100 m:

$$(v_{1x})_B^2 = (v_{0x})_B^2 + 2a_x(x_{1B} - x_{0B}) = 0 \text{ m}^2/\text{s}^2 + 2a_x(100 \text{ m} - 0 \text{ m}) \Rightarrow (v_{1x})_B = \sqrt{(200 \text{ m})a_x}$$

To obtain a_x, we apply Newton's second law to Brian in the x and y directions as follows:

$$\sum (F_{\text{on B}})_x = w_B \sin\theta - f_k = m_B a_x \qquad \sum (F_{\text{on B}})_y = n - w_B \cos\theta = 0 \text{ N} \Rightarrow n = w\cos\theta$$

From the model of kinetic friction, $f_k = \mu_k n = \mu_k w_B \cos\theta$. The x-equation thus becomes

$$w_B \sin\theta - \mu_k w_B \cos\theta = m_B a_x$$

$$\Rightarrow a_x = g(\sin\theta - \mu_k \cos\theta) = (9.8 \text{ m / s}^2)[\sin 20° - (0.06)\cos 20°] = 2.799 \text{ m / s}^2$$

Using this value of a_x, $(v_{1x})_B = \sqrt{(200 \text{ m})(2.799 \text{ m / s}^2)} = 23.66 \text{ m / s}$. In the collision with Ashley the equation $p_{fx} = p_{ix}$ is

$$(m_B + m_A)v_{2x} = m_B(v_{1x})_B \Rightarrow v_{2x} = \frac{m_B}{m_B + m_A}(v_{1x})_B = \frac{80 \text{ kg}}{80 \text{ kg} + 50 \text{ kg}}(23.66 \text{ m / s}) = 14.56 \text{ m / s}$$

Brian+Ashley skiing down the slope:

$$v_{3x}^2 = v_{2x}^2 + 2a_x(x_3 - x_2) = (14.56 \text{ m/s})^2 + 2(2.799 \text{ m / s}^2)(100 \text{ m}) \Rightarrow v_{3x} = 27.8 \text{ m / s}$$

That is, Brian+Ashley arrive at the bottom of the slope with a speed of 27.8 m/s.
Assess: A speed of approximately 62 mph on a ski-slope of 200 m length and 20° slope is reasonable. Also note that we have used the same value of a_x in the first and the last parts of this problem. This is because a_x is independent of mass in this problem.

9.49.   Model: This is an isolated system, so momentum is conserved in the explosion. Momentum is a *vector* quantity, so the direction of the initial velocity vector $\vec{v}_i$ establishes the direction of the momentum vector. The final momentum vector, after the explosion, must still point in the +*x*-direction. The two known pieces continue to move along this line and have no *y*-components of momentum. The missing third piece cannot have a *y*-component of momentum if momentum is to be conserved, so it must move along the *x*-axis – either straight forward or straight backward. We can use conservation laws to find out.

Visualize:

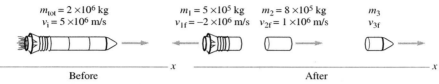

Pictorial representation

Solve: From the conservation of mass, the mass of piece 3 is

$$m_3 = m_{total} - m_1 - m_2 = 7.0 \times 10^5 \text{ kg}$$

To conserve momentum along the *x*-axis, we require

$$\left[p_i = m_{total} v_i \right] = \left[p_f = p_{1f} + p_{2f} + p_{3f} = m_1 v_{1f} + m_2 v_{2f} + p_{3f} \right]$$

$$\Rightarrow p_{3f} = m_{total} v_i - m_1 v_{1f} - m_2 v_{2f} = +1.02 \times 10^{13} \text{ kg m / s}$$

Because $p_{3f} > 0$, the third piece moves in the +*x*-direction, that is, straight forward. Because we know the mass m_3, we can find the velocity of the third piece as follows:

$$v_{3f} = \frac{p_{3f}}{m_3} = \frac{1.02 \times 10^{13} \text{ kg m / s}}{7.0 \times 10^5 \text{ kg}} = 1.46 \times 10^7 \text{ m / s}$$

9.53.   Model: The neutron's decay is an "explosion" of the neutron into several pieces. The neutron is an isolated system, so its momentum should be conserved. The initial momentum is $p_{ix} = 0$ kg m/s. The observed decay products, the electron and proton, move in opposite directions.

Visualize:

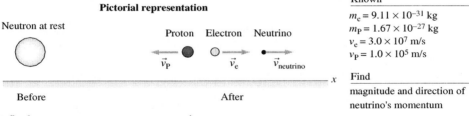

Pictorial representation

Known

$m_e = 9.11 \times 10^{-31}$ kg
$m_P = 1.67 \times 10^{-27}$ kg
$v_e = 3.0 \times 10^7$ m/s
$v_P = 1.0 \times 10^5$ m/s

Find

magnitude and direction of neutrino's momentum

Solve: **(a)** The final momentum $p_{fx} = m_e v_e + m_p v_p$ is

$$2.73 \times 10^{-23} \text{ kg m / s} - 1.67 \times 10^{-22} \text{ kg m / s} = -1.40 \times 10^{-22} \text{ kg m / s}$$

No, momentum does not seem to be conserved.

(b) and **(c)** If the neutrino is needed to conserve momentum, then $p_e + p_p + p_{neutrino} = 0$ kg m / s. This requires

$$p_{neutrino} = -\left(p_e + p_p \right) = +1.40 \times 10^{-22} \text{ kg m / s}$$

The neutrino must "carry away" 1.40×10^{-22} kg m/s of momentum in the same direction as the electron.

9.55.   Model: Model the three balls of clay as particle 1 (moving north), particle 2 (moving west), and particle 3 (moving southeast). The three stick together during their collision, which is perfectly inelastic. The impulse approximation during the brief collision time implies that the momentum of the system is conserved.

Visualize: **Pictorial representation**

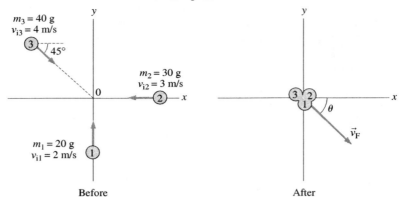

Before   After

Solve: The three initial momenta are

$$\vec{p}_{i1} = m_1\vec{v}_{i1} = (0.02 \text{ kg})(2 \text{ m / s})\hat{j} = 0.04\hat{j} \text{ kg m / s}$$

$$\vec{p}_{i2} = m_2\vec{v}_{i2} = (0.03 \text{ kg})(-3 \text{ m / s } \hat{i}) = -0.09\hat{i} \text{ kg m / s}$$

$$\vec{p}_{i3} = m_3\vec{v}_{i3} = (0.04 \text{ kg})[(4 \text{ m / s})\cos 45°\hat{i} - (4 \text{ m / s})\sin 45°\hat{j}] = (0.113\hat{i} - 0.113\hat{j}) \text{ kg m / s}$$

Since $\vec{p}_f = \vec{p}_i = \vec{p}_{i1} + \vec{p}_{i2} + \vec{p}_{i3}$, we have

$$(m_1 + m_2 + m_3)\vec{v}_f = (0.023\hat{i} - 0.073\hat{j}) \text{ kg m / s} \Rightarrow \vec{v}_f = (0.256\hat{i} - 0.811\hat{j}) \text{ m / s}$$

$$\Rightarrow v_f = \sqrt{(0.256 \text{ m / s})^2 + (-0.811 \text{ m / s})^2} = 0.85 \text{ m / s}$$

$$\theta = \tan^{-1}\frac{|v_{fy}|}{v_{fx}} = \tan^{-1}\frac{0.811}{0.256} = 72.5° \text{ below } +x$$

9.59.   Model: The angular momentum of a particle in circular motion is constant if no tangential force acts on the particle. In the present case, the table is frictionless and the rod is massless. We will represent the block as a particle undergoing circular motion.

Visualize: **Pictorial representation**

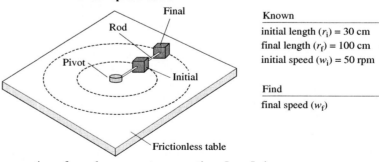

Known

initial length (r_i) = 30 cm
final length (r_f) = 100 cm
initial speed (w_i) = 50 rpm

Find

final speed (w_f)

Solve: The conservation of angular momentum equation $L_f = L_i$ is

$$mv_f r_f = mv_i r_i \Rightarrow (r_f\omega_f)r_f = (r_i\omega_i)r_i \Rightarrow \omega_f = \left(\frac{r_i}{r_f}\right)^2\omega_i = \left(\frac{30 \text{ cm}}{100 \text{ cm}}\right)^2(50 \text{ rpm}) = 4.5 \text{ rpm}$$

Assess: An angular speed of 4.5 rpm is reasonable, since the angular speed varies inversely as the square of the object's distance from the rotation axis.

9.61.   Model: Model the puck and the 200 g weights as particles. The puck is in circular motion and the forces acting on the puck are its weight downward, the radial tension in the string, and a normal force upward. There is no tangential force acting on the puck, and thus the angular momentum of the puck is conserved.

Visualize: **Pictorial representation**

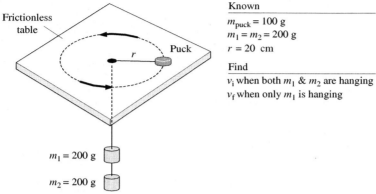

Frictionless table

r Puck

Known
$m_{puck} = 100$ g
$m_1 = m_2 = 200$ g
$r = 20$ cm

Find
v_i when both m_1 & m_2 are hanging
v_f when only m_1 is hanging

$m_1 = 200$ g

$m_2 = 200$ g

Solve: (a) For the puck to move in a circle, the centripetal force is provided by the two 200 g weights. Thus,

$$\left(0.40 \text{ kg}\right)\left(9.8 \text{ m / s}^2\right) = m_{puck}\frac{v_i^2}{r_i} = \left(0.1 \text{ kg}\right)\frac{v_i^2}{\left(0.2 \text{ m}\right)} \Rightarrow v_i = 2.8 \text{ m / s}$$

(b) The conservation of angular momentum equation $L_f = L_i$ implies

$$m_{puck}v_f r_f = m_{puck}v_i r_i \Rightarrow v_f r_f = v_i r_i = \left(2.8 \text{ m / s}\right)\left(0.2 \text{ m}\right) = 0.56 \text{ m}^2 / \text{s}$$

Now for the centripetal force to be equal to the new weight

$$\frac{m_{puck}v_f^2}{r_f} = \left(0.2 \text{ kg}\right)\left(9.8 \text{ m / s}^2\right) \Rightarrow r_f = \frac{m_{puck}v_f^2}{1.96 \text{ kg m / s}^2} = \frac{v_f^2}{19.6 \text{ m / s}^2}$$

Substituting this expression into the conservation of angular momentum equation, we have

$$v_f\left(\frac{v_f^2}{19.6 \text{ m / s}^2}\right) = 0.56 \text{ m}^2 / \text{s} \Rightarrow v_f^3 = 10.976 \text{ m}^3 / \text{s}^3 \Rightarrow v_f = 2.22 \text{ m / s}$$

Now we can obtain r_f as

$$r_f = \frac{v_f^2}{19.6 \text{ m / s}^2} = \frac{\left(2.22 \text{ m / s}\right)^2}{19.6 \text{ m / s}^2} = 0.25 \text{ m}$$

9.65.   Solve: (a) A 150 g lump of clay moving at 1.0 m/s is suddenly observed to break in two. One piece, which has twice the mass of the second, continues in the same direction but at an increased speed of 7.5 m/s. Which direction and at what speed is the second piece seen to leave the explosion? During the breakup or explosion, momentum is conserved.

(b)

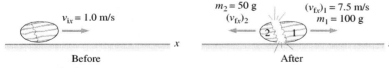

$v_{ix} = 1.0$ m/s

Before

$m_2 = 50$ g
$(v_{fx})_2$

$(v_{fx})_1 = 7.5$ m/s
$m_1 = 100$ g

After

(c) The solution is $\left(v_{fx}\right)_2 = -12 \text{ m / s}$. Thus, the second piece moves backward at 12 m/s.

ENERGY

10.3. **Model:** Model the compact car (C) and the truck (T) as particles.

Visualize:

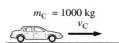

$m_T = 20{,}000$ kg
$v_T = 25$ km/hr

$m_C = 1000$ kg
v_C

Solve: For the kinetic energy of the compact car and the kinetic energy of the truck to be equal,

$$K_C = K_T \Rightarrow \frac{1}{2}m_C v_C^2 = \frac{1}{2}m_T v_T^2 \Rightarrow v_C = \sqrt{\frac{m_T}{m_C}}v_T = \sqrt{\frac{20{,}000 \text{ kg}}{1000 \text{ kg}}}(25 \text{ km/hr}) = 112 \text{ km/hr}$$

Assess: A smaller mass needs a greater velocity for its kinetic energy to be the same as that of a larger mass.

10.5. **Model:** Model the car (C) as a particle. This is an example of free fall, and therefore the sum of kinetic and potential energy does not change as the car falls.

Visualize:

y

y_i — $v_i = 0$ m/s   Before

y_f — $v_f = 30$ m/s   After

Solve: **(a)** The kinetic energy of the car is

$$K_C = \frac{1}{2}m_C v_C^2 = \frac{1}{2}(1500 \text{ kg})(30 \text{ m/s})^2 = 6.75 \times 10^5 \text{ J}$$

(b) Let us relabel K_C as K_f and place our coordinate system at $y_f = 0$ m so that the car's potential energy U_{gf} is zero, its velocity is v_f, and its kinetic energy is K_f. At position y_i, $v_i = 0$ m/s or $K_i = 0$ J, and the only energy the car has is $U_{gi} = mgy_i$. Since the sum $K + U_g$ is unchanged by motion, $K_f + U_{gf} = K_i + U_{gi}$. This means

$$K_f + mgy_f = K_i + mgy_i \Rightarrow K_f + 0 = K_i + mgy_i$$

$$\Rightarrow y_i = \frac{(K_f - K_i)}{mg} = \frac{(6.75 \times 10^5 \text{ J - 0 J})}{(1500 \text{ kg})(9.8 \text{ m/s}^2)} = 45.9 \text{ m}$$

(c) From part (b),

$$y_i = \frac{(K_f - K_i)}{mg} = \frac{\frac{1}{2}mv_f^2 - \frac{1}{2}mv_i^2}{mg} = \frac{(v_f^2 - v_i^2)}{2g}$$

Assess: Free fall does not depend upon the mass.

10.9. Model: Model the skateboarder as a particle. Assuming that the track offers no rolling friction, the sum of the skateboarder's kinetic and gravitational potential energy does not change during its rolling motion.
Visualize:

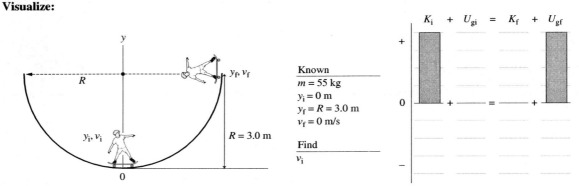

The vertical displacement of the skateboarder is equal to the radius of the track.
Solve: The quantity $K + U_g$ is the same at the upper edge of the quarter-pipe track as it was at the bottom. The energy conservation equation $K_f + U_{gf} = K_i + U_{gi}$ is

$$\frac{1}{2}mv_f^2 + mgy_f = \frac{1}{2}mv_i^2 + mgy_i \Rightarrow v_i^2 = v_f^2 + 2g(y_f - y_i)$$

$$v_i^2 = (0 \text{ m/s})^2 + 2(9.8 \text{ m/s}^2)(3.0 \text{ m} - 0 \text{ m}) = 58.8 \text{ m} \Rightarrow v_i = 7.67 \text{ m/s}$$

Assess: Note that we did not need to know the skateboarder's mass, as is the case with free-fall motion.

10.11. Model: In the absence of frictional and air-drag effects, the sum of the kinetic and gravitational potential energy does not change as the pendulum swings from one side to the other.
Visualize:

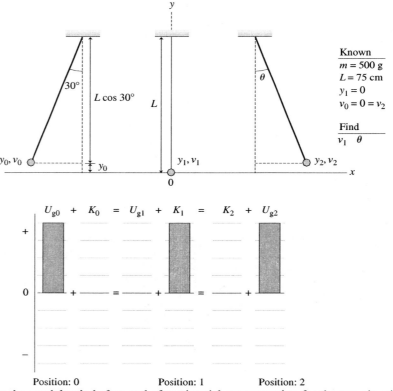

The figure shows the pendulum's before-and-after pictorial representation for the two situations described in parts (a) and (b).

Solve: **(a)** The quantity $K + U_g$ is the same at the lowest point of the trajectory as it was at the highest point. Thus, $K_1 + U_{g1} = K_0 + U_{g0}$ means

$$\frac{1}{2}mv_1^2 + mgy_1 = \frac{1}{2}mv_0^2 + mgy_0 \Rightarrow v_1^2 + 2gy_1 = v_0^2 + 2gy_0$$

$$\Rightarrow v_1^2 + 2g(0 \text{ m}) = (0 \text{ m/s})^2 + 2gy_0 \Rightarrow v_1 = \sqrt{2gy_0}$$

From the pictorial representation, we find that $y_0 = L - L\cos 30°$. Thus,

$$v_1 = \sqrt{2gL(1 - \cos 30°)} = \sqrt{2(9.8 \text{ m/s}^2)(0.75 \text{ m})(1 - \cos 30°)} = 1.403 \text{ m/s}$$

(b) Since the quantity $K + U_g$ does not change, $K_2 + U_{g2} = K_1 + U_{g1}$. We have

$$\frac{1}{2}mv_2^2 + mgy_2 = \frac{1}{2}mv_1^2 + mgy_1 \Rightarrow y_2 = \left(v_1^2 - v_2^2\right)/2g$$

$$\Rightarrow y_2 = [(1.403 \text{ m/s})^2 - (0 \text{ m/s})^2]/(2 \times 9.8 \text{ m/s}^2) = 0.100 \text{ m}$$

Since $y_2 = L - L\cos\theta$, we obtain

$$\cos\theta = \frac{L - y_2}{L} = \frac{(0.75 \text{ m}) - (0.10 \text{ m})}{(0.75 \text{ m})} = 0.8667 \Rightarrow \theta = \cos^{-1}(0.8667) = 30°$$

That is, the pendulum swings to the other side by $30°$.

Assess: The swing angle is the same on either side of the rest position. This result is a consequence of the fact that the sum of the kinetic and gravitational potential energy does not change. This is shown as well in the energy bar chart in the figure.

10.15. **Model:** Assume that the spring is ideal and obeys Hooke's law. We also model the 5.0 kg mass as a particle.
Visualize: We will use the subscript s for the scale and sp for the spring.

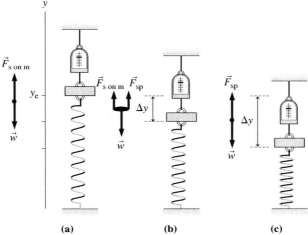

(a)   **(b)**   **(c)**

Solve: **(a)** The y-component of the force acting on the 5 kg mass is given by Newton's second law:

$$\sum (F_{\text{on m}})_y = F_{\text{s on m}} - w = 0 \Rightarrow F_{\text{s on m}} = w = mg = (5.0 \text{ kg})(9.8 \text{ m/s}^2) = 49 \text{ N}$$

(b) In this case, the force is

$$\sum (F_{\text{on m}})_y = F_{\text{s on m}} + F_{\text{sp}} - w = 0 \Rightarrow 20 \text{ N} + k\Delta y - mg = 0$$

$$\Rightarrow k = (mg - 20 \text{ N})/\Delta y = (49 \text{ N} - 20 \text{ N})/0.02 \text{ m} = 1450 \text{ N/m}$$

(c) In this case, the force is

$$\sum (F_{\text{on m}})_y = F_{\text{sp}} - w = 0 \Rightarrow k\Delta y - mg = 0$$

$$\Rightarrow \Delta y = mg/k = (49 \text{ N})/(1450 \text{ N/m}) = 0.0338 \text{ m} = 3.4 \text{ cm}$$

Assess: A spring constant of 1450 N/m or 148 kg/m or 1.48 kg/cm is consistent with a compression of 3.4 cm due to a mass of 5.0 kg.

10.21. Model: Assume an ideal spring that obeys Hooke's law. There is no friction, so the mechanical energy $K + U_s$ is conserved. Also model the book as a particle.

Visualize:

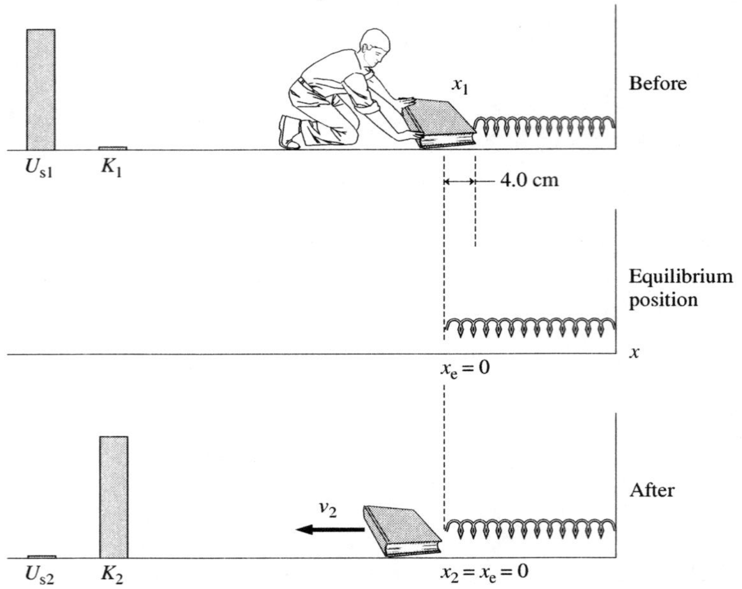

The figure shows a before-and-after pictorial representation. The compressed spring will push on the book until the spring has returned to its equilibrium length. We put the origin of our coordinate system at the equilibrium position of the free end of the spring. The energy bar chart shows that the potential energy of the compressed spring is entirely transformed into the kinetic energy of the book.

Solve: The conservation of energy equation $K_2 + U_{s2} = K_1 + U_{s1}$ is

$$\frac{1}{2}mv_2^2 + \frac{1}{2}k(x_2 - x_e)^2 = \frac{1}{2}mv_1^2 + \frac{1}{2}k(x_1 - x_e)^2$$

Using $x_2 = x_e = 0$ m and $v_1 = 0$ m/s, this simplifies to

$$\frac{1}{2}mv_2^2 = \frac{1}{2}k(x_1 - 0 \text{ m})^2 \Rightarrow v_2 = \sqrt{\frac{kx_1^2}{m}} = \sqrt{\frac{(1250 \text{ N/m})(0.04 \text{ m})^2}{(0.500 \text{ kg})}} = 2.0 \text{ m/s}$$

Assess: This problem can not be solved using constant-acceleration kinematic equations or using Newton's laws. The acceleration is not a constant in this problem, since the spring force, given as $F_s = -k\Delta x$, is directly proportional to Δx or $|x - x_e|$.

10.25. Model: We assume this is a one-dimensional collision that obeys the conservation laws of momentum and mechanical energy.

Visualize:

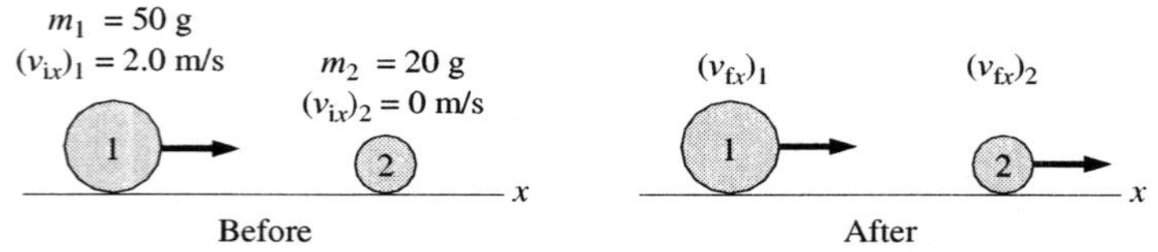

Note that momentum conservation alone is not sufficient to solve this problem because the two final velocities $(v_{fx})_1$ and $(v_{fx})_2$ are unknowns and can not be determined from one equation.

Solve: Momentum conservation: $m_1(v_{ix})_1 + m_2(v_{ix})_2 = m_1(v_{fx})_1 + m_2(v_{fx})_2$

Energy conservation: $\frac{1}{2}m_1(v_{ix})_1^2 + \frac{1}{2}m_2(v_{ix})_2^2 = \frac{1}{2}m_1(v_{fx})_1^2 + \frac{1}{2}m_2(v_{fx})_2^2$

These two equations can be solved for $(v_{fx})_1$ and $(v_{fx})_2$, as shown by Equations 10.39 through 10.43, to give

$$(v_{fx})_1 = \frac{m_1 - m_2}{m_1 + m_2}(v_{ix})_1 = \frac{50 \text{ g} - 20 \text{ g}}{50 \text{ g} + 20 \text{ g}}(2.0 \text{ m/s}) = 0.857 \text{ m/s}$$

$$(v_{fx})_2 = \frac{2m_1}{m_1 + m_2}(v_{ix})_1 = \frac{2(50 \text{ g})}{50 \text{ g} + 20 \text{ g}}(2.0 \text{ m/s}) = 2.86 \text{ m/s}$$

Assess: These velocities are of a reasonable magnitude. Since both these velocities are positive, both balls move along the +*x* direction.

10.29.   **Model:**   For an energy diagram, the sum of the kinetic and potential energy is a constant.
Visualize:

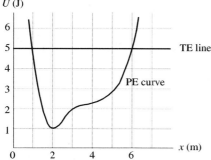

The particle is released from rest at $x = 1.0$ m. That is, $K = 0$ at $x = 1.0$ m. Since the total energy is given by $E = K + U$, we can draw a horizontal total energy (TE) line through the point of intersection of the potential energy curve (PE) and the $x = 1.0$ m line. The distance from the PE curve to the TE line is the particle's kinetic energy. These values are transformed as the position changes, causing the particle to speed up or slow down, but the sum $K + U$ does not change.
Solve: **(a)** We have $E = 5.0$ J and this energy is a constant. For $x < 1.0$, $U > 5.0$ J and, therefore, K must be negative to keep E the same (note that $K = E - U$ or $K = 5.0$ J $- U$). Since negative kinetic energy is unphysical, the particle can not move to the left. That is, the particle will move to the right of $x = 1.0$ m.
(b) The expression for the kinetic energy is $E - U$. This means the particle has maximum speed or maximum kinetic energy when U is minimum. This happens at $x = 2.0$ m. Thus,

$$K_{max} = E - U_{min} = (5.0 \text{ J}) - (1.0 \text{ J}) = 4.0 \text{ J} \qquad \frac{1}{2}mv_{max}^2 = 4.0 \text{ J} \Rightarrow v_{max} = \sqrt{\frac{2(4.0 \text{ J})}{m}} = \sqrt{\frac{8.0 \text{ J}}{0.02 \text{ kg}}} = 20 \text{ m/s}$$

The particle possesses this speed at $x = 2.0$ m.
(c) The total energy (TE) line intersects the potential energy (PE) curve at $x = 1$ m and $x = 6.0$ m. These are the turning points of the motion.

10.31.   **Model:**   For an energy diagram, the sum of the kinetic and potential energy is a constant.
Visualize:

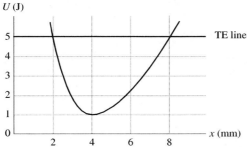

Since the particle oscillates between $x = 2.0$ mm and $x = 8.0$ mm, the speed of the particle is zero at these points. That is, for these values of x, $E = U = 5.0$ J, which defines the total energy (TE) line. The distance from the potential energy (PE) curve to the TE line is the particle's kinetic energy. These values are transformed as the position changes, but the sum $K + U$ does not change.
Solve: The equation for total energy $E = U + K$ means $K = E - U$, so that K is maximum when U is minimum. We have

$$K_{max} = \frac{1}{2}mv_{max}^2 = 5.0 \text{ J} - U_{min}$$

$$\Rightarrow v_{max} = \sqrt{2(5.0 \text{ J} - U_{min})/m} = \sqrt{2(5.0 \text{ J} - 1.0 \text{ J})/0.002 \text{ kg}} = 63.2 \text{ m/s}$$

10.33. **Model:** Model your vehicle as a particle. Assume zero rolling friction, so that the sum of your kinetic and gravitational potential energy does not change as the vehicle coasts down the hill.

Visualize:

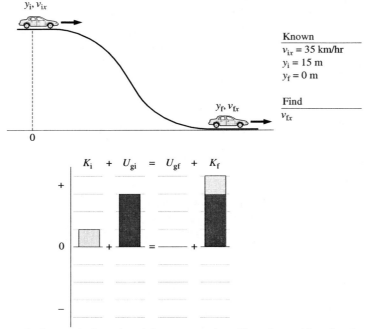

The figure shows a before-and-after pictorial representation. Note that neither the shape of the hill nor the angle of the downward slope is given, since these are not needed to solve the problem. All we need is the change in potential energy as you and your vehicle descend to the bottom of the hill. Also note that

$$35 \text{ km/hr} = (35000 \text{ m}/3600 \text{ s}) = 9.722 \text{ m/s}$$

Solve: Using $y_f = 0$ and the equation $K_i + U_{gi} = K_f + U_{gf}$ we get

$$\frac{1}{2}mv_i^2 + mgy_i = \frac{1}{2}mv_f^2 + mgy_f \Rightarrow v_i^2 + 2gy_i = v_f^2$$

$$\Rightarrow v_f = \sqrt{v_i^2 + 2gy_i} = \sqrt{(9.722 \text{ m/s})^2 + 2(9.8 \text{ m/s})(15 \text{ m})} = 19.7 \text{ m/s} = 71 \text{ km/hr}$$

You are driving over the speed limit. Yes, you will get a ticket.

Assess: A speed of 19.7 m/s or 71 km/hr at the bottom of the hill, when your speed at the top of the hill was 35 km/s, is reasonable. From the energy bar chart, we see that the initial potential energy is completely transformed into the final kinetic energy.

10.37. **Model:** Assume that the rubber band behaves similar to a spring. Also, model the rock as a particle.

Visualize:

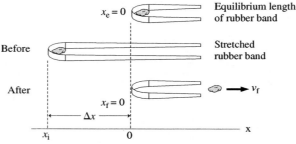

Please refer to Figure P10.37.

Solve: **(a)** The rubber band is stretched to the left since a positive spring force on the rock due to the rubber band results from a negative displacement of the rock. That is, $(F_{sp})_x = -kx$, where x is the rock's displacement from the equilibrium position due to the spring force F_{sp}.

(b) Since the F_{sp} versus x graph is linear with a negative slope and can be expressed as $F_{sp} = -kx$, the rubber band obeys Hooke's law.

(c) From the graph, $|\Delta F_{sp}| = 20$ N for $|\Delta x| = 10$ cm. Thus,

$$k = \frac{|\Delta F_{sp}|}{|\Delta x|} = \frac{20 \text{ N}}{0.10 \text{ m}} = 200 \text{ N/m}$$

(d) The conservation of energy equation $K_f + U_{sf} = K_i + U_{si}$ for the rock is

$$\frac{1}{2}mv_f^2 + \frac{1}{2}kx_f^2 = \frac{1}{2}mv_i^2 + \frac{1}{2}kx_i^2 \Rightarrow \frac{1}{2}mv_f^2 + \frac{1}{2}k(0 \text{ m})^2 = \frac{1}{2}m(0 \text{ m/s})^2 + \frac{1}{2}kx_i^2$$

$$\Rightarrow v_f = \sqrt{\frac{k}{m}}x_i = \sqrt{\frac{200 \text{ N/m}}{0.05 \text{ kg}}}(0.30 \text{ m}) = 19.0 \text{ m/s}$$

Assess: Note that x_i is Δx, which is the displacement relative to the equilibrium position, and x_f is the equilibrium position of the rubber band, which is equal to zero.

10.41. **Model:** Model the marble and the steel ball as particles. We will assume an elastic collision between the marble and the ball, and apply the conservation of momentum and the conservation of energy equations. We will also assume zero rolling friction between the marble and the incline.

Visualize:

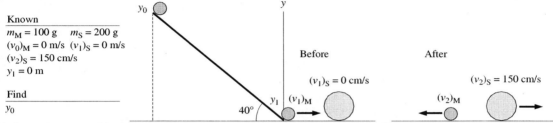

This is a two-part problem. In the first part, we will apply the conservation of energy equation to find the marble's speed as it exits onto a horizontal surface. We have put the origin of our coordinate system on the horizontal surface just where the marble exits the incline. In the second part, we will consider the elastic collision between the marble and the steel ball.

Solve: The conservation of energy equation $K_1 + U_{g1} = K_0 + U_{g0}$ gives us:

$$\frac{1}{2}m_M(v_1)_M^2 + m_M g y_1 = \frac{1}{2}m_M(v_0)_M^2 + m_M g y_0$$

Using $(v_0)_M = 0$ m/s and $y_1 = 0$ m, we get $\frac{1}{2}(v_1)_M^2 = gy_0 \Rightarrow (v_1)_M = \sqrt{2gy_0}$. When the marble collides with the steel ball, conservation of momentum equation $p_{fx} = p_{ix}$ requires

$$m_M(v_2)_M + m_S(v_2)_S = m_M(v_1)_M + m_S(v_1)_S$$

Using $(v_1)_S = 0$, we get $m_M(v_2)_M + m_S(v_2)_S = m_M(v_1)_M \Rightarrow (v_2)_M = (v_1)_M - \left(\frac{m_S}{m_M}\right)(v_2)_S$

The conservation of energy states: $K_f + U_{gf} = K_i + U_{gi}$. Using $U_{gf} = U_{gi} = U_{g2} = U_{g1} = 0$ we get

$$\frac{1}{2}m_M(v_2)_M^2 + \frac{1}{2}m_S(v_2)_S^2 = \frac{1}{2}m_M(v_1)_M^2 + \frac{1}{2}m_S(v_1)_S^2$$

Substituting $(v_1)_S = 0$, $(v_1)_M = \sqrt{2gy_0}$, $(v_2)_S = 150$ cm/s, and $(v_2)_M = (v_1)_M - \left(\frac{m_S}{m_M}\right)(v_2)_S$ into the above energy equation yields:

$$\left[(v_1)_M - \left(\frac{m_S}{m_M}\right)(v_2)_S\right]^2 + \frac{m_S}{m_M}(v_2)_S^2 = (v_1)_M^2 \qquad \left[\sqrt{2gy_0} - \left(\frac{0.200 \text{ kg}}{0.100 \text{ kg}}\right)(1.50 \text{ m/s})\right]^2 + \left(\frac{0.200 \text{ kg}}{0.100 \text{ kg}}\right)(1.50 \text{ m/s})^2 = 2gy_0$$

$$\Rightarrow 2gy_0 + 9.00 \text{ m}^2/\text{s}^2 - (6.00 \text{ m/s})\sqrt{2gy_0} + 4.50 \text{ m}^2/\text{s}^2 = 2gy_0 \Rightarrow \sqrt{2gy_0} = \left(\frac{13.50}{6.00}\right) \text{ m/s} \Rightarrow y_0 = 25.8 \text{ cm}$$

Assess: A height of 25.8 cm on a 40° incline to achieve a speed of $(v_1)_M = \sqrt{2gy_0} = \sqrt{2(9.8 \text{ m/s}^2)(0.258 \text{ m})} = 2.25$ m/s, or 5.04 mph, is reasonable.

10.45. Model: Assume an ideal spring that obeys Hooke's law. Since there is free fall, the mechanical energy $K + U_s + U_g$ is conserved.

Visualize:

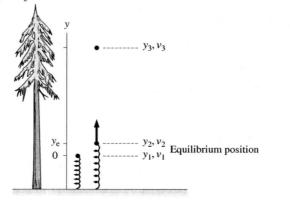

Known
$m = 20$ g
$\Delta x = 20$ cm $x_3 - x_2 = 5.0$ m
$y_3 - y_2 = -1.5$ m
$v_1 = 0$ m/s

Find
k

This is a two-part problem. In the first part, we use kinematic equations to find the ball's initial velocity v_2. This will yield the ball's kinetic energy as it leaves the spring.

Solve: Using the equations of kinematics,

$$x_3 = x_2 + v_{2x}(t_3 - t_2) + \frac{1}{2}a_x(t_3 - t_2)^2 \Rightarrow 5.0 \text{ m} = 0 \text{ m} + (v_2\cos30°)(t_3 - 0 \text{ s}) + 0 \text{ m}$$

$$(v_2\cos30°)t_3 = 5.0 \text{ m} \Rightarrow t_3 = (5.0 \text{ m}/v_2\cos30°)$$

$$y_3 = y_2 + v_{2y}(t_3 - t_2) + \frac{1}{2}a_y(t_3 - t_2)^2$$

$$-1.5 \text{ m} = 0 + (v_2\sin30°)(t_3 - 0 \text{ s}) + \frac{1}{2}(9.8 \text{ m/s}^2)(t_3 - 0 \text{ s})^2$$

Substituting the value for t_3, $(-1.5 \text{ m}) = (v_2\sin30°)\left(\dfrac{5.0 \text{ m}}{v_2\cos30°}\right) - \left(4.9 \text{ m/s}^2\right)\left(\dfrac{5.0 \text{ m}}{v_2\cos30°}\right)^2$

$$\Rightarrow (-1.5 \text{ m}) = +(2.887 \text{ m}) - \frac{163.33}{v_2^2} \Rightarrow v_2 = 6.102 \text{ m/s}$$

The conservation of energy equation $K_2 + U_{s2} + U_{g2} = K_1 + U_{s1} + U_{g1}$ is

$$\frac{1}{2}mv_2^2 + \frac{1}{2}kx_e^2 + mgy_2 = \frac{1}{2}mv_1^2 + \frac{1}{2}k(\Delta x)^2 + mgy_1$$

Using $y_2 = 0$ m, $x_e = 0$ m, $v_1 = 0$ m/s, $\Delta x = 0.2$ m, and $y_1 = -(\Delta x)\sin 30°$, we get

$$\frac{1}{2}mv_2^2 + 0 \text{ J} + 0 \text{ J} = 0 \text{ J} + \frac{1}{2}k(\Delta x)^2 - mg(\Delta x)\sin30° \qquad (\Delta x)^2 k = mv_2^2 + 2mg(\Delta x)\sin30°$$

$$(0.2 \text{ m})^2 k = (0.02 \text{ kg})(6.102 \text{ m/s})^2 + 2(0.02 \text{ kg})(9.8 \text{ m/s}^2)(0.2)(0.5) \Rightarrow k = 19.6 \text{ N/m}$$

Assess: Note that $y_1 = -(\Delta x)\sin30°$ is with a minus sign and hence the gravitational potential energy mgy_1 is $-mg(\Delta x)\sin30°$.

10.47. Model: Assume an ideal spring that obeys Hooke's law. This is a case of free fall, and thus the mechanical energy $K + U_s + U_g$ is conserved.

Visualize:

Known
$k = 1000$ N/m
$m = 400$ g
$y_e - y_1 = 30$ cm
$y_3 = 15$ m
$v_1 = 0$ m/s

Find
v_2

We place the origin of our coordinate system at the spring's compressed position $y_1 = 0$. The rock leaves the spring with velocity v_2 as the spring reaches its equilibrium position.

Solve: (a) The conservation of mechanical energy equation is

$$K_2 + U_{s2} + U_{g2} = K_1 + U_{s1} + U_{g1} \qquad \frac{1}{2}mv_2^2 + \frac{1}{2}k(y_2 - y_e)^2 + mgy_2 = \frac{1}{2}mv_1^2 + \frac{1}{2}k(y_1 - y_e)^2 + mgy_1$$

Using $y_2 = y_e$, $y_1 = 0$ m, and $v_1 = 0$ m/s, this simplifies to

$$\frac{1}{2}mv_2^2 + 0 \text{ J} + mgy_2 = 0 \text{ J} + \frac{1}{2}k(y_1 - y_e)^2 + 0$$

$$\frac{1}{2}(0.4 \text{ kg})v_2^2 + (0.4 \text{ kg})(9.8 \text{ m/s}^2)(0.3 \text{ m}) = \frac{1}{2}(1000 \text{ N/m})(0.3 \text{ m})^2 \Rightarrow v_2 = 14.8 \text{ m/s}$$

(b) Let us use the conservation of mechanical energy equation once again to find the highest position (y_3) of the rock where its speed (v_3) is zero:

$$K_3 + U_{g3} = K_2 + U_{g2} \Rightarrow \frac{1}{2}mv_3^2 + mgy_3 = \frac{1}{2}mv_2^2 + mgy_2$$

$$\Rightarrow 0 + g(y_3 - y_2) = \frac{1}{2}v_2^2 \Rightarrow (y_3 - y_2) = \frac{v_2^2}{2g} = \frac{(14.8 \text{ m/s})^2}{2(9.8 \text{ m/s}^2)} = 11.2 \text{ m}$$

If we assume the spring's length to be 0.5 m, then the distance between ground and fruit is 11.2 m + 0.5 m = 11.7 m. This is much smaller than the distance of 15 m between fruit and ground. So, the rock does not reach the fruit.

10.53.   Model: Because the track is frictionless, the sum of the kinetic and gravitational potential energy does not change during the car's motion.

Visualize:

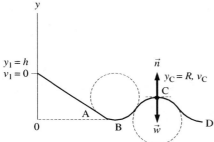

We place the origin of the coordinate system at the ground level directly below the car's starting position. This is a two-part problem. If we first find the maximum speed at the top of the hill (point C), we can use energy conservation to find the maximum initial height.

Solve: Because the its motion is circular, at the top of the hill the car has a downward-pointing centripetal acceleration $\vec{a}_c = -(mv^2/r)\hat{j}$. Newton's second law at the top of the hill is

$$(F_{net})_y = n_y + w_y = n - mg = m(a_c)_y = -\frac{mv^2}{R} \Rightarrow n = mg - \frac{mv^2}{R} = m\left(g - \frac{v^2}{R}\right)$$

If $v = 0$ m/s, $n = mg$ as expected in static equilibrium. As v increases, n gets smaller—the apparent weight of the car and passengers decreases as they go over the top. But n has to remain positive for the car to be on the track, so the maximum speed v_{max} occurs when $n \to 0$. We see that $v_{max} = \sqrt{gR}$. Now we can use energy conservation to relate point C to the starting height:

$$K_C + U_C = K_i + U_i \Rightarrow \frac{1}{2}mv_C^2 + mgy_C = \frac{1}{2}mv_i^2 + mgy_i \Rightarrow \frac{1}{2}mgR + mgR = 0 \text{ J} + mgh_{max},$$

where we used $v_C = v_{max}$ and $y_C = R$. Solving for h_{max} gives $h_{max} = \frac{3}{2}R$.

(b) If $R = 10$ m, then $h_{max} = 15$ m.

10.57. Model: We can divide this problem into two parts. First, we have an elastic collision between the 20 g ball (m) and the 100 g ball (M). Second, the 100 g ball swings up as a pendulum.

Visualize:

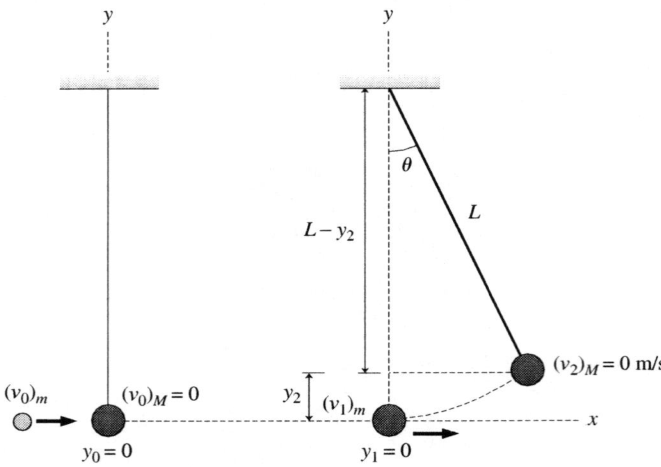

The figure shows three distinct moments of time: the time before the collision, the time after the collision but before the two balls move, and the time the 100 g ball reaches its highest point. We place the origin of our coordinate system on the 100 g ball when it is hanging motionless.

Solve: The momentum conservation equation $p_1 = p_0$ for a perfectly elastic collision is

$$m(v_1)_m + M(v_1)_M = m(v_0)_m + M(v_0)_M$$

$$(0.020 \text{ kg})(v_1)_m + (0.100 \text{ kg})(v_1)_M = (0.020 \text{ kg})(v_0)_m + 0 \text{ kg m/s} \Rightarrow (v_1)_m = (v_0)_m - 5(v_1)_M$$

The kinetic energy conservation equation $K_1 = K_0$ is

$$\frac{1}{2}m(v_1)_m^2 + \frac{1}{2}M(v_1)_M^2 = \frac{1}{2}m(v_0)_m^2 + \frac{1}{2}M(v_0)_M^2 \Rightarrow (v_1)_m^2 + 5(v_1)_M^2 = (v_0)_m^2$$

Substituting the result for $(v_1)_m$ from the momentum conservation equation, the energy equation simplifies to

$$[(v_0)_m - 5(v_1)_M]^2 + 5(v_1)_M^2 = (v_0)_m^2 \Rightarrow 30(v_1)_M\left[(v_1)_M - \frac{1}{3}(v_0)_m\right] = 0$$

$$\Rightarrow (v_1)_M = 0 \text{ m/s (initial condition) and } (v_1)_M = \frac{(v_1)_m}{3}$$

In the second part, the sum of the kinetic and gravitational potential energy is conserved as the 100 g ball swings up after the collision. That is, $K_2 + U_{g2} = K_1 + U_{g1}$. We have

$$\frac{1}{2}M(v_2)_M^2 + Mgy_2 = \frac{1}{2}M(v_1)_M^2 + Mgy_1$$

Using $(v_2)_M = 0$ J, $(v_1)_M = \frac{(v_0)_m}{3}$, $y_1 = 0$ m, and $(L - y_2)/L = \cos\theta$ $(y_2 = L - L\cos\theta)$, the energy equation simplifies to

$$g(L - L\cos\theta) = \frac{1}{2}\frac{(v_0)_m^2}{9}$$

$$\Rightarrow (v_0)_m = \sqrt{18 g L(1 - \cos\theta)} = \sqrt{18(9.8 \text{ m/s}^2)(1.0 \text{ m})(1 - \cos 50°)} = 7.94 \text{ m/s}$$

10.59. Model: Model the balls as particles. We will use the Galilean transformation of velocities (Equation 10.44) to analyze the problem of elastic collisions. We will transform velocities from the lab frame S to a frame S' in which one ball is at rest. This allows us to apply Equations 10.43 to a perfectly elastic collision in S'. After finding the final velocities of the balls in S', we can then transform these velocities back to the lab frame S.

Visualize: Let S' be the frame of the 400-g ball. Denoting masses as $m_1 = 100$ g and $m_2 = 400$ g, the initial velocities in the S frame are $(v_{ix})_1 = +4.0$ m/s and $(v_{ix})_2 = +1.0$ m/s.

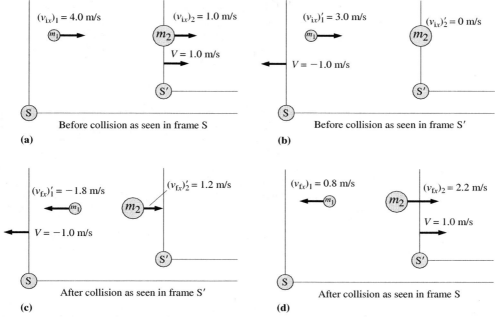

Figures (a) and (b) show the before-collision situations in frames S and S′, respectively. The after-collision velocities in S′ are shown in figure (c). Figure (d) indicates velocities in S after they have been transformed to S from S′.

Solve: In frame S, $(v_{ix})_1 = 4.0$ m/s and $(v_{ix})_2 = 1.0$ m/s. Because S′ is the reference frame of the 400-g ball, $V = 1.0$ m/s. The velocities of the two balls in this frame can be obtained using the Galilean transformation of velocities $v' = v - V$.

So,

$$(v_{ix})_1' = (v_{ix})_1 - V = 4.0 \text{ m/s} - 1.0 \text{ m/s} = 3.0 \text{ m/s} \qquad (v_{ix})_2' = (v_{ix})_2 - V = 1.0 \text{ m/s} - 1.0 \text{ m/s} = 0 \text{ m/s}$$

Figure (b) shows the "before" situation in frame S′ where the ball 2 is at rest.

Now we can use Equations 10.43 to find the after-collision velocities in frame S′:

$$(v_{fx})_1' = \frac{m_1 - m_2}{m_1 + m_2}(v_{ix})_1' = \frac{100 \text{ g} - 400 \text{ g}}{100 \text{ g} + 400 \text{ g}}(3.0 \text{ m/s}) = -1.8 \text{ m/s}$$

$$(v_{fx})_2' = \frac{2m_1}{m_1 + m_2}(v_{ix})_1' = \frac{2(100 \text{ g})}{100 \text{ g} + 400 \text{ g}}(3.0 \text{ m/s}) = 1.2 \text{ m/s}$$

Finally, we need to apply the reverse Galilean transformation $v = v' + V$, with the same V, to transform the after-collision velocities back to the lab frame S.

$$(v_{fx})_1 = (v_{fx})_1' + V = -1.8 \text{ m/s} + 1.0 \text{ m/s} = -0.8 \text{ m/s}$$

$$(v_{fx})_2 = (v_{fx})_2' + V = 1.2 \text{ m/s} + 1.0 \text{ m/s} = 2.2 \text{ m/s}$$

Figure (d) shows the "after" situation in frame S.

Assess: The magnitudes of the after-collision velocities are similar to the magnitudes of the before-collision velocities.

10.61.   Model: We will use the conservation of mechanical energy.

Visualize:

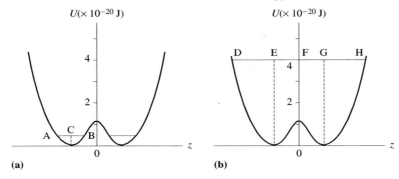

The potential energy (U) of the nitrogen atom as a function of z exhibits a double-minimum behavior; the two minima correspond to the nitrogen atom's position on both sides of the plane containing the three hydrogens.
Solve: **(a)** At room temperature, the nitrogen atom has mechanical energy (E) of 0.4×10^{-20} J. The horizontal line in figure (a) indicates the mechanical energy of the nitrogen atom which will be trapped either on the positive side of the hydrogen triangle or on the negative side. Since $E = U + K$ and $K = \frac{1}{2}mv^2$, we can write

$$v = \sqrt{2(E-U)/m} \text{ or } v \propto \sqrt{(0.4 \times 10^{-20} \text{ J}) - U(z)}$$

At points A and B on the total energy line $U(z) = 0.4 \times 10^{-20}$ J, thus $v = 0$. At point C, $U(z) = 0$ and therefore v will be maximum. That is, on the left side of the potential energy plot, the nitrogen atom will have zero velocity at A, increase its velocity as it moves toward C, and then decrease its velocity as it moves toward B where it will again have zero velocity. Motion on the right side of the potential energy plot is the mirror image of this motion.
(b) The horizontal line in figure (b) indicates $E = 4 \times 10^{-20}$ J. The nitrogen atom will be trapped between D and H on either side of the center of the hydrogen-triangle. The nitrogen atom at D has $v = 0$ and it increases its speed to E. From E to F, the speed decreases slightly as the atom moves to F which is at zero. The velocity of the nitrogen atom increases slightly to G where it is again maximum. As the atom moves further to H, its speed decreases to zero.

10.67. Solve: (a) A spring gun with $k = 400$ N/m and compressed a distance of 10 cm exerts a force on a 500 g block on a frictionless surface. The block then climbs a 10.0 cm slope inclined at 30°. With what speed will the block reach the top of the slope?
(b)

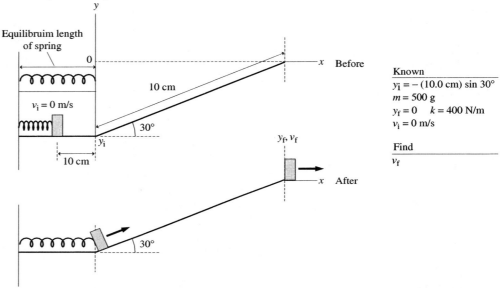

The before-and-after pictorial representation of the block and the spring on a frictionless surface is shown. We place the origin of our coordinate system directly above the bottom of the slope but at the same level as the top of the slope.
(c) Whether the block makes it to the top of the slope can be answered by calculating separately the spring energy and the change in the potential energy of the block:

$$E_s = \frac{1}{2}k(\Delta x)^2 = \frac{1}{2}(400 \text{ N/m})(0.10 \text{ m})^2 = 2 \text{ J}$$

$$\Delta U_g = mg(\Delta y) = (0.500 \text{ kg})(9.8 \text{ m/s}^2)(0.10\sin 30°) \text{ m} = 0.245 \text{ J}$$

Since $E_s > \Delta U_g$, the block reaches the top. Solving the energy conservation equation gives $v_f = 2.65$ m/s.

WORK

11.5. Solve: (a) $W = \vec{F} \cdot \Delta \vec{r} = (6.0\hat{i} - 3.0\hat{j}) \cdot (2.0\hat{i}) \, \text{N} \cdot \text{m} = (12.0\hat{i} \cdot \hat{i} - 3.0\hat{j} \cdot \hat{i}) \, \text{J} = 12.0 \, \text{J}.$
(b) $W = \vec{F} \cdot \Delta \vec{r} = (6.0\hat{i} - 3.0\hat{j}) \cdot (2.0\hat{j}) \, \text{N} \cdot \text{m} = (12.0\hat{i} \cdot \hat{j} - 6.0\hat{j} \cdot \hat{j}) \, \text{J} = -6.0 \, \text{J}.$

11.7. Model: Use the work-kinetic energy theorem to find the work done on the particle.
Visualize:

$\vec{F}$

$v_f = 30 \, \text{m/s}$ $v_i = 30 \, \text{m/s}$
                                          $m = 20 \, \text{g}$

After   Before

Solve: From the work-kinetic energy theorem,

$$W = \Delta K = \frac{1}{2}mv_1^2 - \frac{1}{2}mv_0^2 = \frac{1}{2}m\left(v_1^2 - v_0^2\right) = \frac{1}{2}(0.020 \, \text{kg})[(30 \, \text{m/s})^2 - (-30 \, \text{m/s})^2]^2 = 0 \, \text{J}$$

Assess: Negative work is done in slowing down the particle to rest, and an equal amount of positive work is done in bringing the particle to the original speed but in the opposite direction.

11.9. Model: Model the piano as a particle and use $W = \vec{F} \cdot \Delta \vec{r}$, where W is the work done by the force $\vec{F}$ through the displacement $\Delta \vec{r}$.
Visualize:

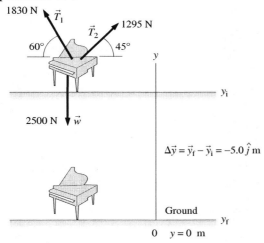

$\Delta \vec{y} = \vec{y}_f - \vec{y}_i = -5.0 \hat{j} \, \text{m}$

Solve: For the force $\vec{w}$:

$$W = \vec{F} \cdot \Delta \vec{r} = \vec{w} \cdot \Delta \vec{y} = (w)(\Delta y)\cos 0° = (2500 \, \text{N})(5.0 \, \text{m})(1) = 1.25 \times 10^4 \, \text{J}$$

For the tension $\vec{T}_1$:

$$W = \vec{T}_1 \cdot \Delta \vec{y} = (T_1)(\Delta y)\cos(150°) = (1830 \, \text{N})(5.0 \, \text{N})(-0.8660) = -7.92 \times 10^3 \, \text{J}$$

For the tension $\vec{T}_2$:

$$W = \vec{T}_2 \cdot \Delta \vec{y} = (T_2)(\Delta y)\cos(135°) = (1295 \, \text{N})(5.0 \, \text{m})(-0.7071) = -4.58 \times 10^3 \, \text{J}$$

Assess: Note that the displacement $\Delta \vec{y}$ in all the above cases is directed downwards along $-\hat{j}$. Also note that the force $\vec{w}$ transfers energy into the piano, but the tensions $\vec{T}_1$ and $\vec{T}_2$ transfer an equal amount of energy out of the piano.

11.11.   Model: Model the 2.0 kg object as a particle, and use the work-kinetic energy theorem.
Visualize: Please refer to Figure Ex11.11. For each of the five intervals the velocity-versus-time graph gives the initial and final velocities. The mass of the object is 2.0 kg.
Solve: According to the work-kinetic energy theorem:

$$W = \Delta K = \frac{1}{2}mv_f^2 = \frac{1}{2}mv_i^2 = \frac{1}{2}m\left(v_f^2 - v_i^2\right)$$

Interval AB: $v_i = 0$ m/s, $v_f = 2$ m/s $\Rightarrow W = \frac{1}{2}(2.0 \text{ kg})[(2 \text{ m/s})^2 - (0 \text{ m/s})^2] = +4.0$ J

Interval BC: $v_i = 2$ m/s, $v_f = 0$ m/s $\Rightarrow W = \frac{1}{2}(2.0 \text{ kg})[(0 \text{ m/s})^2 - (2 \text{ m/s})^2] = -4.0$ J

Interval CD: $v_i = 0$ m/s, $v_f = -2$ m/s $\Rightarrow W = \frac{1}{2}(2.0 \text{ kg})[(-2 \text{ m/s})^2 - (0 \text{ m/s})^2] = +4.0$ J

Interval DE: $v_i = -2$ m/s, $v_f = -2$ m/s $\Rightarrow W = \frac{1}{2}(2.0 \text{ kg})[(-2 \text{ m/s})^2 - (-2 \text{ m/s})^2] = 0$ J

Interval EF: $v_i = -2$ m/s, $v_f = -1$ m/s $\Rightarrow W = \frac{1}{2}(2.0 \text{ kg})[(-1 \text{ m/s})^2 - (-2 \text{ m/s})^2] = -3.0$ J

Assess: The work done is the same in intervals AB and CD. It is not whether v is positive or negative that counts because $K \propto v^2$. What is important is the magnitude of v.

11.15.   Model: Use the work-kinetic energy theorem.
Visualize: Please refer to Figure Ex11.15.
Solve: The work-kinetic energy theorem is

$$\Delta K = W = \int_{x_i}^{x_f} F_x \, dx = \text{area of the } F_x\text{-versus-}x \text{ graph between } x_i \text{ and } x_f$$

$$\frac{1}{2}mv_f^2 - \frac{1}{2}mv_i^2 = \frac{1}{2}(F_{max})(2 \text{ m})$$

Using $m = 0.500$ kg, $v_f = 6.0$ m/s, and $v_i = 2.0$ m/s, the above equation yields $F_{max} = 8.0$ N.
Assess: Problems in which the force is not a constant can not be solved using constant-acceleration kinematic equations.

11.17.   Model: Use the negative derivative of the potential energy to determine the force acting on a particle.
Visualize: Please refer to Figure Ex11.17.
Solve: The force acting on the particle at any point is given by the equation

$$F_x = -\left(\frac{dU}{dx}\right)$$

From the potential energy graph and the relationship between force and potential energy, it is clear that F_x corresponds to the slope of the graph of the potential energy at position x. The slope of the potential energy-versus-x graph between $x = 0$ m and $x = 2$ m is

$$(U_f - U_i)/(x_f - x_i) = (60 \text{ J} - 0 \text{ J})/(2 \text{ m} - 0 \text{ m}) = 30 \text{ N}$$

and between $x = 2$ m and $x = 5$ m is

$$(U_f - U_i)/(x_f - x_i) = (0 \text{ J} - 60 \text{ J})/(5 \text{ m} - 2 \text{ m}) = -20 \text{ J}$$

Thus, $F_x = -30$ N at $x = 1$ m and $F_x = 20$ N at $x = 3$ m.

11.23. Visualize:

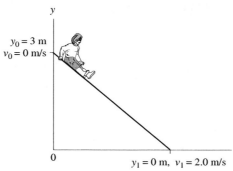

$y_0 = 3$ m
$v_0 = 0$ m/s

0    $y_1 = 0$ m, $v_1 = 2.0$ m/s

Solve: (a) $K_i = K_0 = \frac{1}{2}mv_0^2 = 0$ J $U_i = U_{g0} = mgy_0 = (20 \text{ kg})(9.8 \text{ m/s}^2)(3 \text{ m}) = 588$ J

$W_{ext} = 0$ J $K_f = K_1 = \frac{1}{2}mv_1^2 = \frac{1}{2}(20 \text{ kg})(2.0 \text{ m/s})^2 = 40$ J $U_f = U_{g1} = mgy_1 = 0$ J

At the top of the slide, the child has gravitational potential energy of 588 J. This energy is transformed into thermal energy of the child's pants and the slide and the kinetic energy of the child. This energy transfer and transformation is shown on the energy bar chart.

(b)   Energy (J)

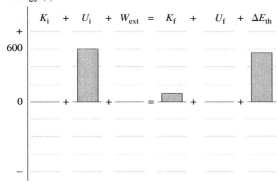

The change in the thermal energy of the slide and of the child's pants is 588 J – 40 J = 548 J.

11.27. Solve: The conservation of energy equation is

$$K_i + U_i + W_{ext} = K_f + U_f + \Delta E_{th} \Rightarrow 0 \text{ J} + 0 \text{ J} + 40 \text{ J} = \frac{1}{2}mv_f^2 + 20 \text{ J} + 0 \text{ J}$$

$$\Rightarrow v_f = \sqrt{(20 \text{ J})(2)/1.02 \text{ kg}} = 6.26 \text{ m/s}$$

The tension of 20 N in the cable is an external force that does work on the block equal to (20 N)(2.0 m) = 40 J, increasing the gravitational potential energy of the block. We placed the origin of our coordinate system on the initial resting position of the block, so we have $U_i = 0$ J and $U_f = mgy_f = (1.02 \text{ kg})(9.8 \text{ m/s}^2)(2.0 \text{ m}) = 20$ J. Also, $K_i = 0$ J, and $\Delta E_{th} = 0$ J. The energy bar chart shows the energy transfers and transformations.

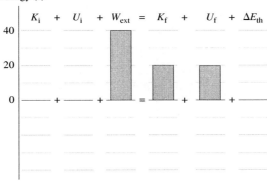

Energy (J)

11.33. Model: Model the sprinter as a particle, and use the constant-acceleration kinematic equations and the definition of power in terms of velocity.

Visualize:

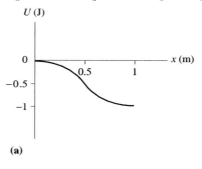

Solve: (a) We can find the acceleration from the kinematic equations and the horizontal force from Newton's second law. We have

$$x = x_0 + v_{0x}(t_1 - t_0) + \frac{1}{2}a_x(t_1 - t_0)^2 \Rightarrow 50 \text{ m} = 0 \text{ m} + 0 \text{ m} + \frac{1}{2}a_x(7.0 \text{ s} - 0 \text{ s})^2 \Rightarrow a_x = 2.04 \text{ m/s}^2$$

$$\Rightarrow F_x = ma_x = (50 \text{ kg})(2.04 \text{ m/s}^2) = 102 \text{ N}$$

(b) We obtain the sprinter's power output by using $P = \vec{F} \cdot \vec{v}$, where $\vec{v}$ is the sprinter's velocity. At $t = 2$ s the power is

$$P = (F_x)[v_{0x} + a_x(t - t_0)] = (102 \text{ N})[0 \text{ m/s} + (2.04 \text{ m/s}^2)(2.0 \text{ s} - 0 \text{ s})] = 416 \text{ W}$$

The power at $t = 4$ s is 832 W and at $t = 6$ s is 1249 W.

11.37. Model: Use the relationship between a conservative force and potential energy.
Visualize: Please refer to Figure P11.37. We will obtain U as a function of x and F_x as a function of x by using the calculus techniques of integration and differentiation.
Solve: (a) For the interval $0 \text{ m} < x < 0.5 \text{ m}$, $F_x = (4x)$ N, where x is in meters. This means

$$\frac{dU}{dx} = -F_x = -4x \Rightarrow U = -2x^2 + C_1 = -2x^2$$

where we have used $U = 0$ J at $x = 0$ m to obtain $C_1 = 0$. For the interval $0.5 \text{ m} < x < 1 \text{ m}$, $F_x = (-4x + 4)$ N. Likewise,

$$\frac{dU}{dx} = 4x - 4 \Rightarrow U = 2x^2 - 4x + C_2$$

Since U should be continuous at the junction, we have the continuity condition

$$(-2x^2)_{x=0.5 \text{ m}} = (2x^2 - 4x + C_2)_{x=0.5 \text{ m}} \Rightarrow -0.5 = 0.5 - 2 + C_2 \Rightarrow C_2 = 1$$

(b) For the interval $0 \text{ m} < x < 0.5 \text{ m}$, $U = +4x$, and for the interval $0.5 \text{ m} < x < 1.0 \text{ m}$, $U = -4x + 4$, where x is in meters. We obtain $F_x = -4$ N and $F_x = +4$ N, respectively.

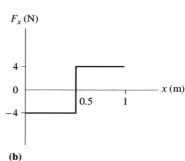

(a)   **(b)**

11.39. Model: Model the elevator as a particle.
Visualize:

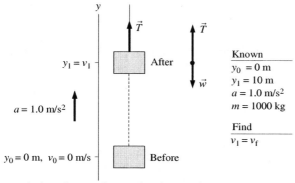

Solve: (a) The work done by gravity on the elevator is
$$W_g = -\Delta U_g = mgy_0 - mgy_1 = -mg(y_1 - y_0) = -(1000 \text{ kg})(9.8 \text{ m/s}^2)(10 \text{ m}) = -9.8 \times 10^4 \text{ J}$$

(b) The work done by the tension in the cable on the elevator is
$$W_T = T(\Delta y)\cos 0° = T(y_1 - y_0) = T(10 \text{ m})$$

To find T we write Newton's second law for the elevator:
$$\sum F_y = T - w = ma_y \Rightarrow T = w + ma_y = m(g + a_y) = (1000 \text{ kg})(9.8 \text{ m/s}^2 + 1.0 \text{ m/s}^2)$$
$$= 1.08 \times 10^4 \text{ N} \Rightarrow W_T = (1.08 \times 10^5 \text{ N})(10 \text{ m}) = 1.08 \times 10^5 \text{ J}$$

(c) The work-kinetic energy theorem is
$$W_{net} = W_g + W_T = \Delta K = K_f - K_i = K_f - \frac{1}{2}mv_0^2 \Rightarrow K_f = W_g + W_T + \frac{1}{2}mv_0^2$$
$$\Rightarrow K_f = (-9.8 \times 10^4 \text{ J}) + (1.08 \times 10^5 \text{ J}) + \frac{1}{2}(1000 \text{ kg})(0 \text{ m/s})^2 = 1.0 \times 10^4 \text{ J}$$

(d) $K_f = \frac{1}{2}mv_f^2 \Rightarrow 1.0 \times 10^4 \text{ J} = \frac{1}{2}(1000 \text{ kg})v_f^2 \Rightarrow v_f = 4.47 \text{ m/s}$

11.41. Model: Model the crate as a particle, and use the work-kinetic energy theorem.
Visualize:

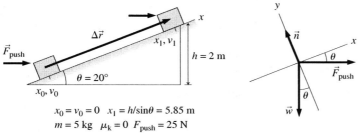

$$x_0 = v_0 = 0 \quad x_1 = h/\sin\theta = 5.85 \text{ m}$$
$$m = 5 \text{ kg} \quad \mu_k = 0 \quad F_{push} = 25 \text{ N}$$

Solve: (a) The work-kinetic energy theorem is $\Delta K = \frac{1}{2}mv_1^2 - \frac{1}{2}mv_0^2 = \frac{1}{2}mv_1^2 = W_{total}$. Three forces act on the box, so $W_{total} = W_{grav} + W_n + W_{push}$. The normal force is perpendicular to the motion, so $W_n = 0$ J. The other two forces do the following amount of work:
$$W_{push} = \vec{F}_{push} \cdot \Delta\vec{r} = F_{push}\Delta x \cos 20° = 137.4 \text{ J} \qquad W_{grav} = \vec{W} \cdot \Delta\vec{r} = W_x\Delta x = (-mg\sin 20°)\Delta x = -98.0 \text{ J}$$

Thus, $W_{total} = 39.4$ J, leading to a speed at the top of the ramp equal to
$$v_1 = \sqrt{\frac{2W_{total}}{m}} = \sqrt{\frac{2(39.4 \text{ J})}{5 \text{ kg}}} = 3.97 \text{ m/s}$$

(b) The x-component of Newton's second law is
$$a_x = a = \frac{(F_{net})_x}{m} = \frac{F_{push}\cos 20° - w\sin 20°}{m} = \frac{F_{push}\cos 20° - mg\sin 20°}{m} = 1.347 \text{ m/s}^2$$

Constant-acceleration kinematics with $x_1 = h/\sin 20° = 5.85$ m gives the final speed

$$v_1^2 = v_0^2 + 2a(x_1 - x_0) = 2ax_1 \Rightarrow v_1 = \sqrt{2ax_1} = \sqrt{2(1.347 \text{ m/s}^2)(5.85 \text{ m})} = 3.97 \text{ m/s}$$

11.45. Model: Model the suitcase as a particle, use the model of kinetic friction, and use the work-kinetic energy theorem.

Visualize:

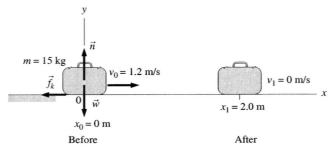

The only force that does work on the suitcase is the force of kinetic friction, $\vec{f}_k$. The forces $\vec{w}$ and $\vec{n}$ are perpendicular to the displacement, and therefore do not do work on the suitcase.

Solve: The work-kinetic energy theorem is

$$W_{\text{net}} = \Delta K = \frac{1}{2}mv_1^2 - \frac{1}{2}mv_0^2 \Rightarrow \vec{f}_k \cdot (\vec{x}_1 - \vec{x}_0) = 0 \text{ J} - \frac{1}{2}mv_0^2 \Rightarrow (f_k)(x_1 - x_0)\cos 180° = -\frac{1}{2}mv_0^2$$

$$\Rightarrow -\mu_k mg(x_1 - x_0) = -\frac{1}{2}mv_0^2 \Rightarrow \mu_k = \frac{v_0^2}{2g(x_1 - x_0)} = \frac{(1.2 \text{ m/s})^2}{2(9.8 \text{ m/s}^2)(2.0 \text{ m} - 0 \text{ m})} = 0.037$$

Assess: Friction does negative work on the suitcase, and thus transfers energy out of the suitcase. In response, the suitcase slows down and comes to rest.

11.47. Model: We will use the spring, the package, and the ramp as the system. We will model the package as a particle.

Visualize:

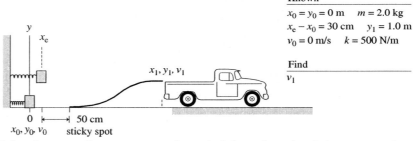

Known
$x_0 = y_0 = 0$ m $m = 2.0$ kg
$x_e - x_0 = 30$ cm $y_1 = 1.0$ m
$v_0 = 0$ m/s $k = 500$ N/m

Find
v_1

We place the origin of our coordinate system on the end of the spring when it is compressed and is in contact with the package to be shot.

Model: (a) The energy conservation equation is

$$K_1 + U_{g1} + U_{s1} + \Delta E_{\text{th}} = K_0 + U_{g0} + U_{s0} + W_{\text{ext}}$$

$$\frac{1}{2}mv_1^2 + mgy_1 + \frac{1}{2}k(x_e - x_e)^2 + \Delta E_{\text{th}} = \frac{1}{2}mv_0^2 + mgy_0 + \frac{1}{2}k(\Delta x)^2 + W_{\text{ext}}$$

Using $y_1 = 1$ m, $\Delta E_{\text{th}} = 0$ J (note the frictionless ramp), $v_0 = 0$ m/s, $y_0 = 0$ m, $\Delta x = 30$ cm, and $W_{\text{ext}} = 0$ J, we get

$$\frac{1}{2}mv_1^2 + mg(1 \text{ m}) + 0 \text{ J} + 0 \text{ J} = 0 \text{ J} + 0 \text{ J} + \frac{1}{2}k(0.30 \text{ m})^2 + 0 \text{ J}$$

$$\frac{1}{2}(2.0 \text{ kg})v_1^2 + (2.0 \text{ kg})(9.8 \text{ m/s}^2)(1 \text{ m}) = \frac{1}{2}(500 \text{ N/m})(0.30 \text{ m})^2$$

$$\Rightarrow v_1 = 1.70 \text{ m/s}$$

(b) We will use the above energy conservation equation again with $\Delta E_{th} = f(0.50 \text{ m}) = \mu n(0.50 \text{ m}) = \mu mg(0.50 \text{ m}) = (0.30)(2.0 \text{ kg})(9.8 \text{ m/s}^2)(0.50 \text{ m}) = 2.94 \text{ J}$. Thus,

$$\frac{1}{2}mv_1^2 + mgy_1 + 0 \text{ J} + \Delta E_{th} = \frac{1}{2}mv_0^2 + mgy_0 + \frac{1}{2}k(\Delta x)^2 + W_{ext}$$

$$\frac{1}{2}(2.0 \text{ kg})v_1^2 + (2.0 \text{ kg})(9.8 \text{ m/s}^2)(1 \text{ m}) + 2.94 \text{ J} = +0 \text{ J} + \frac{1}{2}(500 \text{ N/m})(0.30 \text{ m})^2 + 0 \text{ J}$$

$$(1.0 \text{ kg})v_1^2 + 19.6 \text{ J} + 2.94 \text{ J} = 22.5 \text{ J}$$

This relationship can be interpreted as follows. The package has a total energy of 22.5 J. Out of this energy, 2.94 J is lost as thermal energy leaving an energy of 19.56 J or 19.6 J to three significant figures. An energy of 19.60 J is needed for the package to reach the ramp and make it into the truck. The package, therefore, just makes it into the truck.

11.51. Model: Use the particle model for the ice skater, the model of kinetic/static friction, and the work-kinetic energy theorem.

Visualize:

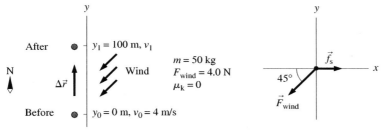

Solve: **(a)** The work-kinetic energy theorem is

$$\Delta K = \frac{1}{2}mv_1^2 - \frac{1}{2}mv_0^2 = W_{wind} + W_{fric}$$

There is no kinetic friction along her direction of motion. Static friction acts to prevent her skates from slipping sideways on the ice, but this force is perpendicular to the motion and does no work: $W_{fric} = 0$ J. The angle between $\vec{F}_{wind}$ and $\Delta \vec{r}$ is $\theta = 135°$, so

$$W_{wind} = \vec{F}_{wind} \cdot \Delta \vec{r} = F_{wind} \Delta y \cos 135° = (4 \text{ N})(100 \text{ m})\cos 135° = -282.8 \text{ J}$$

Thus, her final speed is

$$v_1 = \sqrt{v_0^2 + \frac{2W_{wind}}{m}} = 2.16 \text{ m/s}$$

(b) If the skates don't slip, she has no acceleration in the x-direction and so $(F_{net})_x = 0$ N. That is:

$$f_x - F_{wind}\cos 45° = 0 \text{ N} \Rightarrow f_x = F_{wind}\cos 45° = 2.83 \text{ N}$$

Now there is an upper limit to the static friction: $f_s \leq (f_s)_{max} = \mu_s mg$. To not slip requires

$$\mu_s \geq \frac{f_s}{mg} = \frac{2.83 \text{ N}}{(50 \text{ kg})(9.8 \text{ m/s}^2)} = 0.0058$$

Thus, the minimum value of μ_s is 0.0058.
Assess: The work done by the wind on the ice skater is negative, because the wind slows the skater down.

11.65. Solve: The power output is given by $P = Fv$, where F is the force needed to keep an object moving at a speed v. Since the net force on the horse moving at a steady speed is zero, the motion is opposed by air resistance. As explained in Chapter 5, this means $F_{horse} = \frac{1}{4}Av^2$, where A is the cross-section area of the horse. The power output, therefore, is

$$P = 1 \text{ hp} = F_{horse}v = \frac{1}{4}Av^3 \Rightarrow v^3 = (1 \text{ hp})\frac{4}{A} = (746 \text{ W})\frac{4}{(0.5 \text{ m})(1.8 \text{ m})} = 3315.6 \text{ m}^3/\text{s}^3$$

$$\Rightarrow v = 15 \text{ m/s} \approx 33 \text{ mph}$$

Assess: Not unreasonable, but probably faster than a horse can move.

11.67.   Model: Use the model of static friction, kinematic equations, and the definition of power.
Solve: (a) The rated power of the Porsche is 217 hp = 161,882 W and the weight of the car is (1480 kg)(9.8 m/s^2) = 14504 N. The weight of the car on the drive wheels is (14504)(2/3) = 9670 N. Because the static friction of the tires on road pushes the car forward,

$$F_{max} = \mu_s n = \mu_s mg = (1.0)(9670 \text{ N}) = ma_{max}$$

$$\Rightarrow a_{max} = \frac{9670 \text{ N}}{1480 \text{ kg}} = 6.53 \text{ m/s}^2$$

(b) $P = Fv_{max} \Rightarrow v_{max} = \dfrac{P}{F} = \dfrac{161882 \text{ W}}{9670 \text{ N}} = 16.7 \text{ m/s}$

(c) Using the kinematic equation, $v_{max} = v_0 + a_{max}(t_{min} - t_0)$ with $v_0 = 0$ m/s and $t_0 = 0$ s, we obtain

$$t_{min} = \frac{v_{max}}{a_{max}} = \frac{16.7 \text{ m/s}}{6.53 \text{ m/s}^2} = 2.56 \text{ s}$$

Assess: An acceleration time of 2.56 s for the Porsche to reach a speed of ≈37 mph from rest is reasonable.

11.71.   Solve: (a) A 1500 kg object is being accelerated upward at 1.0 m/s^2 by a rope with a tension T. How much power is required at the instant when the velocity is 2.0 m/s?
(b)

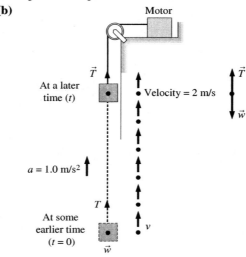

(c) $T = (1500 \text{ kg})(9.8 \text{ m/s}^2) + 1500 \text{ kg}(1.0 \text{ m/s}^2) = 16,200 \text{ N}$

$P = T \cdot 2\text{m/s} = 16200 \text{ N} \times 2.0 \text{ m/s} = 32,400 \text{ W} = 32.4 \text{ kW}$

NEWTON'S THEORY OF GRAVITY

12.3. Model: Model the sun (s) and the earth (e) as spherical masses. Due to the large difference between your size and mass and that of either the sun or the earth, a human body can be treated as a particle.

Solve: $F_{\text{s on you}} = \dfrac{GM_sM_y}{r_{s-e}^2}$ and $F_{\text{e on you}} = \dfrac{GM_eM_y}{r_e^2}$

Dividing these two equations gives

$$\frac{F_{\text{s on y}}}{F_{\text{e on y}}} = \left(\frac{M_s}{M_e}\right)\left(\frac{r_e}{r_{s-e}}\right)^2 = \left(\frac{1.99\times10^{30}\ \text{kg}}{5.98\times10^{24}\ \text{kg}}\right)\left(\frac{6.37\times10^6\ \text{m}}{1.5\times10^{11}\ \text{m}}\right)^2 = 6.00\times10^{-4}$$

12.5. Solve: $F_{\text{sphere on particle}} = \dfrac{GM_sM_p}{r_{s-p}^2}$ and $F_{\text{earth on particle}} = \dfrac{GM_eM_p}{r_e^2}$

Dividing the two equations,

$$\frac{F_{\text{sphere on particle}}}{F_{\text{earth on particle}}} = \left(\frac{M_s}{M_e}\right)\left(\frac{r_e}{r_{s-p}}\right)^2 = \left(\frac{5900\ \text{kg}}{5.98\times10^{24}\ \text{kg}}\right)\left(\frac{6.37\times10^6\ \text{m}}{0.5\ \text{m}}\right)^2 = 1.60\times10^{-7}$$

12.7. Model: Model the earth (e) as a sphere.
Visualize:

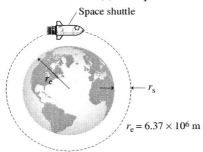

The space shuttle or a 1.0 kg sphere (s) in the space shuttle is $r_e + r_s = 6.37\times10^6\ \text{m} + 0.30\times10^6\ \text{m} = 6.67\times10^6\ \text{m}$ away from the center of the earth.

Solve: (a) $F_{\text{e on s}} = \dfrac{GM_eM_s}{(r_e+r_s)^2} = \dfrac{(6.67\times10^{-11}\ \text{N}\cdot\text{m}^2/\text{kg}^2)(5.98\times10^{24}\ \text{kg})(1.0\ \text{kg})}{(6.67\times10^6\ \text{m})^2} = 8.97\ \text{N}$

(b) Because the sphere and the shuttle are falling with the same acceleration, there cannot be any relative motion between them. That is why the sphere floats around inside the space shuttle.

12.11. Model: Model the earth (e) as a spherical mass.
Visualize: The acceleration due to gravity at sea level (or on the surface) is 9.83 m/s² (see Table 12.1) and $R_e = 6.67\times10^6$ m (see Table 12.2).

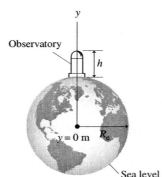

Solve: $g_{\text{observatory}} = \dfrac{GM_e}{(R_e + h)^2} = \dfrac{GM_e}{R_e^2 \left(1 + \dfrac{h}{R_e}\right)^2} = \dfrac{g_{\text{earth}}}{\left(1 + \dfrac{h}{R_e}\right)^2} = (9.83 - 0.0075) \text{ m/s}^2$

$$\Rightarrow 9.8225 \text{ m/s}^2 = \dfrac{9.83 \text{ m/s}^2}{\left(1 + \dfrac{h}{R_e}\right)^2} \Rightarrow h = \left(\sqrt{\dfrac{9.83}{9.8225}} - 1\right) R_e = 2.43 \times 10^3 \text{ m}$$

12.15. **Model:** Model the earth and the projectile as spherical masses. Ignore air resistance. This is an isolated system, so mechanical energy is conserved.

Visualize:

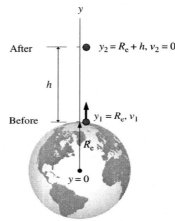

A pictorial representation of the before-and-after events is shown.

Solve: After using $v_2 = 0$ m/s, the energy conservation equation $K_2 + U_2 = K_1 + U_1$ is

$$0 \text{ J} - \dfrac{GM_e m_p}{R_e + h} = \dfrac{1}{2} m_p v_1^2 - \dfrac{GM_e m_p}{R_e}$$

$$\Rightarrow \dfrac{-GM_e m_p}{R_e + h} + \dfrac{GM_e m_p}{R_e} = \dfrac{1}{2} m_p v_1^2 \Rightarrow \dfrac{1}{R_e} - \dfrac{1}{R_e + h} = \dfrac{v_1^2}{2GM_e} = \dfrac{1}{R_e}\left(1 - \dfrac{1}{1 + h/R_e}\right) = \dfrac{v_1^2}{2R_e^2}\left(\dfrac{R_e^2}{GM_e}\right)$$

$$\Rightarrow 1 - \dfrac{1}{1 + h/R_e} = \dfrac{v_1^2}{2R_e}\left(\dfrac{1}{g_{\text{surface}}}\right)$$

$$1 + \dfrac{h}{R_e} = \left[1 - \dfrac{v_1^2}{2R_e g_{\text{surface}}}\right]^{-1} \Rightarrow h = R_e\left\{\left[1 - \dfrac{v_1^2}{2R_e g_{\text{surface}}}\right]^{-1} - 1\right\}$$

Substituting $g_{\text{surface}} = 9.8$ m/s^2, $v_1 = 10{,}000$ km/hr $= 2778$ m/s, and $R_e = 6.37 \times 10^6$ m, we obtain $h = 4.197 \times 10^5$ m $= 420$ km.

12.21.   **Model:**   Model the earth (e) as a spherical mass and the shuttle (s) as a point particle.
Visualize: The shuttle, having mass m_s and velocity v_s orbits the earth in a circle of radius R_s. We will denote the earth's mass by M_e.
Solve: The gravitational force between the earth and the shuttle provides the necessary centripetal force for circular motion. Newton's second law is

$$\frac{GM_e m_s}{R_s^2} = \frac{m_s v_s^2}{R_s} \Rightarrow v_s^2 = \frac{GM_e}{R_s} \Rightarrow v_s = \sqrt{\frac{GM_e}{R_s}}$$

Because $R_s = R_e + 250$ miles $= 6.37 \times 10^6$ m $+ 4.023 \times 10^5$ m $= 6.77 \times 10^6$ m,

$$v_s = \sqrt{\frac{(6.67 \times 10^{-11}\ \text{N} \cdot \text{m}^2/\text{kg}^2)(5.98 \times 10^{24}\ \text{kg})}{(6.77 \times 10^6\ \text{m})}} = 7675\ \text{m/s} = 7.68 \times 10^3\ \text{m/s}$$

$$T_s = \frac{2\pi R_s}{v_s} = \frac{2\pi(6.77 \times 10^6\ \text{m})}{7.675 \times 10^3\ \text{m/s}} = 5542\ \text{s} = 92.4\ \text{minutes}$$

12.23.   **Model:**   Model the earth (e) as a spherical mass and the satellite (s) as a point particle.
Visualize: The satellite has a mass is m_s and orbits the earth with a velocity v_s. The radius of the circular orbit is denoted by R_s and the mass of the earth by M_e.
Solve: The satellite experiences a gravitational force that provides the centripetal force required for circular motion:

$$\frac{GM_e m_s}{R_s^2} = \frac{m_s v_s^2}{R_s} \Rightarrow R_s = \frac{GM_e}{v_s^2} = \frac{(6.67 \times 10^{-11}\text{N} \cdot \text{m}^2/\text{kg}^2)(5.98 \times 10^{24}\ \text{kg})}{(5500\ \text{m/s})^2} = 1.32 \times 10^7\ \text{m}$$

$$\Rightarrow T_s = \frac{2\pi R_s}{v_s} = \frac{(2\pi)(1.32 \times 10^7\ \text{m})}{(5500\ \text{m/s})} = 1.51 \times 10^4 \text{s} = 4.2\ \text{hr}$$

Assess: $\dfrac{R_s}{R_e} = \dfrac{1.32 \times 10^7\ \text{m}}{6.37 \times 10^6\ \text{m}} = 2.07$

where R_e is the radius of the earth. Therefore, the satellite is $1.07 R_e$ above the surface of the earth.

12.27.   **Model:**   Model the moon (m) as a spherical mass and the lander (l) as a particle. This is an isolated system, so mechanical energy is conserved.
Visualize: The initial position of the lunar lander (mass $= m_l$) is at a distance $r_1 = R_m + 50$ km from the center of the moon. The final position of the lunar lander is the orbit whose distance from the center of the moon is $r_2 = R_m + 300$ km.

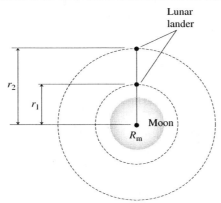

Solve: The energy conservation equation is

$$K_2 + U_2 + \Delta E_{th} = K_1 + U_1 + W_{ext} \qquad \frac{1}{2}m_l v_2^2 - \frac{GM_m m_l}{r_2} + 0\ \text{J} = \frac{1}{2}m_l v_1^2 - \frac{GM_m m_l}{r_1} + W_{thrusters}$$

From Newton's second law:

$$\frac{GM_m m_l}{r_1^2} = \frac{m_l v_1^2}{r_1} \Rightarrow \frac{1}{2}m_l v_1^2 = \frac{1}{2}\frac{GM_m m_l}{r_1} \quad \text{and} \quad \frac{1}{2}m_l v_2^2 = \frac{1}{2}\frac{GM_m m_l}{r_2}$$

The energy equation thus becomes

$$-\frac{1}{2}\frac{GM_m m_1}{r_2} = -\frac{1}{2}\frac{GM_m m_1}{r_1} + W_{thrusters} \Rightarrow W_{thrusters} = \frac{GM_m m_1}{2}\left[\frac{1}{r_1} - \frac{1}{r_2}\right]$$

Using $M_m = 7.36\times10^{22}$ kg, $m_1 = 4\times10^3$ kg, $r_1 = R_m + 50$ km, $r_2 = 300$ km $+ R_m$, and $R_m = 1.74\times10^6$ m, we obtain $W_{thrusters} = 6.72\times10^8$ J.

12.31.   Visualize:

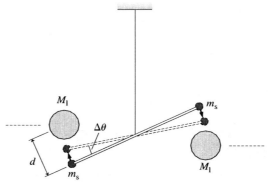

The gravitational force between the lead sphere ($M_1 = 20$ kg) and a smaller sphere ($m_s = 0.200$ kg) leads to a deflection of the suspended rod when the heavier lead spheres are brought closer to the smaller spheres attached to both ends of the rod.

Solve: $F = \dfrac{GM_1 m_s}{d^2} = \dfrac{(6.67\times10^{-11}\text{ N}\cdot\text{m}^2/\text{kg}^2)(20\text{ kg})(0.200\text{ kg})}{(0.15\text{ m})^2} = 1.1858\times10^{-8}\text{ N} = 1.19\times10^{-8}\text{ N}$

Because $F = k\Delta\theta$,

$$\Delta\theta = \frac{F}{k} = \frac{1.1858\times10^{-8}\text{ N}}{1.0\times10^{-5}\text{ N/rad}} = 1.1858\times10^{-3}\text{ rad} = 0.0679\text{ degrees}$$

12.35.   Model: The gravitational potential energy of two masses m_1 and m_2, separated by a distance r_{12}, is defined as $U = -Gm_1 m_2/r_{12}$.

Visualize: We placed the origin of the coordinate system on the 20.0 kg mass (m_1) so that the 5.0 kg mass (m_3) is on the x-axis and the 10.0 kg mass (m_2) is on the y-axis

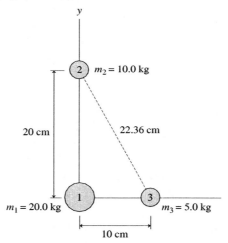

Solution: The gravitational potential energy is a scalar quantity. The gravitational potential energy of the 20.0 kg mass is the scalar sum of the potential energies from the 10.0 kg and 5.0 kg masses and the gravitational potential energy of the 5.0 kg mass is the scalar sum of potential energies from the 20.0 kg and 10 kg masses. Using $G = 6.67 \times 10^{-11}$ N $\cdot$ m^2/kg^2, we obtain

(a) $U_{m_1} = U_{m_2, m_1} + U_{m_1, m_3} = -\dfrac{Gm_1 m_2}{r_{12}} - \dfrac{Gm_1 m_3}{r_{13}}$

$= \dfrac{-G(20.0 \text{ kg})(10.0 \text{ kg})}{(0.20 \text{ m})} - \dfrac{G(20.0 \text{ kg})(5.0 \text{ kg})}{(0.10 \text{ m})} = -1.33 \times 10^{-7}$ J

(b) $U_{m_3} = U_{m_3, m_2} + U_{m_3, m_1} = -\dfrac{Gm_2 m_3}{r_{23}} - \dfrac{Gm_1 m_3}{r_{13}}$

$= \dfrac{-G(10.0 \text{ kg})(5.0 \text{ kg})}{(0.2236 \text{ m})} - \dfrac{G(20.0 \text{ kg})(5.0 \text{ kg})}{(0.10 \text{ m})} = -8.16 \times 10^{-8}$ J

12.41.   **Model:**   Model the planet (p) as a spherical mass and the projectile as a point mass. This is an isolated system, so mechanical energy is conserved.
Visualize: The projectile of mass m was launched on the surface of the planet with an initial velocity v_0.

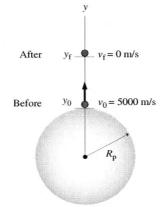

Solve: **(a)** The energy conservation equation $K_f + U_f = K_0 + U_0$ is

$$\frac{1}{2}mv_f^2 - \frac{GM_p m}{R_p + y_f} = \frac{1}{2}mv_0^2 - \frac{GM_p m}{R_p} \Rightarrow \frac{R_p v_0^2}{2GM_p} = \left[1 - \frac{1}{1 + (y_f/R_p)}\right]$$

$$\Rightarrow \frac{(5.0 \times 10^6 \text{ m})(5000 \text{ m/s})^2}{2(6.67 \times 10^{-11} \text{ N} \cdot \text{m}^2/\text{kg}^2)(2.6 \times 10^{24} \text{ kg})} = 1 - \frac{1}{1 + (y_f/R_p)} \Rightarrow y_f = 2.82 \times 10^6 \text{ m}$$

(b) Using the energy conservation equation $K_1 + U_1 = K_0 + U_0$ with $y_1 = 1000$ km $= 100 \times 10^6$ m:

$$\frac{1}{2}mv_1^2 - \frac{GM_p m}{R_p + y_1} = \frac{1}{2}mv_0^2 - \frac{GM_p m}{R_p}$$

$$\Rightarrow v_1^2 = v_0^2 + 2GM_p \left(\frac{1}{R_p + y_1} - \frac{1}{R_p}\right)$$

$$= (5000 \text{ m/s})^2 + 2(6.67 \times 10^{-11} \text{N} \cdot \text{m}^2/\text{kg}^2)(2.6 \times 10^{24} \text{ kg})\left(\frac{1}{(5.0 \times 10^6 \text{ m} + 1.0 \times 10^6 \text{ m})} - \frac{1}{5.0 \times 10^6 \text{ m}}\right)$$

$$= 2.5 \times 10^7 \text{ m}^2/\text{s}^2 + 3.468 \times 10^7 \text{ N} \cdot \text{m}^2/\text{kg}\left(-\frac{1}{3.0 \text{ m}}\right) \Rightarrow v_1 = 3.67 \times 10^3 \text{ m/s}$$

12.51. **Model:** Model the earth (mass = M_e) as a spherical mass and an object (mass = m_o) as a point mass.
Visualize:

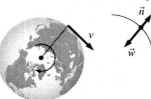

Top view of the Earth

The figure shows the top view of the earth rotating at an angular velocity $\omega = v/R_e$. The forces on an object on the surface of the earth are the normal force $\vec{n}$ and the weight $\vec{w}$.
Solve: Newton's second law on the object is

$$\left(\sum F\right)_r = w - n = \frac{mv^2}{R_e}$$

When the object just begin to "fly off," n is equal to 0 N. Thus,

$$w = \frac{mv^2}{R_e} \Rightarrow \frac{GmM_e}{R_e^2} = \frac{mv^2}{R_e} \Rightarrow v^2 = \frac{GM_e}{R_e} \Rightarrow \left(\frac{2\pi R_e}{T}\right)^2 = \frac{GM_e}{R_e}$$

$$\Rightarrow T = \sqrt{\frac{4\pi^2 R_e^3}{GM_e}} = \sqrt{\frac{4\pi^2 (6.37 \times 10^6 \text{ m})^3}{(6.67 \times 10^{-11} \text{ N} \cdot \text{m}^2/\text{kg}^2)(5.98 \times 10^{24} \text{ kg})}} = 5{,}058 \text{ s} = 1.41 \text{ hrs}$$

Assess: This time period is approximately 17 times smaller than the real time period, implying a much faster rotational motion of the earth.

12.57. **Solve:** **(a)** Taking the logarithm of both sides of $v^p = Cu^q$ gives

$$[\log(v^p) = p\log v] = [\log(Cu^q) = \log C + q\log u] \Rightarrow \log v = \frac{q}{p}\log u + \frac{\log C}{p}$$

But $x = \log u$ and $y = \log v$, so x and y are related by

$$y = \left(\frac{q}{p}\right)x + \frac{\log C}{p}$$

(b) The previous result shows there is a linear relationship between x and y, hence there is a linear relationship between $\log u$ and $\log v$. The graph of a linear relationship is a straight line, so the graph of $\log v$-versus-$\log u$ will be a straight line.
(c) The slope of the straight line represented by the equation $y = (q/p)x + \log C/p$ is q/p. Thus, the slope of the log v-versus-log u graph will be q/p.
(d) From Newton's theory, the period T and radius r of an orbit around the sun are related by

$$T^2 = \left(\frac{4\pi^2}{GM}\right)r^3$$

This equation is of the form $T^p = Cr^q$, with $p = 2$, $q = 3$, and $C = 4\pi^2/GM$. If the theory is correct, we *expect* a graph of log T-versus-log r to be a straight line with slope $q/p = 3/2 = 1.500$. The *experimental measurements* of actual planets yield a straight line graph whose slope is 1.500 to four significant figures. Note that the graph has nothing to do with theory—it is simply a graph of measured values. But the fact that the shape and slope of the graph agree precisely with the prediction of Newton's theory is strong evidence for its correctness.
(e) The predicted y-intercept of the graph is $\log C/p$, and the experimentally determined value is 9.264. Equating these, we can solve for M. Because the planets all orbit the sun, the mass we are finding is $M = M_{sun}$.

$$\frac{1}{2}\log C = \frac{1}{2}\log\left(\frac{4\pi^2}{GM_{sun}}\right) = -9.264 \Rightarrow \frac{4\pi^2}{GM_{sun}} = 10^{-18.528} = \frac{1}{10^{18.528}}$$

$$\Rightarrow M_{sun} = \frac{4\pi^2}{G} \cdot 10^{18.528} = 1.996 \times 10^{30} \text{ kg}$$

The tabulated value, to three significant figures, is $M_{sun} = 1.99 \times 10^{30}$ kg. We have used the orbits of the planets to "weigh the sun!"

12.59. **Model:** Model the earth and the moon as spherical masses.
Solve: Humans use 10^{13} watts of energy which is 10^{13} joules per second. In 100 years this amounts to $10^{13} \times 3600 \times 24 \times 365 \times 100$ J $= 3.154 \times 10^{22}$ J. The mechanical energy of the moon in its orbit is

$$E_{mech} = K + U_g = \frac{1}{2}U_g \Rightarrow \Delta E_{mech} = \frac{1}{2}\Delta U_g = W_{ext}$$

$$\Rightarrow \frac{1}{2}(U_{gf} - U_{gi}) = W_{ext} = -3.1514 \times 10^{22} \text{ J} \Rightarrow U_{gf} = U_{gi} - 6.3028 \times 10^{22} \text{ J}$$

The initial potential energy of the moon is

$$U_{gi} = \frac{-GM_e m_m}{R_{e-m}} = \frac{-(6.67 \times 10^{-11} \text{ N} \cdot \text{m}^2/\text{kg}^2)(5.98 \times 10^{24} \text{ kg})(7.36 \times 10^{22} \text{ kg})}{3.84 \times 10^8 \text{ m}} = -7.6449 \times 10^{28} \text{ J}$$

Thus,

$$U_{gf} = -7.6449 \times 10^{28} \text{ J} - 6.3028 \times 10^{22} \text{ J}$$
$$= -7.6449 \times 10^{28} \text{ J} - 0.0000063 \times 10^{28} \text{ J} = -7.6449 \times 10^{28} \text{ J}$$

Because the number of significant digits is three, the change in the moon's mechanical energy is too small to show up (even in 5 significant figures). However, the percentage change in the moon's energy is

$$\frac{6.3028 \times 10^{22}}{7.6449 \times 10^{28}} \times 100\% = 8.3 \times 10^{-5}\% = \frac{dU_g}{U_g}$$

The percentage change in the orbit radius is also $8.3 \times 10^{-5}\%$ since

$$U_g = \frac{k}{r} \Rightarrow dU_g = -\frac{k\,dr}{r^2} \Rightarrow \frac{dU_g}{U_g} = -\frac{k\,dr}{r^2}\left(\frac{r}{k}\right) = -\frac{dr}{r}$$

Thus $dr = r\dfrac{dU_g}{U_g} = (3.84 \times 10^8 \text{ m})(8.3 \times 10^{-7}) = 319$ m

The percentage change in the time period is $1.25 \times 10^{-4}\%$ since

$$T^2 = kr^3 \Rightarrow 2T\,dT = 3kr^2\,dr \Rightarrow \frac{2T\,dT}{T^2} = \frac{3kr^2\,dr}{kr^3} \Rightarrow \frac{dT}{T} = \frac{3}{2}\frac{dr}{r}$$

Thus $dT = \dfrac{3}{2}\dfrac{dr}{r}T = \dfrac{3}{2}\dfrac{dU_g}{U_g}T = \dfrac{3}{2}(8.3 \times 10^{-7})(27.3 \text{ days})\left(\dfrac{24 \text{ h}}{1 \text{ day}}\right)\left(\dfrac{3600 \text{ s}}{1 \text{ h}}\right) = 3.0$ s

12.63. **Model:** Angular momentum is conserved for a particle following a trajectory of any shape.
Visualize:

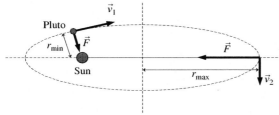

For a particle in an elliptical orbit, the particle's angular momentum is $L = mv_t = mv\sin\beta$, where v is the velocity tangent to the trajectory and β is the angle between $\vec{r}$ and $\vec{v}$.
Solve: At the distance of closest approach (r_{min}) and also at the most distant point, $\beta = 90°$. Since there is no tangential force at these two points (the only force being the radial force), angular momentum must be conserved:

$$m_{Pluto}v_1 r_{min} = m_{Pluto}v_2 r_{max}$$
$$\Rightarrow v_2 = v_1(r_{min}/r_{max}) = (6.12 \times 10^3 \text{ m/s})(4.43 \times 10^{12} \text{ m}/7.30 \times 10^{12} \text{ m}) = 3.71 \text{ km/s}$$

12.65.   Model: For the sun + comet system, the mechanical energy is conserved.
Visualize:

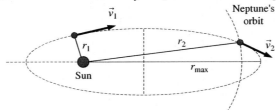

Solve: The conservation of energy equation $K_f + U_f = K_i + U_i$ is

$$\frac{1}{2} M_c v_2^2 - \frac{GM_s M_c}{r_2} = \frac{1}{2} M_c v_1^2 - \frac{GM_s M_c}{r_1}$$

Using $G = 6.67 \times 10^{-11}$ Nm^2/kg^2, $M_s = 1.99 \times 10^{30}$ kg, $r_1 = 8.79 \times 10^{10}$ m, $r_2 = 4.50 \times 10^{12}$ m, and $v_1 = 54.6$ km/s, we get $v_2 = 4.49$ km/s.
Assess: A speed of 4.49 km/s is reasonable.

12.69.   Solve: (a) If a rocket deposited a payload of 1000 kg in a circular orbit around the earth with a speed of 1997 m/s, what would be the radius of the orbit and what multiple of R_{earth} would it be? Does the size of the payload have any effect on the orbit if a speed of 1997 m/s is obtained?
(b)

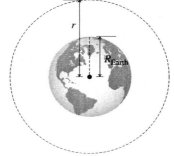

(c) The radius of the orbit is

$$r = \frac{GM_E}{(v_{payload})^2} = \frac{6.67 \times 10^{-11} \text{ N} \cdot \text{m}^2 / \text{kg}^2 (5.98 \times 10^{24} \text{ kg})}{(1997 \text{ m/s})^2} = 1.000 \times 10^8 \text{ m}$$

$$\Rightarrow r = (1.000 \times 10^8 \text{ m}) \frac{R_{earth}}{6.37 \times 10^6 \text{ m}} = 15.7 R_{earth}$$

The size of the payload does not enter our calculation.

12.71.   Solve: (a) Two stars, one the mass of the sun and the other twice the mass of the sun, are released from rest at a separation of 1.0×10^{12} m and allowed to "fall" toward each other. What would be the speed of each star when they are one thousand times closer together?
(b)

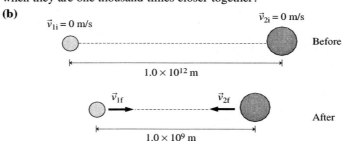

(c) The first equation is the conservation of momentum and can be used in the conservation of energy equation as follows:

$$v_{2f} = -\frac{1}{2}v_{1f} \Rightarrow \frac{1}{2}(1.99\times10^{30}\,\text{kg})v_{1f}^2 + \frac{1}{2}(3.98\times10^{30}\,\text{kg})\frac{1}{4}v_{1f}^2$$

$$= 6.67\times10^{-11}\,\text{N}\cdot\text{m}^2/\text{kg}^2(1.99\times10^{30})\times(3.98\times10^{30}\,\text{kg})\left[\frac{1}{(1\times10^9\,\text{m})} - \frac{1}{(1\times10^{12}\,\text{m})}\right]$$

$$\frac{3}{4}1.99\times10^{30}v_{1f}^2 = 6.67\times10^{-11}\,\text{N}\cdot\text{m}^2/\text{kg}^2(1.99\times10^{30}\,\text{kg})^2(2)\left[\frac{1000}{(1\times10^{12}\,\text{m})} - \frac{1}{(1\times10^{12}\,\text{m})}\right]$$

$$\Rightarrow v_{1f} = 595\,\text{km/s} \quad \text{and} \quad v_{2f} = -297\,\text{km/s}$$

That is, the speeds of the two stars are 595 km/s and 297 km/s.

13

ROTATION OF A RIGID BODY

13.3. **Model:** The wheel is a rotating rigid body.
Solve: **(a)**

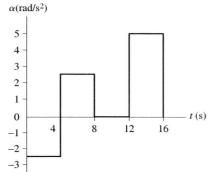

The angular acceleration (α) is the slope of the ω-versus-t graph.
(b) The car is at rest at $t = 0$ s. It gradually speeds up for 4 s and then slows down for 4 s. The car is at rest from $t = 8$ s to $t = 12$ s, and then speeds up in the opposite direction for 4 s.

13.5. **Model:** Spinning skater, whose arms are outstretched, is a rigid rotating body.
Visualize:

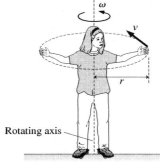

Solve: The speed $v = r\omega$, where $r = 140$ cm/2 $= 0.70$ m. Also, 180 rpm $= (180)2\pi/60$ rad/s $= 6\pi$ rad/s. Thus, $v = (0.70$ m$)(6\pi$ rad/s$) = 13.2$ m/s.
Assess: A speed of 13.2 m/s $\approx$ 29.5 mph for the hands is a little high, but reasonable.

13.7. **Model:** The drill is a rigid rotating body.
Visualize:

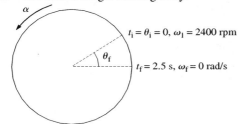

The figure shows the drill's motion from the top.

Solve: (a) The kinematic equation $\omega_f = \omega_i + \alpha(t_f - t_i)$ becomes, after using $\omega_i = 2400$ rpm $= (2400)(2\pi)/60 = 251.3$ rad/s, $t_f - t_i = 2.5$ s $- 0$ s $= 2.5$ s, and $\omega_f = 0$ rad/s,

$$0 \text{ rad} = 251.3 \text{ rad/s} + \alpha(2.5 \text{ s}) \Rightarrow \alpha = -100.5 \text{ rad/s}^2$$

(b) Applying the kinematic equation for angular position yields:

$$\theta_f = \theta_i + \omega_i(t_f - t_i) + \frac{1}{2}\alpha(t_f - t_i)^2$$

$$= 0 \text{ rad} + (251.3 \text{ rad/s})(2.5 \text{ s} - 0 \text{ s}) + \frac{1}{2}(-100.5 \text{ rad/s}^2)(2.5 \text{ s} - 0 \text{ s})^2$$

$$= 314.2 \text{ rad} = 50.0 \text{ rev}$$

Assess: A negative acceleration means a slowing down of rotational motion.

13.11.   Visualize:

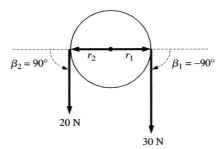

Solve: Torque by a force is defined as $\tau = Fr \sin \beta$ where β is measured counterclockwise from the $\vec{r}$ vector to the $\vec{F}$ vector. The net torque on the pulley about the axle is the torque due to the 30 N force plus the torque due to the 20 N force:

$$(30 \text{ N})r_1 \sin\beta_1 + (20 \text{ N})r_2 \sin\beta_2 = (30 \text{ N})(0.02 \text{ m}) \sin(-90°) + (20 \text{ N})(0.02 \text{ m}) \sin(90°)$$

$$= (-0.60 \text{ Nm}) + (0.40 \text{ Nm}) = -0.20 \text{ Nm}$$

Assess: A negative torque means a clockwise motion of the pulley.

13.15.   Model: The beam is a solid rigid body.
Visualize:

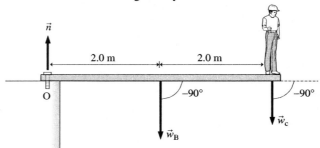

The steel beam experiences a torque due to the construction worker's weight $\vec{w}_C$, the beam's weight $\vec{w}_B$, and the normal force provided by the building's framework and the bolt.
Solve: The normal force exerts no torque since the net torque is calculated about the point where the beam is bolted into place. The net torque on the steel beam about point O is the sum of the torque due to $\vec{w}_C$ and the torque due to $\vec{w}_B$:

$$(w_C)(4.0 \text{ m}) \sin(-90°) + (w_B)(2.0 \text{ m}) \sin(-90°)$$

$$= -(70 \text{ kg})(9.80 \text{ m/s}^2)(4.0 \text{ m}) - (500 \text{ kg})(9.80 \text{ m/s}^2)(2.0 \text{ m}) = -2744 \text{ Nm} - 9800 \text{ Nm}$$

$$= -1.25 \times 10^4 \text{ Nm}$$

Assess: The negative torque means a tendency for the beam to rotate clockwise.

13.19.   Model: The three masses connected by massless rigid rods is a rigid body.
Visualize: Please refer to Figure Ex13.19.

Solve: **(a)** $x_{cm} = \dfrac{\sum m_i x_i}{\sum m_i} = \dfrac{(0.100 \text{ kg})(0 \text{ m}) + (0.200 \text{ kg})(0.06 \text{ m}) + (0.100 \text{ kg})(0.12 \text{ m})}{0.100 \text{ kg} + 0.200 \text{ kg} + 0.100 \text{ kg}} = 0.06 \text{ m}$

$y_{cm} = \dfrac{\sum m_i y_i}{\sum m_i} = \dfrac{(0.100 \text{ kg})(0 \text{ m}) + (0.200 \text{ kg})\left(\sqrt{(0.10 \text{ m})^2 - (0.06 \text{ m})^2}\right) + (0.100 \text{ kg})(0 \text{ m})}{0.100 \text{ kg} + 0.200 \text{ kg} + 0.100 \text{ kg}} = 0.04 \text{ m}$

(b) The moment of inertia about an axis through A and perpendicular to the page is

$I_A = \sum m_i r_i^2 = m_B (0.10 \text{ m})^2 + m_C (0.10 \text{ m})^2 = (0.100 \text{ kg})[(0.10 \text{ m})^2 + (0.10 \text{ m})^2] = 0.002 \text{ kg m}^2$

(c) The moment of inertia about an axis that passes through B and C is

$$I_{BC} = m_A \left(\sqrt{(0.10 \text{ m})^2 - (0.06 \text{ m})^2}\right)^2 = 0.00128 \text{ kg m}^2$$

Assess: Note that mass m_A does not contribute to I_A, and the masses m_B and m_C do not contribute to I_{BC}.

13.21. **Visualize:** Please refer to Figure Ex 13.21.
Solve: From Equation 13.6

$$\omega_f = \omega_i + \text{Area under the angular acceleration } \alpha \text{ curve between } t_i \text{ and } t_f.$$

Because $\tau_{net} = I\alpha$, $\alpha = \dfrac{\tau_{net}}{I}$. Thus the time dependence of α is the same as the time dependence of τ_{net} (shown in Figure Ex 13.21) except that the τ_{net} values are to be divided by $I = 4.0$ kg m^2 at all values of time. Area under the τ_{net} curve between $t = 0$ s and $t = 3$ s is 3 Nm s, which now yields the area under the α curve between $t = 0$ s and $t = 3$ s as

$\dfrac{3 \text{ Nm s}}{I} = \dfrac{3 \text{ Nm s}}{4.0 \text{ kg m}^2} = 0.75$ rad/s.

With $\omega_i = 0$ rad/s, we have

$$\omega_f = 0 \text{ rad/s} + 0.75 \text{ rad/s} = 0.75 \text{ rad/s}.$$

13.25. **Model:** The rod with the mass attached on its right end is a rigid body. To not rotate, it must be in rotational equilibrium.
Visualize:

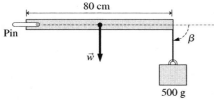

Solve: Rotational equilibrium means

$\tau_{net} = 0 \text{ Nm} = \tau_{500 \text{ gram mass}} + \tau_{rod} + \tau_{pin} \Rightarrow \tau_{pin} = -\tau_{500 \text{ gram mass}} - \tau_{rod}$

$= -(0.500 \text{ kg})(9.80 \text{ m/s}^2)(0.80 \text{ m})\sin(-90°) - (2.0 \text{ kg})(9.80 \text{ m/s}^2)(0.40 \text{ m})\sin(-90°) = 11.8 \text{ Nm}$

Assess: A positive τ_{pin} means that the pin exerts a torque in the counterclockwise direction.

13.33. **Model:** The can is a rigid body rolling across the floor. Assume that the can has uniform mass distribution.
Solve: The rolling motion of the can is a translation of its center of mass plus a rotation about the center of mass. The moment of inertia of the can about the center of mass is $\frac{1}{2}MR^2$, where R is the radius of the can. Also $v_{cm} = R\omega$, where ω is the angular velocity of the can. The total kinetic energy of the can is

$$K = K_{cm} + K_{rot} = \frac{1}{2}Mv_{cm}^2 + \frac{1}{2}I_{cm}\omega^2 = \frac{1}{2}Mv_{cm}^2 + \frac{1}{2}\left(\frac{1}{2}MR^2\right)\left(\frac{v_{cm}}{R}\right)^2$$

$$= \frac{3}{4}Mv_{cm}^2 = \frac{3}{4}(0.5 \text{ kg})(1.0 \text{ m/s})^2 = 0.375 \text{ J}$$

13.39. Solve: (a)
$$\vec{A} \times \vec{B} = (3\hat{i} - \hat{j}) \times (2\hat{i} + 3\hat{j} - \hat{k})$$
$$= 6\hat{i} \times \hat{i} + 9\hat{i} \times \hat{j} - 3\hat{i} \times \hat{k} - 2\hat{j} \times \hat{i} - 3\hat{j} \times \hat{j} + \hat{j} \times \hat{k}$$
$$= 0 + 9\hat{k} - 3(-\hat{j}) - 2(-\hat{k}) - 0 + \hat{i} = \hat{i} + 3\hat{j} + 11\hat{k}$$

(b)

13.43.   Model: The block attached to a massless rod is a rigid rotating body. Assume the block is a particle.
Solve: The moment of inertia of the block about the pivot is
$$I = ML^2 = (0.200 \text{ kg})(0.40 \text{ m})^2 = 0.032 \text{ kg m}^2$$

Since $\tau = I\alpha = 0.050$ Nm,
$$\alpha = \frac{0.050 \text{ Nm}}{I} = \frac{0.050 \text{ Nm}}{0.032 \text{ kg m}^2} = 1.56 \text{ rad/s}^2$$

(a) Substituting $\theta_0 = 0$ rad, $t_0 = 0$ s, and $\omega_0 = 0$ rad/s into the rotational kinematic equation, we get
$$\theta = \theta_0 + \omega_0(t - t_0) + \frac{1}{2}\alpha(t - t_0)^2 \qquad 10(2\pi)\text{rad} = 0 \text{ rad} + 0 \text{ rad} + \frac{1}{2}(1.56 \text{ rad/s}^2)(t - 0 \text{ s})^2 \Rightarrow t = 8.975 \text{ s}$$

(b) The angular momentum is calculated as follows:
$$L = I\omega = I[\omega_0 + \alpha(t - t_0)] = I[0 \text{ rad/s} + \alpha(t - 0 \text{ s})]$$
$$= I\alpha t = (0.032 \text{ kg m}^2)(1.56 \text{ rad/s}^2)(8.975 \text{ s}) = 0.448 \text{ kg m}^2/\text{s}$$

(c) $\dfrac{\Delta L}{\Delta t} = \dfrac{0.448 \text{ kg m}^2/\text{s} - 0 \text{ kg m}^2/\text{s}}{8.975 \text{ s} - 0 \text{ s}} = 0.05 \text{ Nm} = \tau$

Analytically,
$$\frac{\Delta L}{\Delta t} = \frac{I\Delta\omega}{\Delta t} = I\alpha = \tau$$

13.47.   Model: The disk is a rotating rigid body.
Visualize: Please refer to Figure Ex.13.47.
Solve: From Table 13.3, the moment of inertial of the disk about its center is
$$I = \frac{1}{2}MR^2 = \frac{1}{2}(2.0 \text{ kg})(0.02 \text{ m})^2 = 4.0 \times 10^{-4} \text{ kg m}^2$$

The angular velocity ω is 600 rpm = $600 \times 2\pi/60$ rad/s = 20π rad/s. Thus, $L = I\omega = (4.0 \times 10^{-4} \text{ kg m}^2)(20\pi \text{ rad/s}) =$ 0.0251 kg m²/s. If we wrap our right fingers in the direction of the disk's rotation, our thumb will point in the $-x$ direction. Consequently,
$$\vec{L} = (0.0251 \text{ kg m}^2/\text{s}, \ -x \text{ direction})$$

13.51. **Model:** The disk is a rigid rotating body. The axis is perpendicular to the plane of the disk.
Visualize:

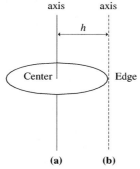

(a)   (b)

Solve: **(a)** From Table 13.3, the moment of inertia of a disk about its center is

$$I = \frac{1}{2}MR^2 = \frac{1}{2}(2.0 \text{ kg})(0.10 \text{ m})^2 = 0.010 \text{ kg m}^2$$

(b) To find the moment of inertia of the disk through the edge, we can make use of the parallel axis theorem:

$$I = I_{center} + Mh^2 = (0.010 \text{ kg m}^2) + (2.0 \text{ kg})(0.10 \text{ m})^2 = 0.030 \text{ kg m}^2$$

Assess: The larger moment of inertia about the edge means there is more inertia to rotational motion about the edge than about the center.

13.53. **Visualize:**

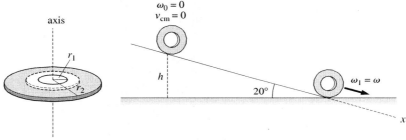

Solve: We solve this problem by dividing the disk between radii r_1 and r_2 into narrow rings of mass dm. Such a ring of radius r and width dr is shown in the figure. Let dA be the area of this ring. The mass dm in this ring is the same fraction of the total mass M as dA is of the total area A.
(a) The moment of inertia can be calculated as follows:

$$I_{disk} = \int r^2 dm \quad \text{and} \quad dm = \frac{M}{A}dA = \frac{M}{\pi(r_2^2 - r_1^2)}(2\pi r)dr$$

$$\Rightarrow I_{disk} = \frac{M}{\pi(r_2^2 - r_1^2)} \int_{r_1}^{r_2} r^2 (2\pi r)dr = \frac{2M}{(r_2^2 - r_1^2)} \int_{r_1}^{r_2} r^3 dr = \frac{2M}{(r_2^2 - r_1^2)} \frac{r^4}{4}\bigg|_{r_1}^{r_2}$$

$$= \frac{2M}{4(r_2^2 - r_1^2)}(r_2^4 - r_1^4) = \frac{M}{2}(r_2^2 + r_1^2)$$

Replacing r_1 with r and r_2 with R, the moment of inertia of the disk through its center is $I_{disk} = \frac{1}{2}M(R^2 + r^2)$.
(b) For $r = 0$ m, $I_{disk} = \frac{1}{2}MR^2$. This is the moment of inertia for a solid disk or cylinder about the center. Additionally, for $r \cong R$, we have $I = MR^2$. This is the expression for the moment of inertia of a cylindrical hoop or ring about the center.
(c) The initial gravitational potential energy of the disk is transformed into kinetic energy as it rolls down. If we choose the bottom of the incline as the zero of potential energy, the energy conservation equation $K_f = U_i$ is

$$\frac{1}{2}I_{cm}\omega^2 + \frac{1}{2}Mv_{cm}^2 = Mgh \Rightarrow \frac{1}{2}\left(\frac{M}{2}\right)(R^2 + r^2)\frac{v_{cm}^2}{R^2} + \frac{1}{2}Mv_{cm}^2 = Mg(0.50 \text{ m})\sin 20°$$

$$\Rightarrow v_{cm}^2\left(\frac{R^2 + r^2}{4R^2}\right) + \frac{1}{2}v_{cm}^2 = v_{cm}^2\left(\frac{1}{2} + \frac{1}{4} + \frac{r^2}{4R^2}\right) = 1.6759 \text{ m}^2/\text{s}^2$$

$$v_{cm}^2\left(\frac{3}{4} + \frac{(0.015 \text{ m})^2}{4(0.020 \text{ m})^2}\right) = 1.6759 \text{ m}^2/\text{s}^2 \Rightarrow v_{cm} = 1.37 \text{ m/s}$$

For a sliding particle on a frictionless surface $K_f = U_i$, so

$$\frac{1}{2}mv^2 = mgh \Rightarrow v = \sqrt{2gh} = \sqrt{2g(0.50 \text{ m})\sin 20°} = 1.83 \text{ m/s} \Rightarrow \frac{v_{cm}}{v} = 0.748$$

That is, v_{cm} is 74.8% of the speed of a particle sliding down a frictionless ramp.

13.59.   Model: Model the beam as a rigid body. For the beam not to fall over, it must be both in translational equilibrium ($\vec{F}_{net} = 0$ N) and rotational equilibrium ($\tau_{net} = 0$ Nm).
Visualize:

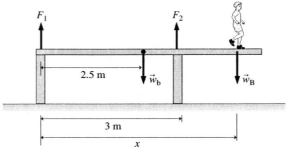

The boy walks along the beam a distance x, measured from the left end of the beam. There are four forces acting on the beam. F_1 and F_2 are from the two supports, $\vec{w}_b$ is the weight of the beam, and $\vec{w}_B$ is the weight of the boy.
Solve: We pick our pivot point on the left end through the first support. The equation for rotational equilibrium is

$$-w_b (2.5 \text{ m}) + F_2 (3.0 \text{ m}) - w_B x = 0 \text{ Nm} \qquad -(20 \text{ kg})(9.80 \text{ m/s}^2)(2.5 \text{ m}) + F_2 (3.0 \text{ m}) - (40 \text{ kg})(9.80 \text{ m/s}^2)x = 0 \text{ Nm}$$

The equation for translation equilibrium is

$$\sum F_y = 0 \text{ N} = F_1 + F_2 - w_b - w_B$$
$$\Rightarrow F_1 + F_2 = w_b + w_B = (20 \text{ kg} + 40 \text{ kg})(9.8 \text{ m/s}^2) = 588 \text{ N}$$

Just when the boy is at the point where the beam tips, $F_1 = 0$ N. Thus $F_2 = 588$ N. With this value of F_2, we can simplify the torque equation to:

$$-(40 \text{ kg})(9.80 \text{ m/s}^2)(2.5 \text{ m}) + (588 \text{ N})(3.0 \text{ m}) - (20 \text{ kg})(9.80 \text{ m/s}^2)x = 0 \text{ Nm}$$

$$\Rightarrow x = 4.0 \text{ m}$$

Thus, the distance from the right end is 5.0 m – 4.0 m = 1.0 m.

13.61.   Model: The two masses connected by a massless rod is a rigid body rotating about its center of mass.
Visualize:

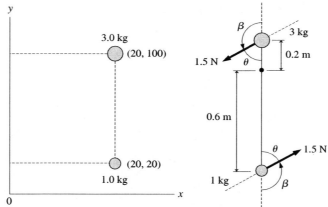

We denote the 1.0 kg and 3.0 kg masses by m_1 and m_2, respectively.

Solve: **(a)** $x_{cm} = \dfrac{m_1 x_1 + m_2 x_2}{m_1 + m_2} = \dfrac{(1.0 \text{ kg})(20 \text{ cm}) + (3.0 \text{ kg})(20 \text{ cm})}{1.0 \text{ kg} + 3.0 \text{ kg}} = 20.0 \text{ cm}$

$y_{cm} = \dfrac{(1.0 \text{ kg})(20 \text{ cm}) + (3.0 \text{ kg})(100 \text{ cm})}{1.0 \text{ kg} + 3.0 \text{ kg}} = 80.0 \text{ cm}$

(b) Relative to the center of mass, the mass m_1 is at a distance of $r_1 = 80 \text{ cm} - 20 \text{ cm} = 60 \text{ cm}$ and m_2 is at a distance of $r_2 = 100 \text{ cm} - 80 \text{ cm} = 20 \text{ cm}$. The moment of inertia is

$$I_{cm} = \sum mr^2 = m_1 r_1^2 + m_2 r_2^2 = (1.0 \text{ kg})(0.60 \text{ m})^2 + (3.0 \text{ kg})(0.20 \text{ m})^2 = 0.48 \text{ kg m}^2$$

(c) Using the rotational kinematic equation $\omega_1 = \omega_0 + \alpha(t_1 - t_0)$, we get

$$\alpha = \frac{\omega_1 - \omega_0}{t_1 - t_0} = \frac{6.25 \text{ rad/s} - 0 \text{ rad/s}}{3.0 \text{ s} - 0 \text{ s}} = 2.083 \text{ rad/s}^2$$

Thus, the torque $\tau = I\alpha = (0.48 \text{ kg m}^2)(2.083 \text{ rad/s}^2) = 1.0 \text{ Nm}$.

(d) To get a torque of 1.0 Nm with forces of 1.5 N on each mass,

$$(1.5 \text{ N})(0.2 \text{ m}) \sin\beta + (1.5 \text{ N})(0.6 \text{ m}) \sin\beta = 1.0 \text{ Nm}$$

$$\Rightarrow 1.2 \text{ Nm} \sin(180° - \theta) = 1.0 \text{ Nm} \quad \text{or} \quad \sin\theta = \frac{1.0}{1.2} \Rightarrow \theta = 56.4°$$

13.65. **Model:** The flywheel is a rigid body rotating about its central axis.

Visualize:

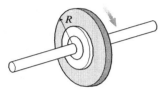

Solve: The radius of the flywheel is $R = (1.5 \text{ m})/2 = 0.75 \text{ m}$ and its mass is $M = 250 \text{ kg}$. The moment of inertia about the axis of rotation is that of a disk:

$$I = \frac{1}{2} MR^2 = \frac{1}{2}(250 \text{ kg})(0.75 \text{ m})^2 = 70.31 \text{ kg m}^2$$

The angular acceleration is calculated as follows:

$$\tau_{net} = I\alpha \Rightarrow \alpha = \tau_{net}/I = (50 \text{ Nm})/(70.31 \text{ kg m}^2) = 0.711 \text{ rad/s}^2$$

(a) Using the kinematic equation for angular velocity gives

$$\omega_1 = \omega_0 + \alpha(t_1 - t_0) = 1200 \text{ rpm} = 0 \text{ rad/s} + 0.711 \text{ rad/s}^2 (t_1 - 0 \text{ s})$$

$$= \frac{1200(2\pi)}{60} \text{ rad/s} = 40\pi \text{ rad/s} \Rightarrow t_1 = 177 \text{ s}$$

(b) The energy stored in the flywheel is rotational kinetic energy:

$$K_{rot} = \frac{1}{2} I\omega_1^2 = \frac{1}{2}(70.31 \text{ kg m}^2)(40\pi \text{ rad/s})^2 = 5.55 \times 10^5 \text{ J}$$

(c) Average power delivered $= \dfrac{\text{energy delivered}}{\text{time interval}} = \dfrac{(5.55 \times 10^5 \text{ J})/2}{2 \text{ s}} = 1.39 \times 10^5 \text{ W}$

(d) Because $\tau = I\alpha$, $\tau_{avg} = I\alpha_{avg} \Rightarrow \tau_{avg} = I\dfrac{\Delta\omega}{\Delta t} = I\left(\dfrac{\omega_{\text{full energy}} - \omega_{\text{half energy}}}{\Delta t}\right)$. $\omega_{\text{full energy}} = \omega_1$ (from part (a)) $= 40\pi \text{ rad/s}$.

$\omega_{\text{half energy}}$ can be obtained as:

$$\frac{1}{2}\omega_{\text{half energy}}^2 = \frac{1}{2} K_{rot} \Rightarrow \omega_{\text{half energy}} = \sqrt{\frac{K_{rot}}{I}} = \sqrt{\frac{5.55 \times 10^5 \text{ J}}{70.31 \text{ kg m}^2}} = 88.85 \text{ rad/s}$$

Thus

$$\tau_{avg} = (70.31 \text{ kg m}^2)\left(\frac{40\pi \text{ rad/s} - 88.85 \text{ rad/s}}{2 \text{ s}}\right) = 1.30 \times 10^3 \text{ Nm}$$

13.67.   Model: The pulley is a rigid rotating body. We also assume that the pulley has the mass distribution of a disk and that the string does not slip.

Visualize:

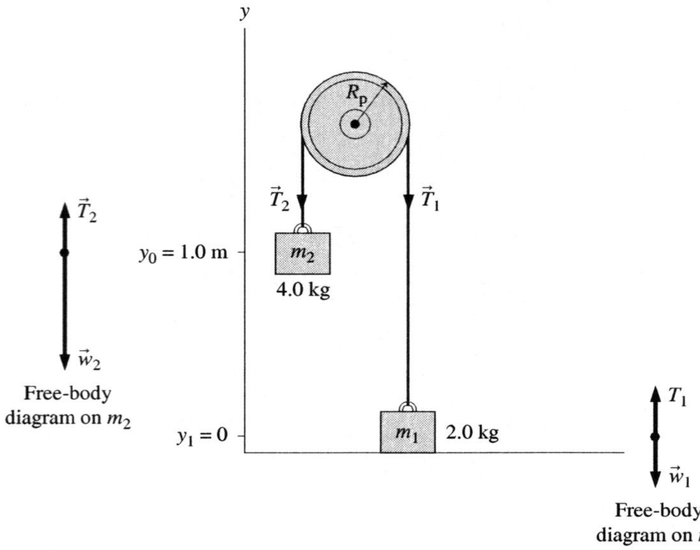

Because the pulley is not massless and frictionless, tension in the rope on both sides of the pulley is not the same.

Solve: Applying Newton's second law to m_1, m_2, and the pulley yields the three equations:

$$T_1 - w_1 = m_1 a_1 \qquad -w_2 + T_2 = m_2 a_2 \qquad T_2 R_p - T_1 R_p - 0.50 \text{ N.m} = I_p \alpha$$

Noting that $-a_2 = a_1 = a$, $I_p = \frac{1}{2} m_p R_p^2$, and $\alpha = a/R_p$, the above equations simplify to

$$T_1 - m_1 g = m_1 a \qquad m_2 g - T_2 = m_2 a \qquad T_2 - T_1 = \left(\frac{1}{2} m_p R_p^2\right)\left(\frac{a}{R_p}\right)\frac{1}{R_p} + \frac{0.50 \text{ N.m}}{R_p} = \frac{1}{2} m_p a + \frac{0.50 \text{ N.m}}{0.06 \text{ m}}$$

Adding these three equations,

$$(m_2 - m_1)g = a\left(m_1 + m_2 + \frac{1}{2} m_p\right) + 8.333 \text{ N}$$

$$\Rightarrow a = \frac{(m_2 - m_1)g - 8.333 \text{ N}}{m_1 + m_2 + \frac{1}{2} m_p} = \frac{(4.0 \text{ kg} - 2.0 \text{ kg})(9.8 \text{ m/s}^2) - 8.333 \text{ N}}{2.0 \text{ kg} + 4.0 \text{ kg} + (2.0 \text{ kg}/2)} = 1.610 \text{ m/s}^2$$

We can now use kinematics to find the time taken by the 4.0 kg block to reach the floor:

$$y_1 = y_0 + v_0(t_1 - t_0) + \frac{1}{2} a_2 (t_1 - t_0)^2 \Rightarrow 0 = 1.0 \text{ m} + 0 + \frac{1}{2}(-1.610 \text{ m/s}^2)(t_1 - 0 \text{ s})^2$$

$$\Rightarrow t_1 = \sqrt{\frac{2(1.0 \text{ m})}{(1.610 \text{ m/s}^2)}} = 1.11 \text{ s}$$

13.73.   Model: The hoop is a rigid body rotating about an axle at the edge of the hoop. The gravitational torque on the hoop causes it to rotate, transforming the gravitational potential energy of the hoop's center of mass into rotational kinetic energy.

Visualize:

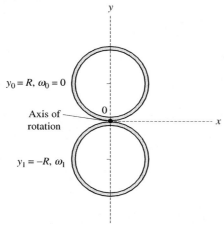

We placed the origin of the coordinate system at the hoop's edge on the axle. In the initial position, the center of mass is a distance R above the origin, but it is a distance R below the origin in the final position.

Solve: (a) Applying the parallel-axis theorem, $I_{edge} = I_{cm} + mR^2 = mR^2 + mR^2 = 2mR^2$. Using this expression in the energy conservation equation $K_f + U_{gf} = K_i + U_{gi}$ yields:

$$\frac{1}{2}I_{edge}\omega_1^2 + mgy_1 = \frac{1}{2}I_{edge}\omega_0^2 + mgy_0 \qquad \frac{1}{2}(2mR^2)\omega_1^2 - mgR = 0 \text{ J} + mgR \Rightarrow \omega_1 = \sqrt{\frac{2g}{R}}$$

(b) The speed of the lowest point on the hoop is

$$v = (\omega_1)(2R) = \sqrt{\frac{2g}{R}}(2R) = \sqrt{8gR}$$

Assess: Note that the speed of the lowest point on the loop involves a radial distance of $2R$ instead of R.

13.77.   Model: The mechanical energy of both the hoop (h) and the sphere (s) is conserved. The initial gravitational potential energy is transformed into kinetic energy as the objects roll down the slope. The kinetic energy is a combination of translational and rotational kinetic energy. We also assume no slipping of the hoop or of the sphere.

Visualize:

The zero of our gravitational potential energy is chosen at the bottom of the slope.

Solve: (a) The energy conservation equation for the sphere or hoop $K_f + U_{gf} = K_i + U_{gi}$ is

$$\frac{1}{2}I(\omega_1)^2 + \frac{1}{2}m(v_1)^2 + mgy_1 = \frac{1}{2}I(\omega_0)^2 + \frac{1}{2}m(v_0)^2 + mgy_0$$

For the sphere, this becomes

$$\frac{1}{2}\left(\frac{2}{5}mR^2\right)\frac{(v_1)_s^2}{R^2} + \frac{1}{2}m(v_1)_s^2 + 0 \text{ J} = 0 \text{ J} + 0 \text{ J} + mgh_s$$

$$\Rightarrow \frac{7}{10}(v_1)_s^2 = gh \Rightarrow (v_1)_s = \sqrt{10gh/7} = \sqrt{10(9.8 \text{ m/s}^2)(0.30 \text{ m})/7} = 2.05 \text{ m/s}$$

For the hoop, this becomes

$$\frac{1}{2}(mR^2)\frac{(v_1)_h^2}{R^2} + \frac{1}{2}m(v_1)_h^2 + 0 \text{ J} = 0 \text{ J} + 0 \text{ J} + mgh_{hoop}$$

$$\Rightarrow h_{hoop} = \frac{(v_1)_h^2}{g}$$

For the hoop to have the same velocity as that of the sphere,

$$h_{hoop} = \frac{(v_1)_s^2}{g} = \frac{(2.05 \text{ m/s})^2}{9.8 \text{ m/s}^2} = 42.86 \text{ cm}$$

(b) As we see in part (a), the speed of a hoop at the bottom depends only on the starting height and not on the mass or radius.

13.81.   Model: The angular momentum of the satellite in the elliptical orbit is a constant.
Visualize: Please refer to Figure P13.81.
Solve: (a) Because the gravitational force is along the same direction as the direction of the moment arm vector, the torque $\tau = r \times F_g$ is zero, but only for parts (a) and (b).
(b) The angular momentum of the satellite at any point on the elliptical trajectory is conserved. We have

$$L_b = L_a \Rightarrow mv_b r_b = mv_a r_a \Rightarrow v_b = \left(\frac{r_a}{r_b}\right) v_a$$

$$r_a = \frac{30,000 \text{ km}}{2} - 9,000 \text{ km} = 6 \times 10^6 \text{ m} \quad \text{and} \quad r_b = \frac{30,000 \text{ km}}{2} + 9,000 \text{ km} = 2.4 \times 10^7 \text{ m}$$

$$\Rightarrow v_b = \left(\frac{6 \times 10^6 \text{ m}}{2.4 \times 10^7 \text{ m}}\right)(8,000 \text{ m/s}) = 2000 \text{ m/s}$$

(c) Using the conservation of angular momentum $L_c = L_a$, we get

$$mv_c r_c \sin \beta = mv_a r_a \Rightarrow v_c = \left(\frac{r_a}{r_c}\right) v_a / \sin \beta \qquad r_c = \sqrt{(9000 \text{ km})^2 + (12,000 \text{ km})^2} = 1.5 \times 10^7 \text{ m}$$

$$\Rightarrow v_c = \left(\frac{6 \times 10^6 \text{ m}}{1.5 \times 10^7 \text{ m}}\right)\frac{(8000 \text{ m/s})}{\sin \beta} = 4000 \text{ m/s}$$

Assess: Note that the radius and velocity vectors are not perpendicular at point C. β is the angle between r and v.

OSCILLATIONS

14.3. **Model:** The air-track glider oscillating on a spring is in simple harmonic motion.
Solve: The glider completes 10 oscillations in 33 s, and it oscillates between the 10 cm mark and the 60 cm mark.

(a)
$$T = \frac{33 \text{ s}}{10 \text{ oscillations}} = 3.3 \text{ s/oscillation} = 3.3 \text{ s}$$

(b)
$$f = \frac{1}{T} = \frac{1}{3.3 \text{ s}} = 0.303 \text{ Hz}$$

(c)
$$\omega = 2\pi f = 2\pi(0.303 \text{ Hz}) = 1.904 \text{ rad/s}$$

(d) The oscillation from one side to the other is equal to 60 cm − 10 cm = 50 cm = 0.50 m. Thus, the amplitude is $\frac{1}{2}(0.50 \text{ m}) = 0.25 \text{ m}$.
(e) The maximum speed is

$$v_{\max} = \omega A = \left(\frac{2\pi}{T}\right)A = (1.904 \text{ rad/s})(0.25 \text{ m}) = 0.476 \text{ m/s}$$

14.9. **Solve:** The position of the object is given by the equation

$$x(t) = A\cos(\omega t + \phi_0) = A\cos(2\pi f t + \phi_0)$$

We can find the phase constant ϕ_0 from the initial condition:

$$0 \text{ cm} = (4.0 \text{ cm})\cos\phi_0 \Rightarrow \cos\phi_0 = 0 \Rightarrow \phi_0 = \cos^{-1}(0) = \pm\tfrac{1}{2}\pi \text{ rad}$$

Since the object is moving to the right, the object is in the lower half of the circular motion diagram. Hence, $\phi_0 = -\tfrac{1}{2}\pi$. The final result is

$$x(t) = (4.0 \text{ cm})\cos\left[(8.0\pi \text{ rad/s})t - \tfrac{1}{2}\pi\right]$$

14.11. **Model:** The air-track glider attached to the spring is in simple harmonic motion.
Solve: **(a)** We can find the phase constant ϕ_0 from the initial conditions for position and velocity.

$$x(t) = A\cos(\omega t + \phi_0) \text{ and } v(t) = -\omega A\sin(\omega t + \phi_0)$$

At $t = 0$ s, these equations are

$$x_0 = -5.0 \text{ cm} = A\cos\phi_0 \text{ and } v_0 = +36.3 \text{ cm/s} = -\omega A\sin\phi_0$$

Using $\omega = 2\pi/T = 2\pi/1.5 \text{ s} = \tfrac{4}{3}\pi \text{ rad/s}$, the above two equations become

$$A\cos\phi_0 = -5.0 \text{ cm and } A\sin\phi_0 = -(36.3 \text{ cm/s})/(\tfrac{4}{3}\pi \text{ rad/s}) = -8.666 \text{ cm}$$

$$\Rightarrow A = \sqrt{(-5.0 \text{ cm})^2 + (-8.666 \text{ cm})^2} = 10.0 \text{ cm and } \phi_0 = \tan^{-1}\left(\frac{8.666 \text{ cm}}{5.0 \text{ cm}}\right) = -\frac{\pi}{3}$$

This choice of ϕ_0 is consistent with the fact that it will yield negative values for both $\cos\phi_0$ and $\sin\phi_0$.
(b) The phase at $t = 0$ s is

$$\phi = \omega t - \frac{2\pi}{3} = -\frac{2\pi}{3} \text{ rad}$$

and the phase at $t = 0.5$ s is

$$\phi = \omega t - \frac{2\pi}{3} = \frac{4\pi}{3}(\text{rad/s})0.5 \text{ s} - \frac{2\pi}{3} = 0 \text{ rad}$$

In the same way the phase at $t = 1.0$ s and $t = 1.5$ s are $\frac{2}{3}\pi$ rad and $\frac{4}{3}\pi$ rad, respectively.

14.15.   Model: The mass attached to the spring oscillates in simple harmonic motion.
Solve: (a) The period $T = 1/f = 1/2.0 \text{ Hz} = 0.5 \text{ s}$.
(b) The angular frequency $\omega = 2\pi f = 2\pi(2 \text{ Hz}) = 4\pi \text{ rad/s}$.
(c) At $t = 0$ s, the position equation becomes

$$x(t) = A\cos(\omega t + \phi_0) \Rightarrow x_0 = A\cos\phi_0$$

and the velocity equation becomes

$$v_x(t) = -A\omega\sin(\omega t + \phi_0) \Rightarrow v_{0x} = -A\omega\sin\phi_0$$

These equations can be written

$$x_0 = A\cos\phi_0 \text{ and } -v_{0x}/\omega = A\sin\phi_0$$

$$\Rightarrow A = \sqrt{(x_0)^2 + (-v_{0x}/\omega)^2} = \sqrt{(5.0 \text{ cm})^2 + \left(\frac{30 \text{ cm/s}}{4\pi \text{ rad/s}}\right)^2} = 5.54 \text{ cm}$$

Alternatively, using energy conservation

$$\tfrac{1}{2}kA^2 = \tfrac{1}{2}kx^2 + \tfrac{1}{2}mv^2$$

Using $x = 5.0$ cm, $v = -30$ cm/s and $k = m\omega^2 = (0.2 \text{ kg})(4\pi \text{ rad/s})^2$, we get $A = 5.54$ cm.
(d) To calculate the phase constant ϕ_0 the above equations are used again:

$$A\cos\phi_0 = x_0 = 5.0 \text{ cm}$$

$$\Rightarrow \phi_0 = \cos^{-1}\left(\frac{5.0 \text{ cm}}{5.54 \text{ cm}}\right) = 0.445 \text{ rad}$$

(e) The maximum speed is $v_{max} = \omega A = (4\pi \text{ rad/s})(5.54 \text{ cm}) = 69.6 \text{ cm/s}$.
(f) The maximum acceleration is

$$a_{max} = \omega^2 A = \omega(\omega A) = (4\pi \text{ rad/s})(69.6 \text{ cm/s}) = 875 \text{ cm/s}^2$$

(g) The total energy is $E = \tfrac{1}{2}mv_{max}^2 = \tfrac{1}{2}(0.200 \text{ kg})(69.6 \text{ cm/s})^2 = 0.0484 \text{ J}$.
(h) The position at $t = 0.40$ s is

$$x_{0.4 \text{ s}} = (5.54 \text{ cm})\cos[(4\pi \text{ rad/s})(0.40 \text{ s}) + 0.445 \text{ rad}] = +3.81 \text{ cm}$$

14.17.   Model: The block attached to the spring is in simple harmonic motion.
Visualize:

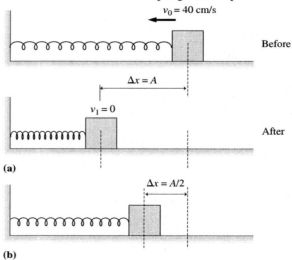

Solve: **(a)** The conservation of mechanical energy equation $K_f + U_{sf} = K_i + U_{si}$ is

$$\tfrac{1}{2}mv_1^2 + \tfrac{1}{2}k(\Delta x)^2 = \tfrac{1}{2}mv_0^2 + 0\text{ J} \Rightarrow 0\text{ J} + \tfrac{1}{2}kA^2 = \tfrac{1}{2}mv_0^2 + 0\text{ J}$$

$$\Rightarrow A = \sqrt{\frac{m}{k}}\,v_0 = \sqrt{\frac{1.0\text{ kg}}{16\text{ N/m}}}(0.40\text{ m/s}) = 0.10\text{ m} = 10.0\text{ cm}$$

(b) We have to find the velocity at a point where $x = A/2$. The conservation of mechanical energy equation $K_2 + U_{s2} = K_i + U_{si}$ is

$$\frac{1}{2}mv_2^2 + \frac{1}{2}k\left(\frac{A}{2}\right)^2 = \frac{1}{2}mv_0^2 + 0\text{ J} \Rightarrow \frac{1}{2}mv_2^2 = \frac{1}{2}mv_0^2 - \frac{1}{4}\left(\frac{1}{2}kA^2\right) = \frac{1}{2}mv_0^2 - \frac{1}{4}\left(\frac{1}{2}mv_0^2\right) = \frac{3}{4}\left(\frac{1}{2}mv_0^2\right)$$

$$\Rightarrow v_2 = \sqrt{\frac{3}{4}}v_0 = \sqrt{\frac{3}{4}}(0.40\text{ m/s}) = 0.346\text{ m/s}$$

Assess: The initial velocity of 40 cm/s becomes 34.6 m/s when the block is halfway at its maximum displacement. This is reasonable.

14.19.   Model: The vertical oscillations constitute simple harmonic motion.
Visualize:

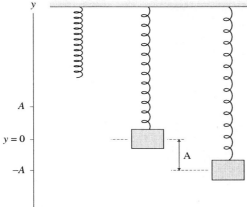

Solve: The period and angular frequency are

$$T = \frac{20\text{ s}}{30\text{ oscillations}} = 0.6667\text{ s} \quad \text{and} \quad \omega = \frac{2\pi}{T} = \frac{2\pi}{0.666\text{ s}} = 9.425\text{ rad/s}$$

(a) The mass can be found as follows:

$$\omega = \sqrt{\frac{k}{m}} \Rightarrow m = \frac{k}{\omega^2} = \frac{15.0\text{ N/m}}{(9.425\text{ rad/s})^2} = 0.169\text{ kg}$$

(b) The maximum speed $v_{max} = \omega A = (9.425\text{ rad/s})(0.06\text{ m}) = 0.565\text{ m/s}.$

14.27.   Model: The motion is a damped oscillation.
Solve: The amplitude of the oscillation at time t is given by Equation 14.55: $A(t) = A_0 e^{-t/2\tau}$, where $\tau = m/b$ is the time constant. Using $x = 0.368\ A$ and $t = 10.0$ s, we get

$$0.368A = Ae^{-10.0\text{ s}/2\tau} \Rightarrow \ln(0.368) = \frac{-10\text{ s}}{2\tau} \Rightarrow \tau = -\frac{10.0\text{ s}}{2\ln(0.368)} = 5.00\text{ s}$$

14.29.   Model: The motion is a damped oscillation.
Solve: The position of the air-track glider is $x(t) = Ae^{-(t/2\tau)}\cos(\omega t + \phi_0)$, where $\tau = m/b$ and

$$\omega = \sqrt{\frac{k}{m} - \frac{b^2}{4m^2}}$$

Using $A = 0.20$ m, $\phi_0 = 0$ rad, and $b = 0.015$ kg/s,

$$\omega = \sqrt{\frac{4.0 \text{ N/m}}{0.250 \text{ kg}} - \frac{(0.015 \text{ kg/s})^2}{4(0.250 \text{ kg})^2}} = \sqrt{16 - 9 \times 10^{-4}} \text{ rad/s}$$

$$= 4\left(1 - \frac{9 \times 10^{-4}}{16}\right)^{\frac{1}{2}} \text{ rad/s} \cong 4\left(1 - \frac{9 \times 10^{-4}}{32}\right) \text{ rad/s} \cong 4 \text{ rad/s}$$

The amplitude at $t = 0$ s is $x_0 = A$ and the amplitude will be equal to $e^{-1}A$ at a time given by

$$\frac{1}{e}A = Ae^{-(t/2\tau)} \Rightarrow t = 2\tau = 2\frac{m}{b} = 33.33 \text{ s}$$

Because the period is

$$T = \frac{2\pi}{\omega} = \frac{2\pi \text{ rad}}{4.0 \text{ rad/s}} = 1.57 \text{ s}$$

the number of complete oscillations in a time of 33.33 s is 21.22 or 21 complete oscillations.

14.31.   Model: The object is undergoing simple harmonic motion.
Visualize:

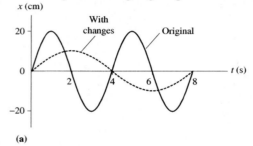

(a)

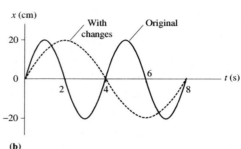

(b)

Solve: The formula for the period is

$$T = \frac{1}{f} = 2\pi\sqrt{\frac{m}{k}}$$

(a) When the frequency f is halved, the period is doubled. That is, the period increases from 4.0 s to 8.0 s.
(b) When the mass m is quadrupled, the period doubles.

14.37.   Model: The block attached to the spring is in simple harmonic motion.
Visualize: The position and the velocity of the block are given by the equations

$$x(t) = A\cos(\omega t + \phi_0) \text{ and } v_x(t) = -A\omega\sin(\omega t + \phi_0)$$

Solve: To graph $x(t)$ we need to determine ω, ϕ_0, and A. These quantities will be found by using the initial ($t = 0$ s) conditions on $x(t)$ and $v_x(t)$. We have

$$T = 2\pi\sqrt{\frac{m}{k}} = 2\pi\sqrt{\frac{1.0 \text{ kg}}{20 \text{ N/m}}} = 1.405 \text{ s} \Rightarrow \omega = \frac{2\pi}{T} = \frac{2\pi \text{ rad}}{1.405 \text{ s}} = 4.472 \text{ rad/s}$$

At $t = 0$ s, $x_0 = A\cos\phi_0$ and $v_{0x} = -A\omega\sin\phi_0$. Dividing these equations,

$$\tan\phi_0 = -\frac{v_x}{\omega x} = -\frac{(-1.0 \text{ m/s})}{(4.472 \text{ rad/s})(0.20 \text{ m})} = 1.1181 \Rightarrow \phi_0 = 0.841 \text{ rad}$$

Because the block is moving with a negative velocity (or to the left), it is in the upper half of the circular motion diagram, indicating a phase constant between 0 and π radians. A positive value of $\phi_0 = +0.841$ radian is also consistent with the above forms of x and v_x at $t = 0$ s. From the initial conditions,

$$x^2 + \left(\frac{v_x}{\omega}\right)^2 = A^2 \Rightarrow A = \sqrt{x^2 + \left(\frac{v_x}{\omega}\right)^2} = \sqrt{(0.20 \text{ m})^2 + \left(\frac{-1.0 \text{ m/s}}{4.472 \text{ rad/s}}\right)^2} = 0.300 \text{ m}$$

The position-versus-time graph can now be plotted using the equation

$$x(t) = (0.300 \text{ m})\cos\left[(4.472 \text{ rad/s})t + 0.841 \text{ rad}\right]$$

Note that the cosine function is a maximum when

$$4.472t + 0.841 = \pi, \ 2\pi, \ 3\pi, \ \ldots$$
$$\Rightarrow t = (\pi - 0.841)/4.472, \ (2\pi - 0.841)/4.472, \ (3\pi - 0.841)/4.472, \ \ldots$$
$$\Rightarrow t = 0.514 \text{ s}, \ 1.217 \text{ s}, \ 1.919 \text{ s}, \ \ldots$$

In addition, $x(t) = 0$ m when

$$4.472t + 0.841 = \pi/2, \ 3\pi/2, \ 5\pi/2, \ \ldots$$
$$t = \left(\frac{\pi}{2} - 0.841\right)\Big/4.472, \ \left(\frac{3\pi}{2} - 0.841\right)\Big/4.472, \ \left(\frac{5\pi}{2} - 0.841\right)\Big/4.472, \ \ldots$$
$$t = 0.163 \text{ s}, \ 0.866 \text{ s}, \ 1.569 \text{ s}, \ \ldots$$

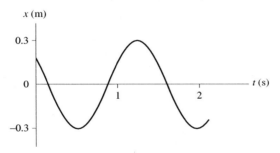

14.39.   Model: The particle is in simple harmonic motion.
Solve: The equation for the velocity of the particle is

$$v_x(t) = -(25 \text{ cm})(10 \text{ rad/s})\sin(10 \text{ t})$$

Substituting into $K = 2U$ gives

$$\frac{1}{2}mv_x^2(t) = 2\left(\frac{1}{2}kx^2(t)\right) \Rightarrow \frac{1}{2}m\left[-(250 \text{ cm/s})\sin(10 \text{ t})\right]^2 = k\left[(25 \text{ cm})\cos(10 \text{ t})\right]^2$$

$$\Rightarrow \frac{\sin^2(10 \text{ t})}{\cos^2(10 \text{ t})} = 2\left(\frac{k}{m}\right)\frac{(25 \text{ cm})^2}{(250 \text{ cm/s})^2} = 2\omega^2\left(\frac{1}{100}\right)\text{s}^2$$

$$\Rightarrow \tan^2(10 \text{ t}) = 2(10 \text{ rad/s})^2\left(\frac{1}{100}\right)\text{s}^2 = 2.0 \Rightarrow t = \frac{1}{10}\tan^{-1}\sqrt{2.0} = 0.0955 \text{ s}$$

14.43.   Model: The ball attached to a spring is in simple harmonic motion.
Solve: (a) Let $t = 0$ s be the instant when $x_0 = -5$ cm and $v_0 = 20$ cm/s. The oscillation frequency is

$$\omega = \sqrt{\frac{k}{m}} = \sqrt{\frac{2.5 \text{ N/m}}{0.10 \text{ kg}}} = 5.0 \text{ rad/s}$$

Using Equation 14.27, the amplitude of the oscillation is

$$A = \sqrt{x_0^2 + \left(\frac{v_0}{\omega}\right)^2} = \sqrt{(-5 \text{ cm})^2 + \left(\frac{20 \text{ cm/s}}{5 \text{ rad/s}}\right)^2} = 6.40 \text{ cm}$$

(b) The maximum acceleration is $a_{max} = \omega^2 A = 160 \text{ cm/s}^2$.

(c) For an oscillator, the acceleration is most positive $(a = a_{max})$ when the displacement is most negative $(x = -x_{max} = -A)$. So the acceleration is maximum when $x = -6.40 \text{ cm}$.

(d) From the oscillatory equations, $x(t) = A\cos(\omega t + \phi_0)$ and $v(t) = -v_{max}\sin(\omega t + \phi_0)$, where $v_{max} = \omega A = 32.0 \text{ cm/s}$.

$$x = 3.0 \text{ cm} = (6.40 \text{ cm})\cos(\omega t + \phi_0) \Rightarrow \cos(\omega t + \phi_0) = \frac{3.0 \text{ cm}}{6.40 \text{ cm}} \Rightarrow \omega t + \phi_0 = 1.083 \text{ rad}.$$

Now,

$$v = -\omega A \sin(\omega t + \phi_0) = -(5 \text{ rad/s})(6.40 \text{ cm})\sin(1.083 \text{ rad}) \Rightarrow v = \pm 28.3 \text{ cm/s}.$$

Or, the speed at $x = 3$ cm is $|v| = 28.3$ cm/s.

Assess: Alternately, we can use the conservation of energy between $x_0 = -5$ cm and $x_1 = 3$ cm:

$$\tfrac{1}{2}mv_0^2 + \tfrac{1}{2}kx_0^2 = \tfrac{1}{2}mv_1^2 + \tfrac{1}{2}kx_1^2 \Rightarrow v_1 = \sqrt{v_0^2 + \frac{k}{m}(x_0^2 - x_1^2)} = 0.283 \text{ m/s} = 28.3 \text{ cm/s}$$

Because k is known in SI units of N/m, the energy calculation *must* be done using SI units of m, m/s, and kg.

14.49.   Model: The block is in simple harmonic motion.
Visualize:

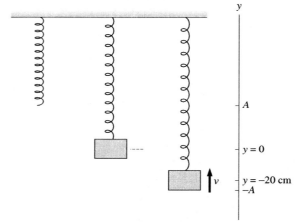

Solve: The position and velocity equations for the block are

$$y(t) = A\cos(\omega t + \phi_0) \text{ and } v_y(t) = -\omega A\sin(\omega t + \phi_0)$$

At $t = 0$ s, these equations become

$$-0.20 \text{ m} = A\cos\phi_0 \Rightarrow A^2\cos^2\phi_0 = 0.04 \text{ m}^2 \text{ and } +1.0 \text{ m/s} = -\omega A\sin\phi_0$$

Using,

$$\omega = \sqrt{\frac{k}{m}} = \sqrt{\frac{10 \text{ N/m}}{0.2 \text{ kg}}} = 7.071 \text{ rad/s}$$

the velocity equation is

$$-\frac{1.0 \text{ m/s}}{7.071 \text{ rad/s}} = A\sin\phi \Rightarrow A^2\sin^2\phi_0 = (0.1414)^2 \text{ m}^2$$

Adding the position and velocity equations,

$$A^2 = 0.04 \text{ m}^2 + (0.1414)^2 \text{ m}^2 \Rightarrow A = 0.245 \text{ m}$$

Dividing the position and velocity equations,

$$\tan\phi_0 = \frac{0.1414}{0.20} \Rightarrow \phi_0 = 0.6154$$

Because $\sin\phi_0$ is negative and $\cos\phi_0$ is also negative, ϕ_0 is in the third quadrant. Thus,

$$\phi_0 = 0.6154 + \pi = 0.6154 + 3.1415 = 3.7569 \text{ rad}$$

(a) The frequency is

$$f = \frac{\omega}{2\pi} = \frac{7.071}{2\pi} = 1.125 \text{ Hz}$$

(b) Substituting the initial condition into the velocity equation, we get

$$(0.50 \text{ m/s}) = -(7.071 \text{ rad/s})(0.245 \text{ m})\sin(\omega t + \phi_0) \Rightarrow \sin(\omega t + \phi_0) = 0.2886$$

$$\Rightarrow \cos(\omega t + \phi_0) = \sqrt{1 - (0.2886)^2} = 0.9574$$

Substituting this expression into the position equation, we get

$$y(t) = (0.245 \text{ m})(0.9574) = 0.235 \text{ m}$$

We can also find y from energy considerations.

$$\tfrac{1}{2}ky^2 + \tfrac{1}{2}mv^2 = \tfrac{1}{2}kA^2$$

Using $k = m\omega^2$

$$\omega^2 y^2 + v^2 = A^2\omega^2 \Rightarrow y = \sqrt{(A^2\omega^2 - v^2)/\omega^2}$$

With $A = 0.245$ m, $\omega = 7.071$ rad/s and $v = 0.50$ m/s, we get $y = 0.235$ m.

(c) The position of the block at $t = 1$ s is

$$y_{1.0\text{ s}} = (0.245 \text{ m})\cos\big[(7.071 \text{ rad/s})(1.0 \text{ s}) + 3.7569 \text{ rad}\big] = -0.049 \text{ m} = -4.9 \text{ cm}$$

Assess: Note how the phase constant ϕ_0 was determined in this problem. The value of ϕ_0 must be consistent with the initial position and velocity equations.

14.55.   Model: Assume simple harmonic motion for the two-block system without the upper block slipping. We will also use the model of static friction between the two blocks.
Visualize: Please refer to Figure A 14.54.
Solve: The net force on the upper block m_1 is the force of friction due to the lower block m_2. The model of static friction gives the maximum force of static friction as

$$f_{s\text{ max}} = \mu_s n = \mu_s(m_1 g) = m_1 a_{max} \Rightarrow a_{max} = \mu_s g$$

$$\Rightarrow \mu_s = \frac{a_{max}}{g} = \frac{\omega^2 A_{max}}{g} = \left(\frac{2\pi}{T}\right)^2\left(\frac{A_{max}}{g}\right) = \left(\frac{2\pi}{1.5 \text{ s}}\right)^2\left(\frac{0.40 \text{ m}}{9.8 \text{ m/s}^2}\right) = 0.716$$

Assess: Because the period is given, we did not need to use the block masses or the spring constant in our calculation.

14.57.   Model: Assume that the pendulum makes a small angle with the vertical so that there is simple harmonic motion.
Solve: The angle θ made by the string with the vertical as a function of time is

$$\theta(t) = \theta_{max}\cos(\omega t + \phi_0)$$

At $t = 0$ s, $\theta = 8.0° = \theta_{max}$, so we get $\cos\phi_0 = 1$ or $\phi_0 = 0$. Thus, $\theta(t) = \theta_{max}\cos\omega t$. To find the time t when the pendulum reaches $4.0°$ on the opposite side:

$$-4.0° = 8.0°\cos\omega t \Rightarrow \omega t = \cos^{-1}(-0.5) = 2.0944 \text{ rad}$$

Using the formula for the angular frequency,

$$\omega = \sqrt{\frac{g}{L}} = \sqrt{\frac{9.8 \text{ m/s}^2}{1.0 \text{ m}}} = 3.1305 \text{ rad/s} \Rightarrow t = \frac{2.0944 \text{ rad}}{\omega} = \frac{2.0944 \text{ rad}}{3.1305 \text{ rad/s}} = 0.669 \text{ s}$$

Assess: Because $T = 2\pi/\omega = 2.00$ s, a value of 0.669 s for the pendulum to cover a little less than half the oscillation is reasonable.

14.59.   Model: Assume a small angle oscillation of the pendulum so that it has simple harmonic motion.
Solve: (a) At the equator, the period of the pendulum is

$$T_{\text{equator}} = 2\pi \sqrt{\frac{1.000 \text{ m}}{9.78 \text{ m/s}^2}} = 2.009 \text{ s}$$

The time for 100 oscillations is 200.9 s.
(b) At the north pole, the period is

$$T_{\text{pole}} = 2\pi \sqrt{\frac{1.000 \text{ m}}{9.83 \text{ m/s}^2}} = 2.004 \text{ s}$$

The time for 100 oscillations is 200.4 s.
(c) The difference between the two answers is 0.5 s, and this difference is quite measurable with a hand-operated stopwatch.
(d) The period on the top of the mountain is 2.010 s. The acceleration due to gravity can be calculated by rearranging the formula for the period:

$$g_{\text{mountain}} = L\left(\frac{2\pi}{T_{\text{mountain}}}\right)^2 = (1.000 \text{ m})\left(\frac{2\pi}{2.010 \text{ s}}\right)^2 = 9.77 \text{ m/s}^2$$

Assess: This last result is reasonable because g decreases with altitude.

14.63.   Model: A completely inelastic collision between the bullet and the block resulting in simple harmonic motion.
Visualize:

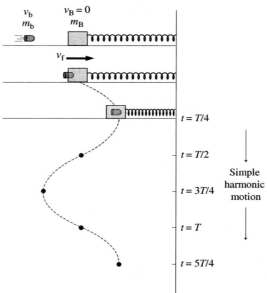

Solve: (a) The equation for conservation of energy after the collision is

$$\frac{1}{2}kA^2 = \frac{1}{2}(m_{\text{b}} + m_{\text{B}})v_{\text{f}}^2 \Rightarrow v_{\text{f}} = \sqrt{\frac{k}{m_{\text{b}} + m_{\text{B}}}}\,A = \sqrt{\frac{2500 \text{ N/m}}{1.010 \text{ kg}}}(0.10 \text{ m}) = 4.975 \text{ m/s}$$

The momentum conservation equation for the perfectly inelastic collision $p_{\text{after}} = p_{\text{before}}$ is

$$(m_{\text{b}} + m_{\text{B}})v_{\text{f}} = m_{\text{b}}v_{\text{b}} + m_{\text{B}}v_{\text{B}}$$

$$(1.010 \text{ kg})(4.975 \text{ m/s}) = (0.010 \text{ kg})v_{\text{b}} + (1.00 \text{ kg})(0 \text{ m/s}) \Rightarrow v_{\text{b}} = 502.5 \text{ m/s}$$

(b) The oscillation frequency will give $\sqrt{k/(m_{\text{b}} + m_{\text{B}})}$, but one still needs to know the amplitude to calculate v_{f} and hence v_{b}.

14.71.   Model: The oscillator is in simple harmonic motion.
Solve: (a) The maximum displacement at time t of a damped oscillator is

$$x_{max}(t) = Ae^{-t/2\tau} \Rightarrow -\frac{t}{2\tau} = \ln\left(\frac{x_{max}(t)}{A}\right)$$

Using $x_{max} = 0.98A$ at $t = 0.5$ s, we can find the time constant τ to be

$$\tau = -\frac{0.5 \text{ s}}{2\ln(0.98)} = 12.375 \text{ s}$$

25 oscillations will be completed at $t = 25T = 12.5$ s. At that time, the amplitude will be

$$x_{max, 12.5 \text{ s}} = (10.0 \text{ cm})e^{-12.5 \text{ s}/(2)(12.375 \text{ s})} = 6.03 \text{ cm}$$

(b) The energy of a damped oscillator decays more rapidly than the amplitude: $E(t) = E_0e^{-t/\tau}$. When the energy is 60% of its initial value, $E(t)/E_0 = 0.60$. We can find the time this occurs as follows:

$$-\frac{t}{\tau} = \ln\left(\frac{E(t)}{E_0}\right) \Rightarrow t = -\tau\ln\left(\frac{E(t)}{E_0}\right) = -(12.375 \text{ s})\ln(0.60) = 6.32 \text{ s}$$

14.73.   Model: Samson on the trapeze is in simple harmonic motion.
Visualize:

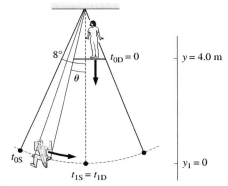

The time $(t_{1D} - t_{0D})$ for Delilah to fall 4.0 m is equal to the time $(t_{1S} - t_{0S})$ Samson takes to swing from the angle θ to the lowest point of the arc.
Solve: Treating Samson as a pendulum, his period is

$$T = 2\pi\sqrt{\frac{l}{g}} = 2\pi\sqrt{\frac{6.0 \text{ m}}{9.8 \text{ m/s}^2}} = 4.916 \text{ s}$$

The time of Delilah's fall can be found from kinematics as follows:

$$y_1 - y_0 = v_{0y}(t_{1D} - t_{0D}) + \tfrac{1}{2}a_y(t_{1D} - t_{0D})^2$$

$$0 \text{ m} - 4.0 \text{ m} = (0 \text{ m/s})(t_{1D} - t_{0D}) + \tfrac{1}{2}(-9.8 \text{ m/s}^2)(t_{1D} - 0 \text{ s})^2 \Rightarrow t_{1D} = 0.9035 \text{ s}$$

The time from the top of swing to the bottom is $\tfrac{1}{4}T = 1.229$ s. We have

$$t_{1D} - t_{0D} = 0.9035 \text{ s} - 0 \text{ s} = t_{1S} - t_{0S} \Rightarrow t_{0S} = t_{1S} - 0.9035 \text{ s} = 1.229 \text{ s} - 0.9035 \text{ s} = 0.3255 \text{ s}$$

If we represent Samson's motion by $\theta = \theta_{max}\cos\omega t$, then $\theta = \theta_{max} = 8°$ when $t = 0$ s and $\theta = 0°$ when $\omega t = \tfrac{1}{2}\pi$. We can thus find θ when $t = t_{0S} = 0.3225$ s:

$$\theta_{0.3225 \text{ s}} = (8.0°)\cos\left[\left(\frac{2\pi}{T}\right)t_{0S}\right] = (8.0°)\cos\left[\left(\frac{2\pi}{4.916 \text{ s}}\right)(0.3255 \text{ s})\right] = 7.32°$$

Delilah should fall just after Samson begins his downward journey.

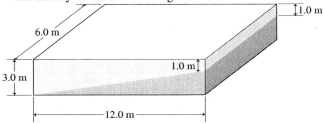

FLUIDS AND ELASTICITY

15.3. Model: The density of water is 1000 kg/m³.
Visualize:

Solve: Volume of water in the swimming pool is

$$V = 6 \text{ m} \times 12 \text{ m} \times 3 \text{ m} - \tfrac{1}{2}(6 \text{ m} \times 12 \text{ m} \times 2 \text{ m}) = 144 \text{ m}^3$$

The mass of water in the swimming pool is

$$m = \rho V = (1000 \text{ kg/m}^3)(144 \text{ m}^3) = 1.44 \times 10^5 \text{ kg}$$

15.5. Model: The density of sea water is 1,030 kg/m³.
Solve: The pressure below sea level can be found from Equation 15.6 as follows:

$$p = p_0 + \rho g d = 1.013 \times 10^5 \text{Pa} + (1030 \text{ kg/m}^3)(9.80 \text{ m/s}^2)(1.1 \times 10^4 \text{ m})$$

$$= 1.013 \times 10^5 \text{ Pa} + 1.1103 \times 10^8 \text{ Pa} = 1.1113 \times 10^8 \text{ Pa} = 1097 \text{ atm}$$

where we have used the conversion $1 \text{ atm} = 1.013 \times 10^5 \text{ Pa}$.
Assess: The pressure deep in the ocean is very large.

15.9. Model: The density of seawater $\rho_{\text{seawater}} = 1030 \text{ kg/m}^2$.
Visualize:

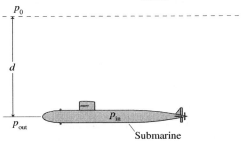

Submarine

Solve: The pressure outside the submarine's window is $p_{\text{out}} = p_0 + \rho_{\text{seawater}} g d$, where d is the maximum safe depth for the window to withstand a force F. This force is $F/A = p_{\text{out}} - p_{\text{in}}$, where A is the area of the window. With $p_{\text{in}} = p_0$, we simplify the pressure equation to

$$p_{\text{out}} - p_0 = \frac{F}{A} = \rho_{\text{seawater}} g d \Rightarrow d = \frac{F}{A\rho_{\text{seawater}} g} \qquad d = \frac{1.0 \times 10^6 \text{ N}}{\pi(0.10 \text{ m})^2 (1030 \text{ kg/m}^2)(9.8 \text{ m/s}^2)} = 3153 \text{ m}$$

Assess: A force of 1.0×10^6 N corresponds to a pressure of

$$\rho = \frac{F}{A} = \frac{1.0 \times 10^6 \text{ N}}{\pi(0.10 \text{ m})^2} = 314 \text{ atm}$$

A depth of 1 km is therefore reasonable.

15.13.   Model: Assume that the oil is incompressible and its density is 900 kg/m³.
Visualize:

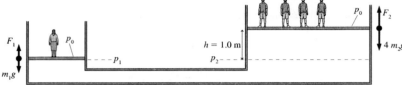

Solve: The pressures p_1 and p_2 are equal. Thus,

$$p_0 + \frac{F_1}{A_1} = p_0 + \frac{F_2}{A_2} + \rho g h \Rightarrow \frac{F_1}{A_1} = \frac{F_2}{A_2} + \rho g h$$

With $F_1 = m_1 g$, $F_2 = 4m_2 g$, $A_1 = \pi r_1^2$, and $A_2 = \pi r_2^2$, we have

$$\frac{m_1 g}{\pi r_1^2} = \frac{4m_2 g}{\pi r_2^2} + \rho g h \Rightarrow r_2 = \left(\frac{4m_2 g}{\pi}\right)^{1/2} \left(\frac{m_1 g}{\pi r_1^2} - \rho g h\right)^{-1/2}$$

Using $m_1 = 55$ kg, $m_2 = 110$ kg, $r_1 = 0.08$ m, $\rho = 900$ kg/m³, and $h = 1.0$ m, the calculation yields $r_2 = 0.276$ m. The diameter is 55.2 cm.
Assess: Both pistons are too small to hold the people as shown, but the ideas are correct.

15.17.   Model: The buoyant force on the sphere is given by Archimedes' principle.
Visualize:

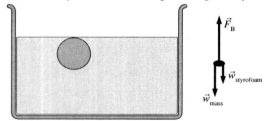

Solve: For the Styrofoam sphere and the mass not to sink, the buoyant force F_B must be equal to the sum of the weight of the Styrofoam sphere and the attached mass.

$$F_B = \rho_{\text{water}} V_{\text{water}} g = (1000 \text{ kg/m}^3) \tfrac{4\pi}{3}(0.25 \text{ m})^3 (9.80 \text{ m/s}^2) = 641.4 \text{ N}$$

$$w_{\text{Styrofoam}} = \rho_{\text{Styrofoam}} V_{\text{Styrofoam}} g = (300 \text{ kg/m}^3)[\tfrac{4}{3}\pi(0.25 \text{ m})^3](9.80 \text{ m/s}^2) = 192.4 \text{ N}$$

Because $w_{\text{Styrofoam}} + mg = F_B$,

$$m = \frac{F_B - w_{\text{Styrofoam}}}{g} = \frac{641.4 \text{ N} - 192.4 \text{ N}}{9.80 \text{ m/s}^2} = 45.8 \text{ kg}$$

15.23.   Model: Treat the water as an ideal fluid so that the flow in the tube follows the continuity equation.
Visualize:

Solve: The equation of continuity is $v_0 A_0 = v_1 A_1$, where $A_0 = L^2$ and $A_1 = \pi\left(\tfrac{1}{2}L\right)^2$. The above equation simplifies to

$$v_0 L^2 = v_1 \pi \left(\frac{L}{2}\right)^2 \Rightarrow v_1 = \left(\frac{4}{\pi}\right) v_0 = 1.27 v_0$$

15.27. **Model:** The load supported by a concrete column creates compressive stress in the concrete column.
Solve: The weight of the load produces tensile stress given by F/A, where A is the cross-sectional area of the concrete column and F equals the weight of the load. From the definition of Young's modulus,

$$Y = \frac{F/A}{\Delta L/L} \Rightarrow \Delta L = \left(\frac{F}{A}\right)\left(\frac{L}{Y}\right) = \left(\frac{200,000 \text{ kg} \times 9.8 \text{ m/s}^2}{\pi(0.25 \text{ m})^2}\right)\left(\frac{3.0 \text{ m}}{3 \times 10^{10} \text{ N/m}^2}\right) = 1.0 \text{ mm}$$

Assess: A compression of 1.0 mm of the concrete column by a load of approximately 200 tons is reasonable.

15.33. **Visualize:**

Solve: **(a)** Because the patient's blood pressure is 140/100, the minimum fluid pressure above atmospheric pressure needed is 100 mm of Hg. Since 760 mm of Hg is equivalent to 1 atm and 1 atm is equivalent to 1.013×10^5 Pa, the minimum pressure is 1.333×10^4 Pa. The pressure in the fluid is due to force F pushing on the internal 6.0-mm-diameter piston that presses against the liquid. Thus, the minimum force the nurse needs to apply to the syringe is

$$F = \text{ fluid pressure } \times \text{ area of plunger} = \left(1.333 \times 10^4 \text{ Pa}\right)\left[\pi(0.003 \text{ m})^2\right] = 0.377 \text{ N}$$

(b) The flow rate is $Q = vA$, where v is the flow speed of the medicine and A is the cross-sectional area of the needle. Thus,

$$v = \frac{Q}{A} = \frac{2.0 \text{ mL}/2.0 \text{ s}}{\pi\left(0.125 \times 10^{-3}\right)^2} = 20.4 \text{ m/s}$$

that the pressure in the fluid is due to F that is not dependent on the size of the plunger pad. Also not drawn to scale. Furthermore, note that a speed of 20.4 m/s is rather large and getting s size in 2 s may not be physically reasonable.

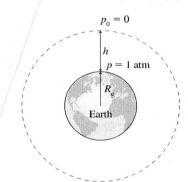

The height of the air column above the earth's surface is h, the atmospheric pressure on the surface of the earth is p, and the pressure beyond the earth's atmosphere is p_0 (= 0 Pa).
Solve: Using the formula $p = p_0 + \rho_{\text{air}}gh$, we can obtain an expression for h:

$$1 \text{ atm} = 0 \text{ atm} + \rho_{\text{air}}gh \Rightarrow h = \frac{1 \text{ atm}}{\rho_{\text{air}}g} = \frac{1.013 \times 10^5 \text{ Pa}}{\rho_{\text{air}}g}$$

The volume of air in the earth's atmosphere is

$$V_{\text{air}} = \frac{4\pi}{3}(R_e + h)^3 - \frac{4\pi}{3}\pi R_e^3 = \frac{4\pi}{3}R_e^3\left[\left(1 + \frac{h}{R_e}\right)^3 - 1\right] \cong \frac{4\pi}{3}R_e^3\left[1 + \frac{3h}{R_e} - 1\right] = 4\pi R_e^2 h$$

where we have assumed that $h/R_e \ll 1$. Thus, the mass of air in the earth's atmosphere is

$$m_{air} = \rho_{air} V_{air} = \rho_{air}\left(4\pi R_e^2 h\right) = \rho_{air}\left[4\pi R_e^2\left(\frac{1.013 \times 10^5 \text{ Pa}}{\rho_{air} g}\right)\right]$$

$$= \frac{4\pi\left(6.37 \times 10^6 \text{ m}\right)^2\left(1.013 \times 10^5 \text{ Pa}\right)}{\left(9.8 \text{ m/s}^2\right)} = 5.27 \times 10^{18} \text{ kg}$$

15.39.   Model: Assume that oil is incompressible and its density is 900 kg/m³.
Visualize: Please refer to Figure P15.39.
Solve: (a) The hydraulic lift is in equilibrium and the pistons on the left and the right are at the same level. Equation 15.11, therefore, simplifies to

$$\frac{F_{\text{left piston}}}{A_{\text{left piston}}} = \frac{F_{\text{right piston}}}{A_{\text{right piston}}} \Rightarrow \frac{w_{\text{student}}}{\pi\left(r_{\text{student}}\right)^2} = \frac{w_{\text{elephant}}}{\pi\left(r_{\text{elephant}}\right)^2}$$

$$\Rightarrow r_{\text{student}} = \sqrt{\left(\frac{w_{\text{student}}}{w_{\text{elephant}}}\right)}\left(r_{\text{elephant}}\right) = \sqrt{\frac{(70 \text{ kg})g}{(1200 \text{ kg})g}}(1.0 \text{ m}) = 0.2415 \text{ m}$$

The diameter of the piston the student is standing on is therefore $2 \times 0.2415 \text{ m} = 0.483 \text{ m}$.
(b) From Equation 15.13, we see that a force ΔF is required to increase the elephant's elevation through a distance d_2. That is,

$$\Delta F = \rho g\left(A_{\text{left piston}} + A_{\text{right piston}}\right)d_2$$

$$\Rightarrow (70 \text{ kg})\left(9.8 \text{ m/s}^2\right) = \left(900 \text{ kg/m}^3\right)\left(9.8 \text{ m/s}^2\right)\pi\left[(0.2415 \text{ m})^2 + (1.0 \text{ m})^2\right]d_2$$

$$\Rightarrow d_2 = 0.0234 \text{ m} = 2.34 \text{ cm}$$

15.43.   Visualize:

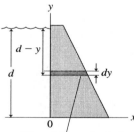

Slice of dam at depth $d - y$
has height dy and width w.

The figure shows a dam with water height d. We chose a coordinate system with the origin at the bottom of the dam. The horizontal slice has height dy, width w (perpendicular to the page), and area $dA = wdy$. The slice is at the depth of $d - y$.
Solve: (a) The water exerts a small force $dF = pdA = pwdy$ on this small piece of the dam, where $p = \rho g(d - y)$ is the pressure at depth $d - y$. Altogether, the force on this small horizontal slice at position y is $dF = \rho gw(d - y)dy$. Note that a force from atmospheric pressure is not included. This is because atmospheric pressure exerts a force on *both* sides of the dam. The total force *of the water* on the dam is found by adding up all the small forces dF for the small slices dy between $y = 0$ m and $y = d$. This summation is expressed as the integral

$$F_{\text{total}} = \int\limits_{\text{all slices}} dF = \int_0^d dF = \rho gw\int_0^d(d - y)dy = \rho gw\left(yd - \frac{1}{2}y^2\right)\Bigg|_0^d = \frac{1}{2}\rho gwd^2$$

(b) The total force is

$$F_{\text{total}} = \tfrac{1}{2}\left(1000 \text{ kg/m}^3\right)\left(9.8 \text{ m/s}^2\right)(100 \text{ m})(60 \text{ m})^2 = 1.76 \times 10^9 \text{ N}$$

15.45.   Visualize:

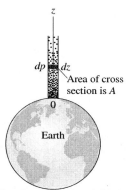

The figure shows a small column of air of thickness dz, of cross-sectional area A, and of density $\rho(z)$. The column is at a height z above the surface of the earth.

Solve: (a) The atmospheric pressure is 1.013×10^5 Pa. That is, the weight of the air column is 1.013×10^5 N/m^2. Consider now the weight of a 1 m^2 slice of thickness dz at a height z:

$$dw = \rho dz g$$

$$= \rho_0 e^{-z/z_0} dz g$$

Integrating from $z = 0$ to $z = \infty$,

$$w = \int_0^\infty \rho_0 g e^{-z/z_0} dz$$

$$= (-\rho_0 g z_0)\left[e^{-z/z_0} \right]_0^\infty$$

$$= \rho_0 g z_0$$

Because $w = 101{,}300$ N $= \rho_0 g z_0$,

$$z_0 = \frac{101{,}300 \text{ N}}{(1.28 \text{ kg/m}^2)(9.8 \text{ m/s}^2)} = 8.08 \times 10^3 \text{ m}$$

(b) Using the density at sea level from Table 15.1,

$$\rho = (1.28 \text{ kg/m}^3)e^{-z/(8.08\times10^3 \text{ m})} = (1.28 \text{ kg/m}^3)e^{-1600 \text{ m}/(8.08\times10^3 \text{ m})} = 1.05 \text{ kg/m}^3$$

15.51.   Model: The buoyant force on the rock is given by Archimedes' principle.
Visualize:

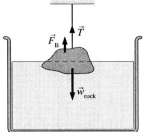

Solve: Because the rock is in static equilibrium, Newton's first law is

$$F_{\text{net}} = T + F_{\text{B}} - w_{\text{rock}} = 0 \text{ N}$$

$$\Rightarrow T = \rho_{\text{rock}} V_{\text{rock}} g - \rho_{\text{water}}\left(\frac{1}{2} V_{\text{rock}}\right)g = \left(\rho_{\text{rock}} - \frac{1}{2}\rho_{\text{water}}\right)V_{\text{rock}} g = \left(\rho_{\text{rock}} - \frac{1}{2}\rho_{\text{water}}\right)\left(\frac{m_{\text{rock}} g}{\rho_{\text{rock}}}\right) = \left(1 - \frac{\rho_{\text{water}}}{2\rho_{\text{rock}}}\right)m_{\text{rock}} g$$

Using $\rho_{\text{rock}} = 4800$ kg/m^3 and $m_{\text{rock}} = 5.0$ kg, we get $T = 43.9$ N.

15.57. Model: The buoyant force on the can is given by Archimedes' principle.
Visualize:

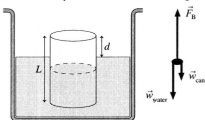

The length of the can above the water level is d, the length of the can is L, and the cross-sectional area of the can is A.
Solve: The can is in static equilibrium, so

$$F_B - w_{can} - w_{water} = 0 \text{ N} \Rightarrow \rho_{water} A(L - d)g = (0.02 \text{ kg})g + m_{water}g$$

The mass of the water in the can is

$$m_{water} = \rho_{water}\left(\frac{V_{can}}{2}\right) = \left(1000 \text{ kg/m}^3\right)\frac{355 \times 10^{-6} \text{ m}^3}{2} = 0.1775 \text{ kg}$$

$$\Rightarrow \rho_{water}A(L - d) = 0.02 \text{ kg} + 0.1775 \text{ kg} = 0.1975 \text{ kg} \Rightarrow d = -\frac{0.1975 \text{ kg}}{\rho_{water}A} + L$$

Because $V_{can} = \pi(0.031 \text{ m})^2 L = 355 \times 10^{-6} \text{ m}^3$, $L = 0.1176$ m. Using this value of L in the above equation, we get
$d = 0.0522$ m $= 5.22$ cm.
Assess: $d/L = 5.22$ cm/11.76 cm $= 0.444$, thus 44.4% of the length of the can is above the water surface. This is
reasonable.

15.59. Model: The buoyant force on the boat is given by Archimedes' principle.
Visualize:

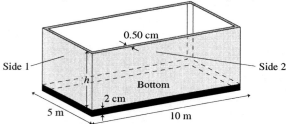

The minimum height of the boat that will enable the boat to float in perfectly calm water is h.
Solve: Archimedes' principle in equation form is $F_B = \rho_w V_{boat}g$. For the boat to float $F_B = w_{boat}$. Let us first
calculate the weight of the boat (with g in m/s^2 and h in m):

$$w_{boat} = w_{bottom} + 2w_{side\ 1} + 2w_{side\ 2}, \text{ where}$$

$$w_{bottom} = \rho_{steel}V_{bottom}g = \left(7900 \text{ kg/m}^3\right)\left(5 \times 10 \times 0.02 \text{ m}^3\right)g = 7900g \text{ N}$$

$$w_{side\ 1} = \rho_{steel}V_{side\ 1}g = \left(7900 \text{ kg/m}^3\right)\left(5 \times h \times 0.005 \text{ m}^3\right)g = 197.5gh \text{ N}$$

$$w_{side\ 2} = \rho_{steel}V_{side\ 2}g = \left(7900 \text{ kg/m}^3\right)\left(10 \times h \times 0.005 \text{ m}^3\right)g = 395gh$$

$$\Rightarrow w_{boat} = \left[7900g + 2(197.5gh) + 2(395gh)\right] \text{ N} = (7900 + 1185h)g \text{ N}$$

Going back to the Archimedes' equation and remembering that h is in meters, we obtain

$$\rho_w V_{boat}g = (7900 + 1185h)g \text{ N} \Rightarrow (1000)(10 \times 5 \times (h + 0.02)) = 7900 + 1185h$$
$$\Rightarrow h = 14.1 \text{ cm}$$

15.61. Model: Treat the water as an ideal fluid obeying Bernoulli's equation. A streamline begins in the bigger
size pipe and ends at the exit of the narrower pipe.
Visualize: The pressure at point 1 is p_1 and the pressure at point 2 is p_2. The pressure at the top of the standing
column of water is p_{atmos}.

Solve: **(a)** The pressure of the water as it exits into the air is $p_2 = p_{atmos}$.
(b) Bernoulli's equation, Equation 15.28, relates the pressure, water speed, and heights at points 1 and 2:

$$p_1 + \tfrac{1}{2}\rho v_1^2 + \rho g y_1 = p_2 + \tfrac{1}{2}\rho v_2^2 + \rho g y_2 \Rightarrow p_1 - p_2 = \tfrac{1}{2}\rho\left(v_2^2 - v_1^2\right) + \rho g\left(y_2 - y_1\right)$$

From the continuity equation,

$$v_1 A_1 = v_2 A_2 = (4 \text{ m/s})(5 \times 10^{-4} \text{ m}^2) = v_1(10 \times 10^{-4} \text{ m}^2) = 20 \times 10^{-4} \text{ m}^3/\text{s} \Rightarrow v_1 = 2 \text{ m/s}$$

Substituting into Bernoulli's equation,

$$p_1 - p_2 = p_1 - p_{atmos} = \tfrac{1}{2}(1000 \text{ kg/m}^3)\left[(4 \text{ m/s})^2 - (2 \text{ m/s})^2\right] + (1000 \text{ kg/m}^3)(9.8 \text{ m/s})(4.0 \text{ m})$$

$$= 6000 \text{ Pa} + 39,200 \text{ Pa} = 45,200 \text{ Pa} = \rho g h$$

$$\Rightarrow h = \frac{45,200 \text{ Pa}}{(1000 \text{ kg/m}^3)(9.8 \text{ m/s}^2)} = 4.61 \text{ m}$$

15.63. **Model:** Treat the air as an ideal fluid obeying Bernoulli's equation.
Solve: **(a)** The pressure above the roof is lower due to the forward motion of the air.
(b) Bernoulli's equation is

$$p_{inside} = p_{outside} + \tfrac{1}{2}\rho_{air}v^2 \Rightarrow \Delta P = \frac{1}{2}\rho_{air}v^2 = \frac{1}{2}(1.28 \text{ kg/m}^3)\left(\frac{130 \times 1000 \text{ m}}{3600 \text{ s}}\right)^2 = 835 \text{ Pa}$$

(c) The force on the roof is $(\Delta P)A = (835 \text{ Pa})(6.0 \text{ m} \times 15.0 \text{ m}) = 7.51 \times 10^4 \text{ N}$. The roof will blow up, because pressure inside the house is greater than pressure on the top of the roof.

15.65. **Model:** The ideal fluid (that is, air) obeys Bernoulli's equation.
Visualize: Please refer to Figure P15.65. There is a streamline connecting points 1 and 2. The air speeds at points 1 and 2 are v_1 and v_2, and the cross-sectional areas of the pipes at these points are A_1 and A_2. Points 1 and 2 are at the same height, so $y_1 = y_2$.
Solve: **(a)** The height of the mercury is 10 cm. So, the pressure at point 2 is larger than at point 1 by

$$\rho_{Hg}g(0.10 \text{ m}) = (13,600 \text{ kg/m}^3)(9.8 \text{ m/s}^2)(0.10 \text{ m}) = 13,328 \text{ Pa} \Rightarrow p_2 = p_1 + 13,328 \text{ Pa}$$

Using Bernoulli's equation,

$$p_1 + \tfrac{1}{2}\rho_{air}v_1^2 + \rho_{air}g y_1 = p_2 + \tfrac{1}{2}\rho_{air}v_2^2 + \rho_{air}g y_2 \Rightarrow p_2 - p_1 = \tfrac{1}{2}\rho_{air}\left(v_1^2 - v_2^2\right)$$

$$\Rightarrow v_1^2 - v_2^2 = \frac{2(p_2 - p_1)}{\rho_{air}} = \frac{2(13,328 \text{ Pa})}{(1.28 \text{ kg/m}^3)} = 20,825 \text{ m}^2/\text{s}^2$$

From the continuity equation, we can obtain another equation connecting v_1 and v_2:

$$A_1 v_1 = A_2 v_2 \Rightarrow v_1 = \frac{A_2}{A_1}v_2 = \frac{\pi(0.005 \text{ m})^2}{\pi(0.001 \text{ m})^2}v_2 = 25 \, v_2$$

Substituting $v_1 = 25v_2$ in the Bernoulli equation, we get

$$(25 \, v_2)^2 - v_2^2 = 20,825 \text{ m}^2/\text{s}^2 \Rightarrow v_2 = 5.78 \text{ m/s}$$

Thus $v_1 = 25v_2 = 144$ m/s.
(b) The volume flow rate $A_2 v_2 = \pi(0.005 \text{ m})^2(5.78 \text{ m/s}) = 0.000454 \text{ m}^3/\text{s} = 454 \text{ mL/s}$.

15.67. **Model:** Treat water as an ideal fluid that obeys Bernoulli's equation. There is a streamline connecting the top of the tank with the hole.
Visualize: Please refer to Figure P15.67. We placed the origin of the coordinate system at the bottom of the tank so that the top of the tank (point 1) is at a height of $h + 1.0$ m and the hole (point 2) is at a height h. Both points 1 and 2 are at atmospheric pressure.
Solve: **(a)** Bernoulli's equation connecting points 1 and 2 is

$$p_1 + \tfrac{1}{2}\rho v_1^2 + \rho g y_1 = p_2 + \tfrac{1}{2}\rho v_2^2 + \rho g y_2$$

$$\Rightarrow p_{atmos} + \tfrac{1}{2}\rho v_1^2 + \rho g(h + 1.0 \text{ m}) = p_{atmos} + \tfrac{1}{2}\rho v_2^2 + \rho g h$$

$$\Rightarrow v_2^2 - v_1^2 = 2 \, g(1.0 \text{ m}) = 19.6 \text{ m}^2/\text{s}^2$$

Using the continuity equation $A_1v_1 = A_2v_2$,

$$v_1 = \left(\frac{A_2}{A_1}\right)v_2 = \frac{\pi(2.0\times10^{-3}\text{ m})^2}{\pi(1.0\text{ m})^2}v_2 = \frac{v_2}{250,000}$$

Because $v_1 << v_2$, we can simply put $v_1 \approx 0$ m/s. Bernoulli's equation thus simplifies to

$$v_2^2 = 19.6\text{ m}^2/\text{s}^2 \Rightarrow v_2 = 4.43\text{ m/s}$$

Therefore, the volume flow rate through the hole is

$$Q = A_2v_2 = \pi(2.0\times10^{-3}\text{ m})^2(4.43\text{ m/s}) = 5.56\times10^{-5}\text{ m}^3/\text{s} = 3.34\text{ L/min}$$

(b) The rate at which the water level will drop is

$$v_1 = \frac{v_2}{250,000} = \frac{4.43\text{ m/s}}{250,000} = 1.77\times10^{-2}\text{ mm/s} = 1.06\text{ mm/min}$$

Assess: Because the hole through which water flows out of the tank has a diameter of only 4.0 mm, a drop in the water level at the rate of 1.06 mm/min is reasonable.

15.71.   Model: Pressure applies a volume stress to water in the cylinder.
Solve: The volume strain of water due to the pressure applied is

$$\frac{\Delta V}{V} = -\frac{p}{B} = -\frac{2\times10^6\text{ Pa}}{0.20\times10^{10}\text{ Pa}} = -1.0\times10^{-3}$$

$$\Rightarrow \Delta V = V' - V = -(1.0\times10^{-3})(1.30\text{ m}^3) = -1.30\times10^{-3}\text{ m}^3 = -1.3\text{ L}$$

As the safety plug on the top of the cylinder bursts, the water comes back to atmospheric pressure. The volume of water that comes out is 1.30 L.

16

A MACROSCOPIC DESCRIPTION OF MATTER

16.3. Solve: The volume of the aluminum cube is 10^{-3} m^3 and its mass is

$$m_{\text{Al}} = \rho_{\text{Al}} V_{\text{Al}} = \left(2700 \text{ kg/m}^3\right)\left(1.0 \times 10^{-3} \text{ m}^3\right) = 2.7 \text{ kg}$$

The volume of the copper sphere with this mass is

$$V_{\text{Cu}} = \frac{4\pi}{3}\left(r_{\text{Cu}}\right)^3 = \frac{m_{\text{Cu}}}{\rho_{\text{Cu}}} = \frac{2.7 \text{ kg}}{8920 \text{ kg/m}^3} = 3.027 \times 10^{-4} \text{ m}^3$$

$$\Rightarrow r_{\text{Cu}} = \left[\frac{3\left(3.027 \times 10^{-4} \text{ m}^3\right)}{4\pi}\right]^{1/3} = 0.04165 \text{ m}$$

The diameter of the copper sphere is 0.0833 m = 8.33 cm.

16.7. Solve: (a) The number density is defined as N/V, where N is the number of particles occupying a volume V. Because Al has a mass density of 2700 kg/m^3, a volume of 1 m^3 has a mass of 2700 kg. We also know that the molar mass of Al is 27 g/mol or 0.027 kg/mol. So, the number of moles in a mass of 2700 kg is

$$n = \left(2700 \text{ kg}\right)\left(\frac{1 \text{ mol}}{0.027 \text{ kg}}\right) = 1.00 \times 10^5 \text{ mol}$$

The number of Al atoms in 1.00×10^5 mols is

$$N = nN_{\text{A}} = \left(1.00 \times 10^5 \text{ mol}\right)\left(6.02 \times 10^{23} \text{ atoms/mol}\right) = 6.02 \times 10^{28} \text{ atoms}$$

Thus, the number density is

$$\frac{N}{V} = \frac{6.02 \times 10^{28} \text{ atoms}}{1 \text{ m}^3} = 6.02 \times 10^{28} \text{ atoms/m}^3$$

(b) Pb has a mass of 11,300 kg in a volume of 1 m^3. Since the atomic mass number of Pb is 207, the number of moles in 11,300 kg is

$$n = \left(11{,}300 \text{ kg}\right)\left(\frac{1 \text{ mole}}{0.207 \text{ kg}}\right)$$

The number of Pb atoms is thus $N = nN_{\text{A}}$, and hence the number density is

$$\frac{N}{V} = \frac{nN_{\text{A}}}{V} = \left(\frac{11300 \text{ kg}}{0.207 \text{ kg}}\right)\left(6.02 \times 10^{23} \frac{\text{atoms}}{\text{mol}}\right)\frac{(1 \text{ mol})}{1 \text{ m}^3} = 3.28 \times 10^{28} \frac{\text{atoms}}{\text{m}^3}$$

16.13. Solve: (a) Referring to Table 16.4, $0°Z \equiv -196°C$ and $1000°Z \equiv +1538°C$. This means an interval of $1000°Z$ is equivalent to $1538°C - (-196°C) = 1734°C$. That is $1°Z = 1.734°C$. Thus, the boiling point of water is $100°C + 196°C = 296°C$ above $0°Z$ on the Z-scale and would be

$$\left(\frac{1°Z}{1.734°C}\right) \times 296°C = 171°Z$$

(b) In the same way,

$$500°Z = (500°Z)\frac{(1.734°C)}{(1°Z)} = 867°C$$

above $-196°C$, which means that it is equal to $671°C$ and $671 + 273 = 944$ K.

16.17.   Solve: The pressure due to seawater at a depth d is

$$p = p_0 + \rho_{sea\,water}gd$$
$$= 1.013 \times 10^5 \text{ Pa} + (1030 \text{ kg/m}^3)(9.8 \text{ m/s}^2)(100 \text{ m}) = 1.1107 \times 10^6 \text{ Pa} \approx 11 \text{ atm}$$

From Figure 16.04, we see that the freezing temperature of water at $p = 11$ atm is below $0°C$ and the boiling temperature is above $100°C$. This is because the solid-liquid transition line has a negative slope, but the liquid-gas transition line has a positive slope.

16.19.   Model: Treat the gas in the sealed container as an ideal gas.
Solve: (a) From the ideal gas law equation $pV = nRT$, the volume V of the container is

$$V = \frac{nRT}{p} = \frac{(2.0 \text{ mol})(8.31 \text{ J/mol K})[(273 + 30) \text{ K}]}{1.013 \times 10^5 \text{ Pa}} = 0.0497 \text{ m}^3$$

(b) The before-and-after relationship of an ideal gas in a sealed container (constant volume) is

$$\frac{p_1 V}{T_1} = \frac{p_2 V}{T_2} \Rightarrow p_2 = p_1 \frac{T_2}{T_1} = (1.0 \text{ atm})\frac{(273 + 130) \text{ K}}{(273 + 30) \text{ K}} = 1.33 \text{ atm}$$

16.25.   Model: Treat the helium gas in the sealed cylinder as an ideal gas.
Solve: The volume of the cylinder is $V = \pi r^2 h = \pi(0.05 \text{ m})^2(0.30 \text{ m}) = 2.356 \times 10^{-3} \text{ m}^3$. The gauge pressure of the gas is $120 \text{ psi} \times \frac{1 \text{ atm}}{14.7 \text{ psi}} \times \frac{1.013 \times 10^5 \text{ Pa}}{1 \text{ atm}} = 8.269 \times 10^5 \text{ Pa}$. So the absolute pressure of the gas is $8.269 \times 10^5 \text{ Pa} + 1.013 \times 10^5 \text{ Pa} = 9.282 \times 10^5 \text{ Pa}$.

The temperature of the gas is $T = (273 + 30) \text{ K} = 293 \text{ K}$. The number of moles of the gas in the cylinder is

$$n = \frac{pV}{RT} = \frac{(9.282 \times 10^5 \text{ Pa})(2.356 \times 10^{-3} \text{ m}^3)}{(8.31 \text{ J/mol K})(293 \text{ K})} = 0.898 \text{ mol}$$

(a) The number of atoms is

$$N = nN_A = (0.898 \text{ mol})(6.02 \times 10^{23} \text{ mol}^{-1}) = 5.407 \times 10^{23} \approx 5.41 \times 10^{23} \text{ atoms}.$$

(b) The mass of the helium is

$$M = nM_{mol} = (0.898 \text{ mol})(4 \text{ g/mol}) = 3.59 \text{ g} = 3.59 \times 10^{-3} \text{ kg}$$

(c) The number density is

$$\frac{N}{V} = \frac{5.407 \times 10^{23} \text{ atoms}}{2.356 \times 10^{-3} \text{ m}^3} = 2.29 \times 10^{26} \text{ atoms/m}^3$$

(d) The mass density is

$$\rho = \frac{M}{V} = \frac{3.59 \times 10^{-3} \text{ kg}}{2.356 \times 10^{-3} \text{ m}^3} = 1.52 \text{ kg/m}^3$$

16.29.   Model: In an isochoric process, the volume of the container stays unchanged. Argon gas in the container is assumed to be an ideal gas.
Solve: (a) The container has only argon inside with $n = 0.1$ mol, $V_1 = 50 \text{ cm}^3 = 50 \times 10^{-6} \text{ m}^3$, and $T_1 = 20°C = 293$ K. This produces a pressure

$$p_1 = \frac{nRT}{V_1} = \frac{(0.1 \text{ mol})(8.31 \text{ J/mol K})(293 \text{ K})}{50 \times 10^{-6} \text{ m}^3} = 4.87 \times 10^6 \text{ Pa} = 4870 \text{ kPa}$$

An ideal gas process has $p_2 V_2/T_2 = p_1 V_1/T_1$. Isochoric heating to a final temperature $T_2 = 300°C = 573$ K has $V_2 = V_1$, so the final pressure is

$$p_2 = \frac{V_1}{V_2} \frac{T_2}{T_1} p_1 = 1 \times \frac{573}{293} \times 4870 \text{ kPa} = 9520 \text{ kPa}$$

Note that it is essential to express temperatures in kelvins.

(b)

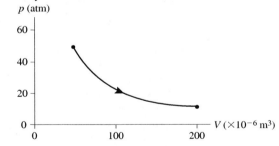

16.31. Model: In an isothermal expansion, the temperature stays the same. The argon gas in the container is assumed to be an ideal gas.

Solve: **(a)** The before-and-after relationship of an ideal gas under isothermal conditions is

$$\frac{p_1 V_1}{T_1} = \frac{p_2 V_2}{T_2} \implies p_2 = p_1 \frac{V_1}{V_2}$$

Using the ideal-gas law $p_1 V_1 = nRT_1$, our equation for p_2 becomes

$$p_2 = nR \frac{T_1}{V_1} \frac{V_1}{V_2} = \frac{nRT_1}{V_2} = \frac{(0.10 \text{ mol})(8.31 \text{ J/mol K})[(273 + 20) \text{ K}]}{200 \times 10^{-6} \text{ m}^3} = 1.217 \times 10^6 \text{ Pa} = 12.02 \text{ atm}$$

(b) Substituting into the equation for an isothermal expansion,

$$p_1 = p_2 \frac{V_2}{V_1} = (12.02 \text{ atm}) \frac{200 \times 10^{-6} \text{ m}^3}{50 \times 10^{-6} \text{ m}^3} = 48.1 \text{ atm}$$

The process can be presented on a pV diagram. The two pV coordinates are (46.9 atm, 50×10^{-6} m³) and (11.7 atm, 200×10^{-6} m³), and p varies inversely with V.

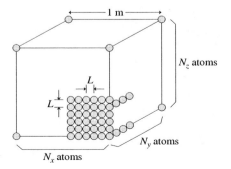

16.35. Visualize:

Solve: Suppose we have a 1 m × 1 m × 1 m block of copper of mass M containing N atoms. The atoms are spaced a distance L apart along all three axes of the cube. There are N_x atoms along the x-edge of the cube, N_y atoms along the y-edge, and N_z atoms along the z-edge. The total number of atoms is $N = N_x N_y N_z$. If L is expressed in meters, then the number of atoms along the x-edge is $N_x = (1\text{ m})/L$. Thus,

$$N = \frac{1\text{ m}}{L} \times \frac{1\text{ m}}{L} \times \frac{1\text{ m}}{L} = \frac{1\text{ m}^3}{L^3} \Rightarrow L = \left(\frac{1\text{ m}^3}{N}\right)^{1/3}$$

This relates the spacing between atoms to the number of atoms in a 1-meter cube. The mass of the large cube of copper is

$$M = \rho_{Cu} V = (8920\text{ kg/m}^3)(1\text{ m}^3) = 8920\text{ kg}$$

But $M = mN$, where $m = 64\text{ u} = 64 \times (1.661 \times 10^{-27}\text{ kg})$ is the mass of an individual copper atom. Thus,

$$N = \frac{M}{m} = \frac{8920\text{ kg}}{64 \times (1.661 \times 10^{-27}\text{ kg})} = 8.39 \times 10^{28}\text{ atoms}$$

$$\Rightarrow L = \left(\frac{1\text{ m}^3}{8.39 \times 10^{28}}\right)^{1/3} = 2.28 \times 10^{-10}\text{ m} = 0.228\text{ nm}$$

16.41.   Model: Assume that the gas in the vacuum chamber is an ideal gas.
Solve: (a) The fraction is

$$\frac{p_{\text{vacuum chamber}}}{p_{\text{atmosphere}}} = \frac{1.0 \times 10^{-10}\text{ mm of Hg}}{760\text{ mm of Hg}} = 1.316 \times 10^{-13}$$

(b) The volume of the chamber $V = \pi(0.20\text{ m})^2(0.30\text{ m}) = 0.03770\text{ m}^3$. From the ideal-gas equation $pV = nRT$, the number of molecules of gas in the chamber is

$$N = nN_A = \frac{pVN_A}{RT} = \frac{(1.316 \times 10^{-3})(1.013 \times 10^5\text{ Pa})(0.03770\text{ m}^3)(6.02 \times 10^{25}\text{ mol})}{(8.31\text{ J/kg mol})(293\text{ K})} = 1.24 \times 10^{11}\text{ molecules}$$

16.45.   Model: Assume that the steam (as water vapor) is an ideal gas.
Solve: The volume of the liquid water is

$$V = \frac{m}{\rho} = \frac{nM_{\text{mol}}}{\rho} = \left(\frac{pV}{RT}\right)\frac{M_{\text{mol}}}{\rho} = \frac{20(1.013 \times 10^5\text{ Pa})(10{,}000 \times 10^{-6}\text{ m}^3)(0.018\text{ kg/mol})}{(8.31\text{ J/mol K})(473\text{ K})(1000\text{ kg/m}^3)}$$

$$= 9.28 \times 10^{-5}\text{ m}^3 = 92.8\text{ cm}^3$$

16.47.   Model: We assume that the volume of the tire and that of the air in the tire is constant.
Solve: A gauge pressure of 30 psi corresponds to an absolute pressure of (30 psi) + (14.7 psi) = 44.7 psi. Using the before-and-after relationship of an ideal gas for an isochoric (constant volume) process,

$$\frac{p_1}{T_1} = \frac{p_2}{T_2} \Rightarrow p_2 = \frac{T_2}{T_1}p_1 = \left(\frac{273+45}{273+15}\right)(44.7\text{ psi}) = 49.4\text{ psi}$$

This pressure of 49.4 psi corresponds to a gauge pressure of 34.7 psi.

16.51.   Model: The gas can be treated as an ideal gas.
Visualize:

He
200 cm³
50°C

25 cm

Solve: **(a)** Because the liquid on the right is *below* that on the left, the "height" of the mercury column is $h = -25$ cm $= -0.25$ m. Thus, the gas pressure in the cell is

$$p_{gas} = 1 \text{ atm} + \rho g h = 101{,}300 \text{ Pa} + (13{,}600 \text{ kg/m}^3)(9.8 \text{ m/s}^2)(-0.25 \text{ m}) = 68{,}000 \text{ Pa}$$

We can find the number of atoms from the version of the ideal-gas law that reads $pV = NkT$ (Equation 16.12):

$$N = \frac{pV}{kT} = \frac{(68{,}000 \text{ Pa})(200 \text{ cm}^3 \times 10^{-6} \text{ m}^3/\text{cm}^3)}{(1.38 \times 10^{-23} \text{ J/K})(50°C + 273°C)} = 3.05 \times 10^{21} \text{ atoms}$$

Notice how all quantities were converted to SI units.
(b) The mass of an atom is $m = 4$ u $= 4 \times (1.661 \times 10^{-27}$ kg$) = 6.644 \times 10^{-27}$ kg. The total mass is

$$M = mN = (6.644 \times 10^{-27} \text{ kg/atom})(3.05 \times 10^{21} \text{ atoms}) = 2.02 \times 10^{-5} \text{ kg} = 20.2 \text{ mg}$$

16.55. **Model:** Assume that the gas is an ideal gas.
Solve:

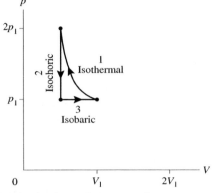

Assess: For the isothermal process, the pressure must double as the volume is halved. This is because p is proportional to $1/V$ for isothermal processes.

16.57. **Model:** Assume the nitrogen gas is an ideal gas.
Visualize: Please refer to Figure P16.57.
Solve: **(a)** The number of moles of nitrogen is

$$n = \frac{M}{M_{mol}} = \frac{1 \text{ g}}{28 \text{ g/mol}} = \left(\frac{1}{28}\right) \text{ mol}$$

Using the ideal-gas equation,

$$p_1 = \frac{nRT_1}{V_1} = \frac{\text{mol}}{28} \frac{(8.31 \text{ J/mol K})(298 \text{ K})}{(100 \times 10^{-6} \text{ m}^3)} = 8.844 \times 10^5 \text{ Pa} = 8.731 \text{ atm}$$

(b) For the process from state1 to state 3:

$$\frac{p_1 V_1}{T_1} = \frac{p_3 V_3}{T_3} \Rightarrow T_3 = T_1 \frac{p_3}{p_1} \frac{V_3}{V_1} = (298 \text{ K})\left(\frac{1.5 p_1}{p_1}\right)\left(\frac{50 \text{ cm}^3}{100 \text{ cm}^3}\right) = 223.5 \text{ K} = -49.5°C$$

For the process from state 3 to state 2:

$$\frac{p_2 V_2}{T_2} = \frac{p_3 V_3}{T_3} \Rightarrow T_2 = T_3 \left(\frac{p_2}{p_3}\right)\left(\frac{V_2}{V_3}\right) = (223.5 \text{ K})\left(\frac{2.0 p_1}{1.5 p_1}\right)\left(\frac{100 \text{ cm}^3}{50 \text{ cm}^3}\right) = 596 \text{ K} = 323°C$$

For the process from state1 to state 4:

$$\frac{p_4 V_4}{T_4} = \frac{p_1 V_1}{T_1} \Rightarrow T_4 = T_1 \frac{p_4}{p_1} \frac{V_4}{V_1} = (298 \text{ K})\left(\frac{1.5 p_1}{p_1}\right)\left(\frac{150 \text{ cm}^3}{100 \text{ cm}^3}\right) = 670.5 \text{ K} = 397.5°C$$

16.59.   Model: Assume the gas is an ideal gas.
Visualize: Please refer to Figure P16.59.
Solve: (a) We can find the temperatures directly from the ideal-gas law after we convert all quantities to SI units:

$$T_1 = \frac{p_1 V_1}{nR} = \frac{(3 \text{ atm} \times 101,300 \text{ Pa/atm})(1000 \text{ cm}^3 \times 10^{-6} \text{ m}^3/\text{cm}^3)}{(0.1 \text{ mol})(8.31 \text{ J/mol K})} = 366 \text{ K}$$

$$T_2 = \frac{p_2 V_2}{nR} = \frac{(1 \text{ atm} \times 101,300 \text{ Pa/atm})(3000 \text{ cm}^3 \times 10^{-6} \text{ m}^3/\text{cm}^3)}{(0.1 \text{ mol})(8.31 \text{ J/mol K})} = 366 \text{ K}$$

(b) $T_2 = T_1$, so this is an isothermal process.
(c) A constant volume process has $V_3 = V_2$. Because $p_1 = 3p_2$, restoring the pressure to its original value means that $p_3 = 3p_2$. From the ideal gas law,

$$\frac{p_3 V_3}{T_3} = \frac{p_2 V_2}{T_2} \Rightarrow T_3 = \left(\frac{p_3}{p_2}\right)\left(\frac{V_3}{V_2}\right)T_2 = 3 \times 1 \times T_2 = 3 \times 366 \text{ K} = 1098 \text{ K} = 825°C$$

16.61.   Model: Assume CO_2 gas is an ideal gas.
Solve: (a) The molar mass for CO_2 is $M_{mol} = 44$ g/mol, so a 10 g piece of dry ice is 0.2273 mol. With $V_1 = 10,000$ cm^3 = 0.010 m^3 and $T_1 = 0°C = 273$ K, the pressure is

$$p_1 = \frac{nRT_1}{V_1} = \frac{(0.2773 \text{ mol})(8.31 \text{ J/mol K})(273 \text{ K})}{0.010 \text{ m}^3} = 5.156 \times 10^4 \text{ Pa} = 0.509 \text{ atm}$$

(b) From the isothermal compression,

$$p_2 V_2 = p_1 V_1 \Rightarrow V_2 = V_1 \frac{p_1}{p_2} = (0.010 \text{ m}^3)\left(\frac{0.509 \text{ atm}}{3.0 \text{ atm}}\right) = 1.70 \times 10^{-3} \text{ m}^3 = 1700 \text{ cm}^3$$

From the isobaric compression,

$$T_3 = T_2 \frac{V_3}{V_2} = (273 \text{ K})\left(\frac{1000 \text{ cm}^3}{1700 \text{ cm}^3}\right) = 161 \text{ K} = -112°C$$

(c)

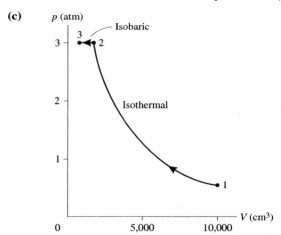

16.65.   Solve: (a) A gas is compressed isothermally from a volume 300 cm^3 at 2 atm to a volume of 100 cm^3. What is the final pressure?

(b)

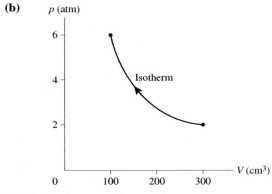

(c) The final pressure is $p_2 = 6$ atm.

16.67.   Solve: (a) We are given a gas at 50°C in a volume of 200 cm³. The temperature is changed in an isobaric process to 400°C. What will be the new volume?

(b)

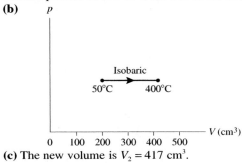

(c) The new volume is $V_2 = 417$ cm³.

WORK, HEAT, AND THE FIRST LAW OF THERMODYNAMICS

17.3. **Model:** The work done on a gas is the negative of the area under the pV curve.
Visualize: Please refer to Figure Ex17.3. The gas is compressing, so we expect the work to be positive. This is because the force on the gas by the environment is in the direction of the displacement.
Solve: The work done on the gas is

$$W = -\int p\,dV = -(\text{area under the } pV \text{ curve})$$

$$= -\left(-(200 \text{ cm}^3)(200 \text{ kPa})\right) = (200 \times 10^{-6} \text{ m}^3)(2 \times 10^5 \text{ Pa}) = 40 \text{ J}$$

Assess: The area under the curve is negative because the integration direction is to the left. Thus, the environment does positive work on the gas, that is, energy is transferred into the gas.

17.5. **Visualize:** Please refer to Figure Ex17.5.
Solve: The work done on gas in an isobaric process is

$$W = -\int p\,dV = -p\Delta V = -p(V_f - V_i)$$

Substituting into this equation,

$$80 \text{ J} = -(200 \times 10^3 \text{ Pa})(V_1 - 3V_1) \Rightarrow V_i = 2 \times 10^{-4} \text{ m}^3 = 200 \text{ cm}^3$$

Assess: The work done on a gas is positive for a compressing gas.

17.7. **Visualize:**

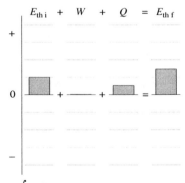

Solve: Because $W = -\int p\,dV$ and this is an isochoric process, $W = 0$ J. The final point is on a higher isotherm than the initial point, so $T_f > T_i$. Heat energy is thus transferred into the gas ($Q > 0$) and the thermal energy of the gas increases ($E_{\text{th f}} > E_{\text{th i}}$) as the temperature increases.

17.11. Visualize:

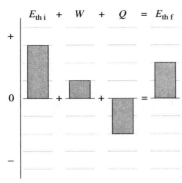

$$E_{\text{th i}} \quad + \quad W \quad + \quad Q \quad = \quad E_{\text{th f}}$$

Solve: This is a case of gas compression and therefore $W = -\int pdV$ is a positive quantity. The final point is on a lower isotherm than the initial point, so $T_f < T_i$. Heat energy is transferred out of the gas ($Q < 0$ J) and the thermal energy of the gas decreases as the temperature falls. That is, $E_{\text{th f}} < E_{\text{th i}}$. To bring about this process: (1) The locking pin is removed so the piston can slide up and down. (2) The masses on the top of the piston are not changed. (3) The ice block is brought into contact with the bottom of the cylinder. (4) The water in the cylinder walls is turned off so that it does not circulate.

17.13. Solve: The first law of thermodynamics is
$$\Delta E_{\text{th}} = W + Q \Rightarrow -200 \text{ J} = 500 \text{ J} + Q \Rightarrow Q = -700 \text{ J}$$
The negative sign means a transfer of energy from the system to the environment.
Assess: Because $W > 0$ means a transfer of energy into the system, Q must be less than zero and larger in magnitude than W so that $E_{\text{th f}} < E_{\text{th i}}$.

17.17. Model: Heating the mercury at its boiling point changes its thermal energy without a change in temperature.
Solve: The mass of the mercury is $M = 20$ g $= 2.0 \times 10^{-2}$ kg, the specific heat $c_{\text{mercury}} = 140$ J/kg K, the boiling point $T_b = 357$ K, and the heat of vaporization $L_V = 2.96 \times 10^5$ J/kg. The heat required for the mercury to change to the vapor phase starting from room temperature (295 K) is the sum of two steps. The first step is
$$Q_1 = Mc_{\text{mercury}}\Delta T = (2.0 \times 10^{-2} \text{ kg})(140 \text{ J/kg K})(357 \text{ K} - 295 \text{ K}) = 173.6 \text{ J}$$
The second step is
$$Q_2 = ML_V = (2.0 \times 10^{-2} \text{ kg})(2.96 \times 10^5 \text{ J/kg}) = 5920 \text{ J}$$
The total heat needed is 6094 J.

17.21. Model: We have a thermal interaction between the copper pellets and water. There are two possible outcomes. First, the water temperature will become 100°C or less. Second, the water temperature will become 100°C and some water will vaporize.
Solve: The heat needed to raise the temperature of 100 mL of water at 20°C to boiling temperature (100°C) is
$$Q = Mc_{\text{water}}\Delta T = (100 \times 10^{-6} \text{ m}^3)(1000 \text{ kg/m}^3)(4190 \text{ J/kg K})(373 \text{ K} - 293 \text{ K}) = 33{,}520 \text{ J}$$
The heat available from 30 g of copper pellets at 300°C to cool down to 100°C is
$$Q = (0.030 \text{ kg})(385 \text{ J/kg K})(-200 \text{ K}) = -2310 \text{ J}$$
Because the heat given out from the copper pellets is less than the heat needed to increase the water's temperature, the final temperature of the pellets + water mixture is less than 100°C. To find this final temperature,
$$Q_{\text{copper}} + Q_{\text{water}} = M_{\text{copper}} c_{\text{copper}}(T_f - 573 \text{ K}) + M_{\text{water}} c_{\text{water}}(T_f - 293 \text{ K}) = 0 \text{ J}$$
$$\Rightarrow (0.030 \text{ kg})(385 \text{ J/kg K})(T_f - 573 \text{ K}) + (100 \times 10^{-6} \text{ m}^3)(1000 \text{ kg/m}^3)(4190 \text{ J/kg K})(T_f - 293 \text{ K})$$
$$= (11.55 \text{ J/k})T_f - 6618.15 \text{ J} + 419T_f - 122{,}767 \text{ J} = 0 \text{ J}$$
Solving this equation gives $T_f = 300.5$ K $= 27.5$°C.

17.29. **Model:** The O_2 gas has $\gamma = 1.40$ and is an ideal gas.
Solve: **(a)** For an adiabatic process, pV^γ remains a constant. That is,

$$p_i V_i^\gamma = p_f V_f^\gamma \Rightarrow p_f = p_i \left(\frac{V_i}{V_f}\right)^\gamma = (3.0 \text{ atm})\left(\frac{V_i}{2V_i}\right)^{1.40} = (3.0 \text{ atm})\left(\frac{1}{2}\right)^{1.40} = 1.14 \text{ atm}$$

(b) Using the ideal-gas law, the final temperature of the gas is calculated as follows:

$$\frac{p_i V_i}{T_i} = \frac{p_f V_f}{T_f} \Rightarrow T_f = T_i \frac{p_f}{p_i}\frac{V_f}{V_i} = (423 \text{ K})\left(\frac{1.14 \text{ atm}}{3.0 \text{ atm}}\right)\left(\frac{2V_i}{V_i}\right) = 321.5 \text{ K} = 48.5°C$$

17.31. **Model:** γ is 1.40 for a diatomic gas and 1.67 for a monoatomic gas.
Solve: **(a)** We will assume that air is a diatomic gas. For an adiabatic process,

$$p_i V_i^\gamma = p_f V_f^\gamma \Rightarrow \left(\frac{V_i}{V_f}\right)^\gamma = \frac{p_f}{p_f}$$

Using the ideal-gas law,

$$\frac{p_i V_i}{T_i} = \frac{p_f V_f}{T_f} \Rightarrow \frac{p_f}{p_i} = \left(\frac{T_f}{T_i}\right)\left(\frac{V_i}{V_f}\right)$$

Combining the two equations,

$$\left(\frac{V_i}{V_f}\right)^\gamma = \left(\frac{T_f}{T_i}\right)\left(\frac{V_i}{V_f}\right) \Rightarrow \left(\frac{V_i}{V_f}\right) = \left(\frac{T_f}{T_i}\right)^{\frac{1}{\gamma-1}} = \left(\frac{1123 \text{ K}}{303 \text{ K}}\right)^{\frac{1}{1.40-1}} = 26.4$$

(b) For a monatomic gas,

$$\left(\frac{V_i}{V_f}\right) = \left(\frac{1123 \text{ K}}{303 \text{ K}}\right)^{\frac{1}{1.67-1}} = 7.07$$

17.33. **Solve:** The area of the garden pond is $A = \pi(2.5 \text{ m})^2 = 19.635 \text{ m}^2$ and its volume is $V = A(0.30 \text{ m}) = 5.891 \text{ m}^3$. The mass of water in the pond is

$$M = \rho V = (1000 \text{ kg/m}^3)(19.635 \text{ m}^3) = 5891 \text{ kg}$$

The water absorbs all the solar power which is

$$(400 \text{ W/m}^2)(19.635 \text{ m}^2) = 7854 \text{ W}$$

This power is used to raise the temperature of the water. That is,

$$Q = (7854 \text{ W})t = Mc_{water}\Delta T = (5891 \text{ kg})(4190 \text{ J/kg K})(10 \text{ K}) \Rightarrow t = 31,425 \text{ s} = 8.73 \text{ hr}$$

17.37. **Model:** There are three interacting systems: aluminum, copper, and ethyl alcohol.
Solve: The aluminum, copper, and alcohol form a closed system, so $Q = Q_{Al} + Q_{Cu} + Q_{eth} = 0 \text{ J}$. The mass of the alcohol is

$$M_{eth} = \rho V = (790 \text{ kg/m}^3)(50 \times 10^{-6} \text{ m}^3) = 39.5 \times 10^{-3} \text{ kg}$$

Expressed in terms of specific heats and using the fact that $\Delta T = T_f - T_i$, the $Q = 0 \text{ J}$ condition is

$$M_{Al}c_{Al}\Delta T_{Al} + M_{Cu}c_{Cu}\Delta T_{Cu} + M_{eth}c_{eth}\Delta T_{eth} = 0 \text{ J}$$

Substituting into this expression,

$$(0.010 \text{ kg})(900 \text{ J/kg K})(298 \text{ K} - 473 \text{ K}) + (0.020 \text{ kg})(385 \text{ J/kg K})(298 \text{ K} - T)$$

$$+ (39.5 \times 10^{-3} \text{ kg})(2400 \text{ J/kg m}^3)(298 \text{ K} - 288 \text{ K}) = -1575 \text{ J} + (7.7 \text{ J/K})(298 - T) + 948 \text{ J} = 0 \text{ J}$$

$$\Rightarrow T = 216.6 \text{ K} = -56.4°C$$

17.41.   Model: Heating the water raises its thermal energy and its temperature. We have two interacting systems: heater and water.
Solve: For the closed system, $Q = Q_{heater} + Q_{water} = 0$ J. $Q_{heater} = -(5.0 \text{ kW})t$, where t is the time the heater delivers energy to the water in raising its temperature from 65°F to 140°F, that is, from 18.33°C to 60°C. We have

$$Q_{water} = M_{water}c_{water}\Delta T = \rho V_{water}c_{water}\Delta T = (1000 \text{ kg/m}^3)(150 \times 10^{-3} \text{ m}^3)(4190 \text{ J/kg K})(60°C - 18.33°C) = 2.619 \times 10^7 \text{ J}$$

The $Q = 0$ J condition becomes

$$(-5000 \text{ W})t + 2.619 \times 10^7 \text{ J} = 0 \text{ J}$$

This means $t = 5238$ s $= 87.3$ min.
Assess: A time of ≈ 1.5 hours to heat 40 gallons of water with a 5.0 kW heater is reasonable.

17.43.   Model: Heating the material increases its thermal energy.
Visualize: Please refer to Figure P17.43. The material melts at 300°C and undergoes a solid-liquid phase change. The material's temperature increases from 300°C to 1500°C. Boiling occurs at 1500°C and the material undergoes a liquid-gas phase change.
Solve: (a) In the liquid phase, the specific heat of the liquid can be obtained as follows:

$$\Delta Q = Mc\Delta T \Rightarrow c = \frac{1}{M}\frac{\Delta Q}{\Delta T} = \left(\frac{1}{0.200 \text{ kg}}\right)\left(\frac{20 \text{ kJ}}{1200 \text{ K}}\right) = 83.3 \text{ J/kg K}$$

(b) The latent heat of vaporization is

$$L_v = \frac{Q}{M} = \frac{40 \text{ kJ}}{(0.200 \text{ kg})} = 2 \times 10^5 \text{ J/kg}$$

17.45.   Model: There are two interacting systems: coffee and ice. Changing the coffee temperature from 90°C to 60°C requires four steps: (1) raise the temperature of ice from −20°C to 0°C, (2) change ice at 0°C to water at 0°C, (c) raise the water temperature from 0°C to 60°C, and (4) lower the coffee temperature from 90°C to 60°C.
Solve: For the closed coffee-ice system,

$$Q = Q_{ice} + Q_{coffee} = (Q_1 + Q_2 + Q_3) + (Q_4) = 0 \text{ J}$$

$$Q_1 = M_{ice}c_{ice}\Delta T = M_{ice}(2090 \text{ J/kg K})(20 \text{ K}) = M_{ice}(41,800 \text{ J/kg})$$

$$Q_2 = M_{ice}L_f = M_{ice}(330,000 \text{ J/kg})$$

$$Q_3 = M_{ice}c_{water}\Delta T = M_{ice}(4190 \text{ J/kg K})(60 \text{ K}) = M_{ice}(251,400 \text{ J/kg})$$

$$Q_4 = M_{coffee}c_{coffee}\Delta T = (300 \times 10^{-6} \text{ m}^3)(1000 \text{ kg/m}^3)(4190 \text{ J/kg K})(-30 \text{ K}) = -37,000 \text{ J}$$

The $Q = 0$ J equation thus becomes

$$M_{ice}(41,800 + 330,000 + 251,400) \text{ J/kg} - 37,710 \text{ J} = 0 \text{ J} \Rightarrow M_{ice} = 0.0605 \text{ kg} = 60.5 \text{ g}$$

Visualize: 60.5 g is the mass of approximately 1 ice cube.

17.49.   Model: For a gas, the thermal energy is the total kinetic energy of the moving molecules. That is, $E_{th} = K_{micro}$. Also, the work W done on an expanding gas is negative.
Solve: (a) The thermal energy of N molecules is $E_{th} = NK_{avg}$, where $K_{avg} = \frac{1}{2}m(v_{avg})^2$ is the average kinetic energy per molecule. The mass of a hydrogen molecule is

$$m = 2 \text{ u} = 2 \times (1.661 \times 10^{-27} \text{ kg}) = 3.32 \times 10^{-27} \text{ kg}$$

The number of molecules in a 1 g $= 0.001$ kg sample is

$$N = \frac{M}{m} = \frac{0.001 \text{ kg}}{3.32 \times 10^{-27} \text{ kg}} = 3.01 \times 10^{23}$$

The average kinetic energy per molecule is

$$K_{avg} = \frac{1}{2}m(v_{avg})^2 = \frac{1}{2}(3.32 \times 10^{-27} \text{ kg})(700 \text{ m/s})^2 = 8.13 \times 10^{-22} \text{ J}$$

Thus, the thermal energy in the 1-gram sample of the gas is

$$E_{th} = NK_{avg} = (3.01 \times 10^{23})(8.13 \times 10^{-22} \text{ J}) = 245 \text{ J}$$

(b) The first law of thermodynamics tells us the change of thermal energy when work is done and heat is added:

$$\Delta E_{th} = W + Q = -300 \text{ J} + 500 \text{ J} = 200 \text{ J}$$

Here W is negative because work is done *by* the system on the environment. The work and heat raise the thermal energy of the gas by 200 J to $E_{th} = 445$ J. Now the average kinetic energy is

$$K_{avg} = E_{th}/N = 1.487 \times 10^{-21} \text{ J} = \tfrac{1}{2}m\left(v_{avg}\right)^2$$

Solving for the new average speed gives

$$v_{avg} = \sqrt{\frac{2K_{avg}}{m}} = \sqrt{\frac{2\left(1.478 \times 10^{-21} \text{ J}\right)}{3.32 \times 10^{-27} \text{ kg}}} = 944 \text{ m/s}$$

17.53.   Model: This is an isobaric process.
Visualize: **Pictorial representation**

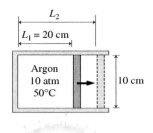

Solve: (a) The initial conditions are $p_1 = 10$ atm $= 1.013 \times 10^6$ Pa, $T_1 = 50°C = 323$ K, $V_1 = \pi r^2 L_1 = \pi (0.05 \text{ m})^2$ $(0.20 \text{ m}) = 1.57 \times 10^{-3}$ m³. The gas is heated at a constant pressure, so heat and temperature change are related by $Q = nC_P \Delta T$. From the ideal gas law, the number of moles of gas is

$$n = \frac{p_1 V_1}{RT_1} = \frac{\left(1.013 \times 10^6 \text{ Pa}\right)\left(1.57 \times 10^{-3} \text{ m}^3\right)}{\left(8.31 \text{ J/mol K}\right)\left(323 \text{ K}\right)} = 0.593 \text{ mol}$$

The temperature change due to the addition of $Q = 2500$ J of heat is thus

$$\Delta T = \frac{Q}{nC_P} = \frac{2500 \text{ J}}{\left(0.593 \text{ mol}\right)\left(20.8 \text{ J/mol K}\right)} = 203 \text{ K}$$

The final temperature is $T_2 = T_1 + \Delta T = 526$ K $= 253°C$.
(b) Noting that the volume of a cylinder is $V = \pi r^2 L$ and that r doesn't change, the ideal gas relationship for an isobaric process is

$$\frac{V_2}{T_2} = \frac{V_1}{T_1} \Rightarrow \frac{L_2}{T_2} = \frac{L_1}{T_1} \Rightarrow L_2 = \frac{T_2}{T_1}L_1 = \frac{526 \text{ K}}{323 \text{ K}}(20 \text{ cm}) = 32.6 \text{ cm}$$

17.57.   Model: The gas is an ideal gas and it goes through an isobaric and an isochoric process.
Solve: (a) The initial conditions are $p_1 = 3$ atm $= 304,000$ Pa and $T_1 = 293$ K. Nitrogen has an atomic mass number $A = 28$, so 5 g of nitrogen gas has $n = M/A = 0.1786$ mol. From this, we can find the initial volume:

$$V_1 = \frac{nRT_1}{p_1} = \frac{\left(0.1786 \text{ mol}\right)\left(8.31 \text{ J/mol K}\right)\left(293 \text{ K}\right)}{304,000 \text{ Pa}} = 1.430 \times 10^{-3} \text{ m}^3 = 1430 \text{ cm}^3$$

The volume triples, so $V_2 = 3V_1 = 4290$ cm³. The expansion is isobaric ($p_2 = p_1 = 3$ atm), so

$$\frac{V_2}{T_2} = \frac{V_1}{T_1} \Rightarrow T_2 = \frac{V_2}{V_1}T_1 = (3)293 \text{ K} = 879 \text{ K} = 606°C$$

(b) The process is isobaric, so

$$Q = nC_P\Delta T = (0.1786 \text{ mol})(29.1 \text{ J/mol K})(879 \text{ K} - 293 \text{ K}) = 3050 \text{ J}$$

(c) The pressure is decreased at constant volume ($V_3 = V_2 = 4290$ cm³) until the original temperature is reached ($T_3 = T_1 = 293$ K). For an isochoric process,

$$\frac{p_3}{T_3} = \frac{p_2}{T_2} \Rightarrow p_3 = \frac{T_3}{T_2}p_2 = \frac{293 \text{ K}}{879 \text{ K}}(3 \text{ atm}) = 1 \text{ atm}$$

(d) The process is isochoric, so

$$Q = nC_V \Delta T = (0.1786 \text{ mol})(20.8 \text{ J/mol K})(293 \text{ K} - 879 \text{ K}) = -2180 \text{ J}$$

So, 2180 J of heat was removed to decrease the pressure.

(e)

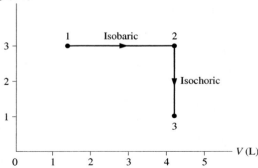

17.59.   Model: The two processes are isochoric and isobaric.
Visualize: Please refer to Figure P17.59.
Solve: Process A is isochoric which means

$$T_f/T_i = p_f/p_i \Rightarrow T_f = T_i(p_f/p_i) = T_i(1 \text{ atm}/3 \text{ atm}) = \tfrac{1}{3}T_i$$

From the ideal-gas equation,

$$T_i = \frac{p_i V_i}{nR} = \frac{(3 \times 1.013 \times 10^5 \text{ Pa})(2000 \times 10^{-6} \text{ m}^3)}{(0.10 \text{ mol})(8.31 \text{ J/mol K})} = 731.4 \text{ K} \Rightarrow T_f = \tfrac{1}{3}T_i = 243.8 \text{ K}$$

$$\Rightarrow T_f - T_i = -487.6 \text{ K}$$

Thus, the heat required for process A is

$$Q_A = nC_V \Delta T = (0.10 \text{ mol})(20.8 \text{ J/mol K})(-487.6 \text{ K}) = -1010 \text{ J}$$

Process B is isobaric which means

$$T_f/V_f = T_i/V_i \Rightarrow T_f = T_i(V_f/V_i) = T_i(3000 \text{ cm}^3/1000 \text{ cm}^3) = 3T_i$$

From the ideal-gas equation,

$$T_i = \frac{p_i V_i}{nR} = \frac{(2 \times 1.013 \times 10^5 \text{ Pa})(1000 \times 10^{-6} \text{ m}^3)}{(0.10 \text{ mol})(8.31 \text{ J/mol K})} = 243.8 \text{ K}$$

$$\Rightarrow T_f = 3T_i = 731.4 \text{ K} \Rightarrow T_f - T_i = 487.6 \text{ K}$$

Thus, heat required for process B is

$$Q_B = nC_p \Delta T = (0.10 \text{ mol})(29.1 \text{ J/mol K})(487.6 \text{ K}) = 1419 \text{ J}$$

Assess: Heat is transferred out of the gas in process A, but transferred into the gas in process B.

17.63.   Model: Assume that the gas is an ideal gas.
Solve: **(a)** For container A,

$$V_{iA} = \frac{nRT_{iA}}{p_{iA}} = \frac{(0.10 \text{ mol})(8.31 \text{ J/mol K})(300 \text{ K})}{3 \times 1.013 \times 10^5 \text{ Pa}} = 8.20 \times 10^{-4} \text{ m}^3$$

For an isothermal process $p_{fA}V_{fA} = p_{iA}V_{iA}$. This means $T_{fA} = T_{iA} = 300 \text{ K}$ and

$$V_{fA} = V_{iA}(p_{iA}/p_{fA}) = (8.20 \times 10^{-4} \text{ m}^3)(3.0 \text{ atm}/1.0 \text{ atm}) = 2.46 \times 10^{-3} \text{ m}^3$$

For the gas in container B,

$$p_{fB}V_{fB}^\gamma = p_{iB}V_{iB}^\gamma \Rightarrow V_{fB} = V_{iB}\left(\frac{p_{iB}}{p_{fB}}\right)^{1/\gamma} = (8.20 \times 10^{-4}\text{m}^3)\left(\frac{3.0 \text{ atm}}{1.0 \text{ atm}}\right)^{3/5} = 1.585 \times 10^{-3} \text{ m}^3$$

The final temperature T_{fB} can now be obtained by using the ideal-gas equation:

$$T_{fB} = T_{iB}\frac{p_{fB}}{p_{iB}}\frac{V_{fB}}{V_{iB}} = (300\ \mathrm{K})\left(\frac{1.0\ \mathrm{atm}}{3.0\ \mathrm{atm}}\right)\left(\frac{1.585\times10^{-3}\ \mathrm{m}^3}{8.2\times10^{-4}\ \mathrm{m}^3}\right) = 193\ \mathrm{K}$$

(b)

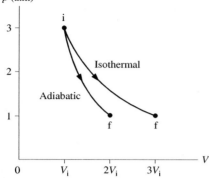

17.71. Model: The helium gas is assumed to be an ideal gas that is subjected to an isothermal process.
Solve: (a) The number of moles in 2.0 g of helium gas is

$$n = \frac{M}{M_{\mathrm{mol}}} = \frac{2.0\ \mathrm{g}}{4.0\ \mathrm{g/mol}} = 0.5\ \mathrm{mol}$$

At $T_i = 100°\mathrm{C} = 373\ \mathrm{K}$ and $p_i = 1.0\ \mathrm{atm} = 1.013\times10^5\ \mathrm{Pa}$, the gas has a volume

$$V_i = \frac{nRT_i}{p_i} = 0.0153\ \mathrm{m}^3 = 15.3\ \mathrm{L}$$

For an isothermal process $(T_f = T_i)$ that doubles the volume $V_f = 2V_i$,

$$p_f V_f = p_i V_i \Rightarrow p_f = p_i(V_i/V_f) = (1\ \mathrm{atm})(\tfrac{1}{2}) = 0.5\ \mathrm{atm}$$

(b) The work done by the environment on the gas is

$$W = -\int p\,dV = -nRT_i\int\frac{dV}{V} = -nRT_i\ln(V_f/V_i) = -(0.5\ \mathrm{mol})(8.31\ \mathrm{J/mol\ K})(373\ \mathrm{K})\ln(2) = -1074\ \mathrm{J}$$

(c) Because $\Delta E_{\mathrm{th}} = Q + W = 0\ \mathrm{J}$ for an isothermal process, the heat input to the gas is $Q = -W = 1074\ \mathrm{J}$.
(d) The change in internal energy $\Delta E_{\mathrm{th}} = 0\ \mathrm{J}$.
(e)

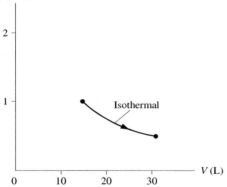

17.75. Solve: (a) 50 J of work are done on a gas sample to compress it to one-third of its original volume at a constant temperature of 77°C. How many moles of the gas are in the sample?
(b) The number of moles is

$$n = \frac{50\ \mathrm{J}}{-(8.31\ \mathrm{J/mol\ K})(350\ \mathrm{K})(\ln\tfrac{1}{3})} = 0.0156\ \mathrm{mol}$$

18

THE MICRO/MACRO CONNECTION

18.1. Solve: We can use the ideal-gas law in the form $pV = Nk_BT$ to determine the Loschmidt number (N/V):

$$\frac{N}{V} = \frac{p}{k_BT} = \frac{\left(1.013 \times 10^5 \text{ Pa}\right)}{\left(1.38 \times 10^{-23} \text{ J/K}\right)(273 \text{ K})} = 2.69 \times 10^{25} \text{ m}^{-3}$$

The Loschmidt number can also be determined from $pV = nRT$:

$$n = \frac{pV}{RT} = \frac{\left(1.013 \times 10^5 \text{ Pa}\right)\left(1 \text{ m}^3\right)}{(8.31 \text{ J/mol K})273 \text{ K}} = 44.65 \text{ mol} = 44.65 \text{ mol} \times \frac{6.02 \times 10^{23}}{\text{mol}} = 2.69 \times 10^{25}$$

18.5. Solve: Neon is a monatomic gas and has a radius $r \approx 5.0 \times 10^{-11}$ m. Using the ideal-gas equation,

$$\frac{N}{V} = \frac{p}{k_BT} = \frac{(150)\left(1.013 \times 10^5 \text{ Pa}\right)}{\left(1.38 \times 10^{-23} \text{ J / K}\right)(298 \text{ K})} = 3.695 \times 10^{27} \text{ m}^{-3}$$

Thus, the mean free path of a neon atom is

$$\lambda = \frac{1}{4\sqrt{2}\pi(N/V)r^2} = \frac{1}{4\sqrt{2}\pi\left(3.695 \times 10^{27} \text{ m}^{-3}\right)\left(5.0 \times 10^{-11} \text{ m}\right)^2} = 6.091 \times 10^{-9} \text{ m}$$

Since the atomic diameter of neon is $2 \times 5.0 \times 10^{-11}$ m $= 1.0 \times 10^{-10}$ m,

$$\lambda = \frac{6.091 \times 10^{-9} \text{ m}}{1.0 \times 10^{-10} \text{ m}} = 60.9 \text{ atomic diameters}$$

18.9. Solve: (a) The atomic mass number of argon is 40. This means the mass of an argon atom is

$$m = \frac{40 \text{ g/mol}}{6.022 \times 10^{23} \text{ mol}} = 6.64 \times 10^{-26} \text{ kg}$$

The pressure of the gas is

$$p = \tfrac{1}{3}\left(\frac{N}{V}\right)mv_{rms}^2 = \tfrac{1}{3}\left(2.0 \times 10^{25} \text{ m}^{-3}\right)\left(6.64 \times 10^{-26} \text{ kg}\right)(455 \text{ m / s})^2 = 9.164 \times 10^4 \text{ Pa}$$

(b) The temperature of the gas in the container can be obtained from the ideal-gas equation in the form $pV = Nk_BT$:

$$T = \frac{pV}{Nk_B} = \frac{9.164 \times 10^4 \text{ Pa}}{\left(2.0 \times 10^{25} \text{ m}^{-3}\right)\left(1.38 \times 10^{-23} \text{ J / K}\right)} = 332 \text{ K}$$

18.11. Solve: The pressure on the wall with area $A = 10 \text{ cm}^2 = 10 \times 10^{-4} \text{ m}^2$ is

$$p = \frac{F}{A} = \frac{\Delta(mv)N}{A\Delta t}$$

where $N/\Delta t$ is the number of N_2 molecules colliding with the wall every second and Δmv is the change in momentum for one collision. Using the atomic mass number of oxygen, the number of collisions per second is

$$\frac{N}{\Delta t} = \frac{pA}{\Delta(mv)} = \frac{\left(1.013 \times 10^5 \text{ Pa}\right)\left(10 \times 10^{-4} \text{ m}^2\right)}{\left(32 \times 1.66 \times 10^{-27} \text{ kg}\right)(500 \text{ m / s} - (-500 \text{ m / s}))} = 1.91 \times 10^{24} \text{ s}^{-1}$$

18.13. Solve: The average translational kinetic energy per molecule in a gas is

$$\varepsilon_{avg} = \frac{1}{2}mv_{rms}^2 = \frac{3}{2}k_B T \Rightarrow v_{rms} = \sqrt{\frac{3k_B T}{m}}$$

The mass of a helium molecule is

$$m = 4 \text{ u} = 4(1.66 \times 10^{-27} \text{ kg}) = 6.64 \times 10^{-27} \text{ kg}$$

$$\Rightarrow v_{rms} = \sqrt{\frac{3(1.38 \times 10^{-23} \text{ J / K})(1273 \text{ K})}{6.64 \times 10^{-27} \text{ kg}}} = 2820 \text{ m / s}$$

For argon $m = 40$ u, so the root-means-square speed is

$$v_{rms} = \sqrt{\frac{3(1.38 \times 10^{-23} \text{ J / K})(1273 \text{ K})}{40 \times 1.66 \times 10^{-27} \text{ kg}}} = 891 \text{ m / s}$$

18.15. Solve: Because the neon and argon atoms in the mixture are in thermal equilibrium, the temperature of each gas in the mixture must be the same. That is, using Equation 18.26,

$$m_A v_{rms\,A}^2 = m_{Ne} v_{rms\,Ne}^2$$

$$v_{rms\,A} = v_{rms\,Ne}\sqrt{\frac{m_{Ne}}{m_A}} = (400 \text{ m / s})\sqrt{\frac{20 \text{ u}}{40 \text{ u}}} = 283 \text{ m / s}$$

18.21. Solve: (a) The total kinetic energy of a gas is $K_{micro} = \frac{3}{2}N_A k_B T = \frac{3}{2}nRT$. For H_2 gas at STP,

$$K_{micro} = \frac{3}{2}(1.0 \text{ mol})(8.31 \text{ J / mol K})(273 \text{ K}) = 3400 \text{ J}$$

(b) For He gas at STP,

$$K_{micro} = \frac{3}{2}(1.0 \text{ mol})(8.31 \text{ J / mol K})(273 \text{ K}) = 3400 \text{ J}$$

(c) For O_2 gas at STP, $K_{micro} = 3400$ J.

18.25. Solve: The volume of the air is $V = 6.0 \text{ m} \times 8.0 \text{ m} \times 3.0 \text{ m} = 144.0 \text{ m}^3$, the pressure $p = 1$ atm $= 1.013 \times 10^5$ Pa, and the temperature $T = 20°C = 293$ K. The number of moles of the gas is

$$n = \frac{pV}{RT} = 5991 \text{ mols}$$

This means the number of molecules is

$$N = nN_A = (5991 \text{ mols})(6.022 \times 10^{23} \text{ mol}^{-1}) = 3.608 \times 10^{27} \text{ molecules.}$$

Since air is a diatomic gas, the room's thermal energy is

$$E_{th} = N\varepsilon_{avg} = N\left(\frac{5}{2}k_B T\right) = 3.65 \times 10^7 \text{ J}$$

Assess: The room's thermal energy can also be obtained as follows:

$$E_{th} = nC_V T = (5991 \text{ mols})(20.8 \text{ J/mol K})(293 \text{ K}) = 3.65 \times 10^7 \text{ J}$$

18.29. Visualize: Refer to Figure 18.13.
Solve: (a) The number of moles of diatomic hydrogen gas in the rigid container is

$$\frac{0.20 \text{ g}}{2 \text{ g / mol}} = 0.1 \text{ mol}$$

The heat needed to change the temperature of the gas from 50 K to 100 K at constant volume is

$$Q = \Delta E_{th} = nC_V \Delta T = (0.1 \text{ mol})(12.5 \text{ J/mol K})(100 \text{ K} - 50 \text{ K}) = 62.4 \text{ J}$$

(b) To raise the temperature from 250 K to 300 K,

$$Q = \Delta E_{th} = (0.1 \text{ mol})(20.8 \text{ J/mol K})(300 \text{ K} - 250 \text{ K}) = 104 \text{ J}$$

(c) To raise the temperature from 550 K to 600 K, $Q = 104$ J.

(d) To raise the temperature from 2250 K to 2300 K, $Q = \Delta E_{th} = nC_V\Delta T = (0.01 \text{ mol})(29.0 \text{ J/mol K})(50 \text{ K}) = 145$ J.

18.31. Solve: (a) The thermal energy of a monatomic gas is

$$E_{th} = \tfrac{3}{2}Nk_BT = \tfrac{3}{2}nRT \Rightarrow T = \frac{2}{3}\frac{E_{th}}{n}\frac{1}{R}$$

$$\Rightarrow T_A = \left(\frac{2}{3}\right)\left(\frac{5000 \text{ J}}{2.0 \text{ mol}}\right)\frac{1}{(8.31 \text{ J / mol K})} = 201 \text{ K}$$

$$T_B = \left(\frac{2}{3}\right)\left(\frac{8000 \text{ J}}{3.0 \text{ mol}}\right)\frac{1}{(8.31 \text{ J / mol K})} = 214 \text{ K}$$

Thus, gas B has the higher initial temperature.

(b) The equilibrium condition is $(\varepsilon_A)_{avg} = (\varepsilon_B)_{avg} = (\varepsilon_{tot})_{avg}$. This means

$$\frac{E_{Af}}{n_A} = \frac{E_{Bf}}{n_B} = \frac{E_{tot}}{n_A + n_B}$$

$$\Rightarrow E_{Af} = \frac{n_A}{n_A + n_B}E_{tot} = \left(\frac{2 \text{ mols}}{2 \text{ mols} + 3 \text{ mols}}\right)(5000 \text{ J} + 8000 \text{ J}) = 5200 \text{ J}$$

$$E_{Bf} = \frac{n_B}{n_A + n_B}E_{tot} = \left(\frac{3 \text{ mols}}{5 \text{ mols}}\right)(13,000 \text{ J}) = 7800 \text{ J}$$

18.35. Solve: (a) To identify the gas, we need to determine its atomic mass number A or, equivalently, the mass m of each atom or molecule. The mass density ρ and the number density (N/V) are related by $\rho = m(N/V)$, so the mass is $m = \rho(V/N)$.

From the ideal-gas law, the number density is

$$\frac{N}{V} = \frac{p}{kT} = \frac{50,000 \text{ Pa}}{(1.38 \times 10^{-23} \text{ J / K})(300 \text{ K})} = 1.208 \times 10^{25} \text{ m}^{-3}$$

Thus, the mass of an atom is

$$m = \rho\frac{V}{N} = \frac{8.02 \times 10^{-2} \text{ kg / m}^3}{1.208 \times 10^{25} \text{ m}^{-3}} = 6.64 \times 10^{-27} \text{ kg}$$

Converting to atomic mass units,

$$A = 6.64 \times 10^{-27} \text{ kg} \times \frac{1 \text{ u}}{1.661 \times 10^{-27} \text{ kg}} = 4.00 \text{ u}$$

This is the atomic mass of helium.

(b) Knowing the mass, we find v_{rms} to be

$$v_{rms} = \sqrt{\frac{3k_BT}{m}} = \sqrt{\frac{3(1.38 \times 10^{-23} \text{ J / K})(300 \text{ K})}{6.64 \times 10^{-27} \text{ kg}}} = 1367 \text{ m / s}$$

(c) A typical atomic radius is $r \approx 0.5 \times 10^{-10}$ m. The mean free path is thus

$$\lambda = \frac{1}{4\sqrt{2}\pi(N/V)r^2} = \frac{1}{4\sqrt{2}\pi(1.208 \times 10^{25} \text{ m}^{-3})(0.5 \times 10^{-10} \text{ m})^2} = 1.86 \times 10^{-6} \text{ m} = 1.86 \,\mu\text{m}$$

18.41. Solve: (a) The cylinder volume is $V = \pi r^2 L$. Thus, the number density is

$$\frac{N}{V} = \frac{2 \times 10^{22}}{1.571 \times 10^{-3} \text{ m}^3} = 1.273 \times 10^{25} \text{ m}^{-3}$$

(b) The mass of an argon atom is

$$m = 40 \text{ u} = 40(1.661 \times 10^{-27} \text{ kg}) = 6.64 \times 10^{-26} \text{ kg}$$

$$\Rightarrow v_{\text{rms}} = \sqrt{\frac{3k_B T}{m}} = \sqrt{\frac{3(1.38 \times 10^{-23} \text{ J / K})(323 \text{ K})}{6.64 \times 10^{-26} \text{ kg}}} = 449 \text{ m / s}$$

(c) v_{rms} is the square root of the average of v^2. That is,

$$v_{\text{rms}}^2 = \left(v^2\right)_{\text{avg}} = \left(v_x^2\right)_{\text{avg}} + \left(v_y^2\right)_{\text{avg}} + \left(v_z^2\right)_{\text{avg}}$$

An atom is equally likely to move in the x, y, or z direction, so *on average* $\left(v_x^2\right)_{\text{avg}} = \left(v_y^2\right)_{\text{avg}} = \left(v_z^2\right)_{\text{avg}}$. Hence,

$$v_{\text{rms}}^2 = 3\left(v_x^2\right)_{\text{avg}} \Rightarrow \left(v_x\right)_{\text{rms}} = \sqrt{\left(v_x^2\right)_{\text{avg}}} = \frac{v_{\text{rms}}}{\sqrt{3}} = 259 \text{ m / s}$$

(d) When we considered all the atoms to have the same velocity, we found the collision rate to be $\frac{1}{2}(N/V)Av_x$ (see Equation 18.10). Because the atoms move with different speeds, we need to replace v_x with $(v_x)_{\text{rms}}$. The end of the cylinder has area $A = \pi r^2 = 7.85 \times 10^{-3} \text{ m}^2$. Therefore, the number of collisions per second is

$$\tfrac{1}{2}(N / V)A\left(v_x\right)_{\text{rms}} = \tfrac{1}{2}(1.273 \times 10^{25} \text{ m}^{-3})(7.85 \times 10^{-3} \text{ m}^2)(259 \text{ m / s}) = 1.296 \times 10^{25} \text{ s}^{-1}$$

(e) From kinetic theory, the pressure is

$$p = \tfrac{1}{3}\left(\frac{N}{V}\right)m\left(v^2\right)_{\text{avg}} = \tfrac{1}{3}\left(\frac{N}{V}\right)mv_{\text{rms}}^2 = \tfrac{1}{3}(1.273 \times 10^{25} \text{ m}^{-3})(6.64 \times 10^{-26} \text{ kg})(449 \text{ m / s})^2 = 56,800 \text{ Pa}$$

(f) From the ideal gas law, the pressure is

$$p = \frac{Nk_B T}{V} = \frac{(2 \times 10^{22})(1.38 \times 10^{-23} \text{ J / K})(323 \text{ K})}{1.571 \times 10^{-3} \text{ m}^3} = 56,700 \text{ Pa}$$

Assess: The very slight difference with part (e) is due to rounding off errors.

18.43.   Solve: (a) The number of molecules of helium is

$$N_{\text{helium}} = \frac{pV}{k_B T} = \frac{(2.0 \times 1.013 \times 10^5 \text{ Pa})(100 \times 10^{-6} \text{ m}^3)}{(1.38 \times 10^{-23} \text{ J / K})(373 \text{ K})} = 3.936 \times 10^{21}$$

$$\Rightarrow n_{\text{helium}} = \frac{3.936 \times 10^{21}}{6.022 \times 10^{23} \text{ mol}^{-1}} = 6.536 \times 10^{-3} \text{ mol}$$

The initial internal energy of helium is

$$E_{\text{helium i}} = \tfrac{3}{2} N_{\text{helium}} k_B T = \tfrac{3}{2}\left(\frac{pV}{k_B T}\right)k_B T = \tfrac{3}{2} pV = 30.39 \text{ J}$$

The number of molecules of argon is

$$N_{\text{argon}} = \frac{pV}{k_B T} = \frac{(4.0 \times 1.013 \times 10^5 \text{ Pa})(200 \times 10^{-6} \text{ m}^3)}{(1.38 \times 10^{-23} \text{ J / K})(673 \text{ K})} = 8.726 \times 10^{21}$$

$$\Rightarrow n_{\text{argon}} = \frac{8.726 \times 10^{21}}{6.022 \times 10^{23} \text{ mol}^{-1}} = 1.449 \times 10^{-2} \text{ mol}$$

The initial thermal energy of argon is

$$E_{\text{argon i}} = \tfrac{3}{2} N_{\text{argon}} k_B T = \tfrac{3}{2} pV = 121.56 \text{ J}$$

(b) The equilibrium condition for monatomic gases is

$$(\varepsilon_{\text{helium f}})_{\text{avg}} = (\varepsilon_{\text{argon f}})_{\text{avg}} = (\varepsilon_{\text{total}})_{\text{avg}}$$

$$\Rightarrow \frac{E_{\text{helium f}}}{n_{\text{helium}}} = \frac{E_{\text{argon f}}}{n_{\text{argon}}} = \frac{E_{\text{tot}}}{n_{\text{tot}}} = \frac{(30.39 \text{ J} + 121.56) \text{ J}}{(6.536 \times 10^{-3} + 1.449 \times 10^{-2}) \text{ mol}} = 7227 \text{ J / mol}$$

$$\Rightarrow E_{\text{helium f}} = (7227 \text{ J / mol})n_{\text{helium}} = (7227 \text{ J / mol})(6.536 \times 10^{-3} \text{ mol}) = 47.23 \text{ J}$$

$$E_{\text{argon f}} = (7227 \text{ J / mol})n_{\text{argon}} = (7227 \text{ J / mol})(1.449 \times 10^{-2} \text{ mol}) = 104.72 \text{ J}$$

(c) The amount of heat transferred is

$$E_{\text{helium f}} - E_{\text{helium i}} = 47.23 \text{ J} - 30.39 \text{ J} = 16.84 \text{ J} \qquad E_{\text{argon f}} - E_{\text{argon i}} = 104.72 \text{ J} - 121.56 \text{ J} = -16.84 \text{ J}$$

The helium box loses 16.84 J of heat energy and the argon box loses 16.84 J.
(d) The equilibrium condition for monatomic gases is

$$\left(\varepsilon_{\text{helium}}\right)_{\text{avg}} = \left(\varepsilon_{\text{argon}}\right)_{\text{avg}} \Rightarrow \frac{E_{\text{helium f}}}{N_{\text{helium}}} = \frac{E_{\text{argon f}}}{N_{\text{argon}}} = \tfrac{3}{2} k_B T_f$$

Substituting the above values,

$$\frac{47.23 \text{ J}}{3.936 \times 10^{21}} = \frac{104.72 \text{ J}}{8.726 \times 10^{21}} = \tfrac{3}{2}\left(1.38 \times 10^{-23} \text{ J / K}\right)T_f = 1.20 \times 10^{-20} \text{ J} = (2.07 \times 10^{-23} \text{ J/K})T_f$$

$$\Rightarrow T_F = 580 \text{ K}$$

(e) The final pressure of the helium and argon are

$$p_{\text{helium f}} = \frac{N_{\text{helium}} k_B T}{V_{\text{helium}}} = \frac{\left(3.936 \times 10^{21}\right)\left(1.38 \times 10^{-23} \text{ J / K}\right)(580 \text{ K})}{100 \times 10^{-6} \text{ m}^3} = 3.15 \times 10^5 \text{ Pa} = 3.11 \text{ atm}$$

$$p_{\text{argon f}} = \frac{N_{\text{argon}} k_B T}{V_{\text{argon}}} = \frac{\left(8.726 \times 10^{21}\right)\left(1.38 \times 10^{-23} \text{ J / K}\right)(580 \text{ K})}{200 \times 10^{-6} \text{ m}^3} = 3.49 \times 10^5 \text{ Pa} = 3.45 \text{ atm}$$

18.51. Solve: **(a)** The thermal energy of a monatomic gas of N molecules is $E_{\text{th}} = N\varepsilon_{\text{avg}}$, where $\varepsilon_{\text{avg}} = \tfrac{3}{2} k_B T$. A monatomic gas molecule has 3 degrees of freedom. However, a two-dimensional monatomic gas molecule has only 2 degrees of freedom. Thus,

$$E_{\text{th}} = N\left(\tfrac{2}{2} k_B T\right) = N k_B T = nRT$$

If the temperature changes by ΔT, then the thermal energy changes by $\Delta E_{\text{th}} = nR\Delta T$. Comparing this form with $\Delta E_{\text{th}} = nC_V \Delta T$, we have $C_V = R = 8.31$ J/mol K.
(b) A two-dimensional solid has 2 degrees of freedom associated with the kinetic energy and 2 degrees of freedom associated with the potential energy (or 2 spring directions), giving a total of 4 degrees of freedom. Thus, $E_{\text{th}} = N\varepsilon_{\text{avg}}$ and $\varepsilon_{\text{avg}} = \tfrac{4}{2} k_B T$. Or $E_{\text{th}} = 2N k_B T = 2nRT$. For a temperature change of ΔT, $\Delta E_{\text{th}} = 2nR\Delta T = nC_V\Delta T \Rightarrow C_V = 2R = 16.6$ J / mol K.

18.53. Solve: **(a)** The average translational kinetic energy for a diatomic gas is

$$\varepsilon_{\text{avg}} = \tfrac{1}{2} m v_{\text{rms}}^2 = \tfrac{5}{2} k_B T \Rightarrow v_{\text{rms}} = \sqrt{\frac{5 k_B T}{m}} \Rightarrow \frac{v_{\text{rms hydrogen}}}{v_{\text{rms oxygen}}} = \sqrt{\frac{T_{\text{hydrogen}}}{T_{\text{oxygen}}} \frac{32 \text{ u}}{2 \text{ u}}} = 4$$

(b) The ratio of the average translational energies is

$$\frac{\varepsilon_{\text{avg hydrogen}}}{\varepsilon_{\text{avg oxygen}}} = \frac{T_{\text{hydrogen}}}{T_{\text{oxygen}}} = 1$$

(c) The internal energy of the hydrogen is

$$E_{\text{th hydrogen}} = \tfrac{5}{2} N_{\text{hydrogen}} k_B T_{\text{hydrogen}} = \tfrac{5}{2} n_{\text{hydrogen}} R T_{\text{hydrogen}}$$

$$\Rightarrow \frac{E_{\text{th hydrogen}}}{E_{\text{th oxygen}}} = \frac{n_{\text{hydrogen}}}{n_{\text{oxygen}}} = \frac{2.0 \text{ g / mol}}{m_{\text{hydrogen}}} \frac{m_{\text{oxygen}}}{32.0 \text{ g / mol}} = \frac{1}{16} \Rightarrow \frac{m_{\text{hydrogen}}}{2.0 \text{ g / mol}} \frac{32.0 \text{ g / mol}}{m_{\text{oxygen}}} = 16$$

18.55. Solve: The thermal energy of a monatomic gas of n_1 moles is $E_1 = \tfrac{3}{2} n_1 RT$. The thermal energy of a diatomic gas of n_2 moles is $E_2 = \tfrac{5}{2} n_2 RT$. The total thermal energy of the mixture is

$$E_{\text{th}} = E_1 + E_2 = \tfrac{1}{2}\left(3n_1 + 5n_2\right)RT \Rightarrow \Delta E_{\text{th}} = \tfrac{1}{2}\left(3n_1 + 5n_2\right)R\Delta T$$

Comparing this expression with

$$\Delta E_{\text{th}} = Q + W(= 0 \text{ J}) = \left(n_1 + n_2\right)C_V \Delta T$$

we get

$$\left(n_1 + n_2\right)C_V = \frac{\left(3n_1 + 5n_2\right)}{2}R$$

The requirement that the ratio of specific heats is 1.5 means

$$\gamma = 1.5 = \frac{C_P}{C_V} = \frac{C_V + R}{C_V} = 1 + \frac{R}{C_V} \Rightarrow C_V = 2R$$

The above equation thus simplifies to

$$\left(n_1 + n_2\right)(2\,R) = \frac{\left(3n_1 + 5n_2\right)}{2}R \Rightarrow 4n_1 + 4n_2 = 3n_1 + 5n_2 \Rightarrow n_1 = n_2$$

Thus, monatomic and diatomic molecules need to be mixed in the ratio 1:1. Or the fraction of the molecules that are diatomic is $\frac{1}{2}$.

HEAT ENGINES AND REFRIGERATORS

19.1. **Model:** The heat engine follows a closed cycle, starting and ending in the original state. The cycle consists of three individual processes.
Visualize: Please refer to Figure Ex19.1.
Solve: **(a)** The work done by the heat engine per cycle is the area enclosed by the p-versus-V graph. We get

$$W_{out} = \tfrac{1}{2}(200 \text{ kPa})(100 \times 10^{-6} \text{ m}^3) = 10 \text{ J}$$

The heat energy transferred into the engine is $Q_H = 120$ J. Because $W_{out} = Q_H - Q_C$, the heat energy exhausted is

$$Q_C = Q_H - W_{out} = 120 \text{ J} - 10 \text{ J} = 110 \text{ J}$$

(b) The thermal efficiency of the engine is

$$\eta = \frac{W_{out}}{Q_H} = \frac{10 \text{ J}}{120 \text{ J}} = 0.0833$$

Assess: Practical engines have thermal efficiencies in the range $\eta \approx 0.1 - 0.4$.

19.5. **Solve:** **(a)** The engine has a thermal efficiency of $\eta = 40\% = 0.40$ and a work output of 100 J per cycle. The heat input is calculated as follows:

$$\eta = \frac{W_{out}}{Q_H} \Rightarrow 0.40 = \frac{100 \text{ J}}{Q_H} \Rightarrow Q_H = 250 \text{ J}$$

(b) Because $W_{out} = Q_H - Q_C$, the heat exhausted is

$$Q_C = Q_H - W_{out} = 250 \text{ J} - 100 \text{ J} = 150 \text{ J}$$

19.9. **Solve:** The amount of heat discharged per second is calculated as follows:

$$\eta = \frac{W_{out}}{Q_H} = \frac{W_{out}}{Q_C + W_{out}} \Rightarrow Q_C = W_{out}\left(\frac{1}{\eta} - 1\right) = (900 \text{ MW})\left(\frac{1}{0.32} - 1\right) = 1.913 \times 10^9 \text{ W}$$

That is, each second the electric power plant discharges 1.913×10^9 J of energy in the ocean. Since a typical American house needs 2.0×10^4 J of energy per second for heating, the number of houses that could be heated with the waste heat is $(1.913 \times 10^9 \text{ J})/(2.0 \times 10^4 \text{ J}) = 9.6 \times 10^4$.

19.11. **Model:** Process A is isochoric, process B is isothermal, process C is adiabatic, and process D is isobaric.
Visualize: Please refer to Figure Ex19.11.
Solve: Process A is isochoric, so the increase in pressure increases the temperature and hence the thermal energy. Because $\Delta E_{th} = Q - W_s$ and $W_s = 0$ J, Q increases for process A. Process B is isothermal, so T is constant and hence $\Delta E_{th} = 0$ J. The work done W_s is positive because the process leads to an increase in volume. Because $Q = W_s + \Delta E_{th}$, Q is positive for process B. Process C is adiabatic, so $Q = 0$ J. W_s is positive because of the increase in volume. Since $Q = 0$ J $= W_s + \Delta E_{th}$, ΔE_{th} is negative for process C. Process D is isobaric, so the decrease in volume leads to a decrease in temperature and hence a decrease in the thermal energy. Due to the decrease in volume, W_s is negative. Because $Q = W_s + \Delta E_{th}$, Q also decreases for process D.

	ΔE_{th}	W_s	Q
A	+	0	+
B	0	+	+
C	−	+	0
D	−	−	−

19.17.   Model: The Brayton cycle involves two adiabatic processes and two isobaric processes.

Solve: From Equation 19.21, the efficiency of a Brayton cycle is $\eta_B = 1 - r_p^{(1-\gamma)/\gamma}$, where r_p is the pressure ratio p_{max}/p_{min}. The specific heat ratio for a diatomic gas is

$$\gamma = \frac{C_P}{C_V} = \frac{\frac{7}{2}R}{\frac{5}{2}R} = 1.4$$

Solving the above equation for r_p,

$$(1 - \eta_B) = r_p^{(1-\gamma)/\gamma} \Rightarrow r_p = (1 - \eta_B)^{\frac{\gamma}{1-\gamma}} = (1 - 0.60)^{\frac{-1.4}{0.4}} = 24.7$$

19.19.   Model: The efficiency of a Carnot engine (η_{Carnot}) depends only on the temperatures of the hot and cold reservoirs. On the other hand, the thermal efficiency (η) of a heat engine depends on the heats Q_H and Q_C.

Visualize: Please refer to Figure Ex19.19.

Solve: **(a)** According to the first law of thermodynamics, $Q_H = W_{out} + Q_C$. For engine (a), $Q_H = 50$ J, $Q_C = 20$ J and $W_{out} = 30$ J, so the first law of thermodynamics is obeyed. For engine (b), $Q_H = 10$ J, $Q_C = 7$ J and $W_{out} = 4$ J, so the first law is violated. For engine (c) the first law of thermodynamics is obeyed.

(b) For the three heat engines, the maximum or Carnot efficiency is

$$\eta_{Carnot} = 1 - \frac{T_C}{T_H} = 1 - \frac{300 \text{ K}}{600 \text{ K}} = 0.50$$

Engine (a) has

$$\eta = 1 - \frac{Q_C}{Q_H} = \frac{W_{out}}{Q_H} = \frac{30 \text{ J}}{50 \text{ J}} = 0.60$$

This is larger than η_{Carnot}, thus violating the second law of thermodynamics. For engine (b),

$$\eta = \frac{W_{out}}{Q_H} = \frac{4 \text{ J}}{10 \text{ J}} = 0.40 < \eta_{Carnot}$$

so the second law is obeyed. Engine (c) has a thermal efficiency that is

$$\eta = \frac{10 \text{ J}}{30 \text{ J}} = 0.333 < \eta_{Carnot}$$

so the second law of thermodynamics is obeyed.

19.23.   Model: The efficiency of an ideal engine (or Carnot engine) depends only on the temperatures of the hot and cold reservoirs.

Solve: **(a)** The engine's thermal efficiency is

$$\eta = \frac{W_{out}}{Q_H} = \frac{W_{out}}{Q_C + W_{out}} = \frac{10 \text{ J}}{15 \text{ J} + 10 \text{ J}} = 0.40 = 40\%$$

(b) The efficiency of a Carnot engine is $\eta_{Carnot} = 1 - T_C/T_H$. The minimum temperature in the hot reservoir is found as follows:

$$0.40 = 1 - \frac{293 \text{ K}}{T_H} \Rightarrow T_H = 488 \text{ K} = 215°C$$

Assess: In a real engine, the hot-reservoir temperature would be higher than 215°C because no real engine can match the Carnot efficiency.

19.29.   Model: Assume that the refrigerator is an ideal or Carnot refrigerator.

Solve: **(a)** For the refrigerator, the coefficient of performance is

$$K = \frac{Q_C}{W_{in}} \Rightarrow Q_C = KW_{in} = (5.0)(10 \text{ J}) = 50 \text{ J}$$

The heat energy exhausted per cycle is

$$Q_H = Q_C + W_{in} = 50\text{ J} + 10\text{ J} = 60\text{ J}$$

(b) If the hot-reservoir temperature is 27°C = 300 K, the lowest possible temperature of the cold reservoir can be obtained as follows:

$$K_{Carnot} = \frac{T_C}{T_H - T_C} \Rightarrow 5.0 = \frac{T_C}{300\text{ K} - T_C} \Rightarrow T_C = 250\text{ K} = -23°\text{C}$$

19.31.   Solve: The work-kinetic energy theorem is that the work done by the car engine is equal to the change in the kinetic energy. Thus,

$$W_{out} = \Delta K = \tfrac{1}{2} mv^2 = \tfrac{1}{2}(1500\text{ kg})(15\text{ m / s})^2 = 168{,}750\text{ J}$$

Using the definition of thermal efficiency,

$$\eta = \frac{W_{out}}{Q_H} \Rightarrow Q_H = \frac{W_{out}}{\eta} = \frac{168{,}750\text{ J}}{0.20} = 8.44 \times 10^5 \text{ J}$$

That is, the burning of gasoline transfers into the engine 8.44×10^5 J of heat energy.

19.39.   Model: We will use the Carnot engine to find the maximum possible efficiency of a floating power plant.
Solve: The efficiency of a Carnot engine is

$$\eta_{Carnot} = 1 - \frac{T_C}{T_H} = 1 - \frac{(273 + 5)\text{ K}}{(273 + 30)\text{ K}} = 0.0825 = 8.25\%$$

19.45.   Model: A heat pump is a refrigerator that is cooling the already cold outdoors and warming the indoors with its exhaust heat.
Solve: (a) The coefficient of performance for this heat pump is $K = 5.0 = Q_C / W_{in}$, where Q_C is the amount of heat removed from the cold reservoir. Q_H is the amount of heat exhausted into the hot reservoir. $Q_H = Q_C + W_{in}$, where W_{in} is the amount of work done on the heat pump. We have

$$Q_C = 5.0 W_{in} \Rightarrow Q_H = 5.0 W_{in} + W_{in} = 6.0 W_{in}$$

If the heat pump is to deliver 15 kJ of heat per second to the house, then

$$Q_H = 15\text{ kJ} = 6.0 W_{in} \Rightarrow W_{in} = \frac{15\text{ kJ}}{6.0} = 2.5\text{ kJ}$$

In other words, 2.5 kW of electric power is used by the heat pump to deliver 15 kJ/s of heat energy to the house.
(b) The monthly heating cost in the house using an electric heater is

$$\frac{15\text{ kJ}}{\text{s}} \times 200\text{ hrs} \times \frac{3600\text{ s}}{1\text{ hr}} \times \frac{1\$}{40\text{ MJ}} = \$270$$

The monthly heating cost in the house using a heat pump is

$$\frac{2.5\text{ kJ}}{\text{s}} \times 200\text{ hrs} \times \frac{3600\text{ s}}{1\text{ hr}} \times \frac{1\$}{40\text{ MJ}} = \$45$$

19.47.   Model: The power plant is to be treated as a heat engine.
Solve: (a) Every hour 300 metric tons or 3×10^5 kg of coal is burnt. The volume of coal is

$$\frac{3 \times 10^5 \text{ kg}}{1\text{ hour}} \times \frac{\text{m}^3}{1500\text{ kg}} \times 24\text{ hour} = 4800\text{ m}^3$$

The height of the room will be 48 m.
(b) The thermal efficiency of the power plant is

$$\eta = \frac{W_{out}}{Q_H} = \frac{7.50 \times 10^8 \text{ J / s}}{\dfrac{3 \times 10^5 \text{ kg}}{1\text{ hr}} \times \dfrac{28 \times 10^6 \text{ J}}{\text{kg}} \times \dfrac{1\text{ hr}}{3600\text{ s}}} = \frac{7.50 \times 10^8 \text{ J}}{2.333 \times 10^9 \text{ J}} = 0.321 = 32.1\%$$

Assess: An efficiency of 32.1% is reasonable.

19.51.   Visualize:

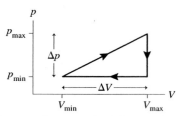

Solve: This problem does not have a unique answer. There are many three-step engines that meet these criteria. However, simple cycles consist of three straight-line segments and form a triangle in the pV diagram. The figure above shows an example. The work done by the gas during one cycle is the area enclosed within the curve. We have

$$\left(W_s\right)_{cycle} = \tfrac{1}{2}\Delta p \Delta V$$

We know that

$$\Delta p = p_{max} - p_{min} = 3 \text{ atm} - 1 \text{ atm} = 2 \text{ atm} = 202,600 \text{ Pa}$$

$$\Rightarrow \Delta V = \frac{2\left(W_s\right)_{cycle}}{\Delta p} = \frac{2(40.5 \text{ J})}{202,600 \text{ Pa}} = 4.00 \times 10^{-4} \text{ m}^3 = 400 \text{ cm}^3$$

The maximum volume is

$$V_{max} = V_{min} + \Delta V = 500 \text{ cm}^3$$

The figures below show possible pV diagram of this heat engine.

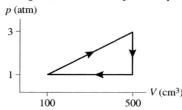
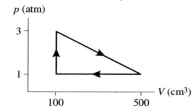
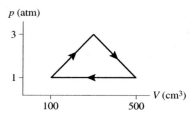

19.53.   Model: The heat engine follows a closed cycle. For a diatomic gas, $C_V = \tfrac{5}{2}R$ and $C_P = \tfrac{7}{2}R$.
Visualize: Please refer to Figure P19.53.
Solve: (a) Since $T_1 = 293$ K, the number of moles of the gas is

$$n = \frac{p_1 V_1}{RT_1} = \frac{\left(0.5 \times 1.013 \times 10^5 \text{ Pa}\right)\left(10 \times 10^{-6} \text{ m}^3\right)}{(8.31 \text{ J / mol K})(293 \text{ K})} = 2.08 \times 10^{-4} \text{ mol}$$

At point 2, $V_2 = 4V_1$ and $p_2 = 3p_1$. The temperature is calculated as follows:

$$\frac{p_1 V_1}{T_1} = \frac{p_2 V_2}{T_2} \Rightarrow T_2 = \frac{p_2}{p_1}\frac{V_2}{V_1}T_1 = (3)(4)(293 \text{ K}) = 3516 \text{ K}$$

At point 3, $V_3 = V_2 = 4V_1$ and $p_3 = p_1$. The temperature is calculated as before:

$$T_3 = \frac{p_3}{p_1}\frac{V_3}{V_1}T_1 = (1)(4)(293 \text{ K}) = 1172 \text{ K}$$

For process $1 \rightarrow 2$, the work done is the area under the p-versus-V curve. That is,

$$W_s = (0.5 \text{ atm})\left(40 \text{ cm}^3 - 10 \text{ cm}^3\right) + \tfrac{1}{2}(1.5 \text{ atm} - 0.5 \text{ atm})\left(40 \text{ cm}^3 - 10 \text{ cm}^3\right)$$

$$= \left(30 \times 10^{-6} \text{ m}^3\right)(1 \text{ atm})\left(\frac{1.013 \times 10^5 \text{ Pa}}{1 \text{ atm}}\right) = 3.039 \text{ J}$$

The change in the thermal energy is

$$\Delta E_{th} = nC_V \Delta T = \left(2.08 \times 10^{-4} \text{ mol}\right)\tfrac{5}{2}(8.31 \text{ J / mol K})(3516 \text{ K} - 293 \text{ K}) = 13.927 \text{ J}$$

The heat is $Q = W_s + \Delta E_{th} = 16.97$ J. For process $2 \rightarrow 3$, the work done $W_s = 0$ J and

$$Q = \Delta E_{th} = nC_V\Delta T = n\left(\tfrac{5}{2}R\right)\left(T_3 - T_2\right)$$
$$= \left(2.08 \times 10^{-4} \text{ mol}\right)\tfrac{5}{2}(8.31 \text{ J / mol K})(1172 \text{ K} - 3516 \text{ K}) = -10.13 \text{ J}$$

For process $3 \rightarrow 1$,

$$W_s = (0.5 \text{ atm})\left(10 \text{ cm}^3 - 40 \text{ cm}^3\right) = \left(0.5 \times 1.013 \times 10^5 \text{ Pa}\right)\left(-30 \times 10^{-6} \text{ m}^3\right) = -1.5195 \text{ J}$$

$$\Delta E_{th} = nC_V\Delta T = \left(2.08 \times 10^{-4} \text{ mol}\right)\tfrac{5}{2}(8.31 \text{ J / mol K})(293 \text{ K} - 1172 \text{ K}) = -3.7983 \text{ J}$$

The heat is $Q = \Delta E_{th} + W_s = -5.318$ J .

	W_s (J)	Q (J)	ΔE_{th}
$1 \rightarrow 2$	3.04	16.97	13.93
$2 \rightarrow 3$	0	−10.13	−10.13
$3 \rightarrow 1$	−1.52	−5.32	−3.80
Net	1.52	1.52	0

(b) The efficiency of the engine is

$$\eta = \frac{W_{net}}{Q_H} = \frac{1.52 \text{ J}}{16.97 \text{ J}} = 0.0896 = 8.96\%$$

(c) The power output of the engine is

$$500 \, \frac{\text{revolutions}}{\text{min}} \times \frac{1 \text{ min}}{60 \text{ s}} \times \frac{W_{net}}{\text{revolution}} = \frac{500}{60} \times 1.52 \text{ J / s} = 12.7 \text{ W}$$

Assess: For a closed cycle, as expected, $(W_s)_{net} = Q_{net}$ and $(\Delta E_{th})_{net} = 0$ J.

19.57. Model: For the closed cycle of the heat engine, process $1 \rightarrow 2$ is adiabatic, process $2 \rightarrow 3$ is isothermal, and process $3 \rightarrow 1$ is isochoric. For a diatomic gas $C_V = \tfrac{5}{2}R$ and $\gamma = \tfrac{7}{5}$.
Visualize: Please refer to Figure P19.57.
Solve: **(a)** From the ideal-gas equation $p_2 V_2 = nRT_2$,

$$nR = \frac{p_2 V_2}{T_2} = \frac{\left(4.0 \times 10^5 \text{ Pa}\right)\left(1000 \times 10^{-6} \text{ m}^3\right)}{400 \text{ K}} = 1.0 \text{ J / K}$$

Using $p_1 V_1^\gamma = p_2 V_2^\gamma$, and reading V_1 from the graph,

$$p_1 = p_2\left(\frac{V_2}{V_1}\right)^\gamma = \left(4.0 \times 10^5 \text{ Pa}\right)\left(\tfrac{1}{4}\right)^{7/5} = 5.743 \times 10^4 \text{ Pa}$$

With p_1, V_1, and nR having been determined, we can find T_1 using the ideal-gas equation:

$$T_1 = \frac{p_1 V_1}{nR} = \frac{\left(5.743 \times 10^4\right)\left(4000 \times 10^{-6} \text{ m}^3\right)}{1.0 \text{ J / K}} = 229.7 \text{ K}$$

(b) For adiabatic process $1 \rightarrow 2$, $Q = 0$ J and

$$W_s = \frac{p_2 V_2 - p_1 V_1}{1 - \gamma} = \frac{nR(T_2 - T_1)}{1 - 1.4} = \frac{(1.0 \text{ J / K})(400 \text{ K} - 229.7 \text{ K})}{(-0.4)} = -425.7 \text{ K}$$

Because $\Delta E_{th} = -W_s + Q$, $\Delta E_{th} = -W_s = 425.7$ K. For isothermal process $2 \rightarrow 3$, $\Delta E_{th} = 0$ J. From Equation 17.15,

$$W_s = nRT_2 \ln\frac{V_3}{V_2} = (1.0 \text{ J / K})(400 \text{ K})\ln(4) = 554.5 \text{ J}$$

From the first law of thermodynamics, $Q = W_s = 554.5$ J for process $2 \rightarrow 3$. For isochoric process $3 \rightarrow 1$, $W_s = 0$ J and

$$Q = \Delta E_{th} = nC_V\Delta T = n\left(\tfrac{5}{2}R\right)\left(T_1 - T_3\right) = \tfrac{5}{2}(nR)(T_1 - T_3) = \tfrac{5}{2}(1.0 \text{ J / K})(229.7 \text{ K} - 400 \text{ K}) = -425.7 \text{ J}$$

	ΔE_{th} (J)	W_s (J)	Q (J)
$1 \rightarrow 2$	425.7	−425.7	0
$2 \rightarrow 3$	0	554.5	554.5
$3 \rightarrow 1$	−425.7	0	−425.7
Net	0	128.8	128.8

(c) The thermal efficiency of the engine is

$$\eta = \frac{W_s}{Q_H} = \frac{128.8 \text{ J}}{554.5 \text{ J}} = 0.232 = 23.2\%$$

Assess: As expected, for a closed cycle $(W_s)_{net} = Q_{net}$ and $(\Delta E_{th})_{net} = 0$ J. Also note that $Q_{net} = Q_H - Q_C$.

19.59.   Model: Process $1 \rightarrow 2$ of the cycle is isochoric, process $2 \rightarrow 3$ is isothermal, and process $3 \rightarrow 1$ is isobaric. For a monatomic gas, $C_V = \frac{3}{2}R$, where $R = 8.31$ J/mol K.

Visualize: Please refer to Figure P19.59.

Solve: (a) At point 1: The pressure $p_1 = 1$ atm $= 1.013 \times 10^5$ Pa and the volume $V_1 = 1000 \times 10^{-6}$ m^3 = 1.0×10^{-3} m^3. The number of moles is

$$n = \frac{120 \times 10^{-3} \text{ g}}{4 \text{ g / mol}} = 0.03 \text{ mol}$$

Using the ideal-gas law,

$$T_1 = \frac{p_1 V_1}{nR} = \frac{(1.013 \times 10^5 \text{ Pa})(1.0 \times 10^{-3} \text{ m}^3)}{(0.03 \text{ mol})(8.31 \text{ J / mol K})} = 406.34 \text{ K} = 406 \text{ K}$$

At point 2: The pressure $p_2 = 5$ atm $= 5.065 \times 10^5$ Pa and $V_2 = 1.0 \times 10^{-3}$ m^3. The temperature is

$$T_2 = \frac{p_2 V_2}{nR} = \frac{(5.065 \times 10^5 \text{ Pa})(1.0 \times 10^{-3} \text{ m}^3)}{(0.03 \text{ mol})(8.31 \text{ J / mol K})} = 2031.7 \text{ K} = 2030 \text{ K}$$

At point 3: The pressure is $p_3 = 1$ atm $= 1.013 \times 10^5$ Pa and the temperature is $T_3 = T_2 = 2031.7$ K. The volume is

$$V_3 = V_2 \frac{p_2}{p_3} = (1.0 \times 10^{-3} \text{ m}^3)\left(\frac{5 \text{ atm}}{1 \text{ atm}}\right) = 5.0 \times 10^{-3} \text{ m}^3$$

(b) For isochoric process $1 \rightarrow 2$, $W_{1\rightarrow 2} = 0$ J and

$$Q_{1\rightarrow 2} = nC_V \Delta T = (0.03 \text{ mol})(\tfrac{3}{2}R)(2031.7 \text{ K} - 406.34 \text{ K}) = 607.8 \text{ J}$$

For isothermal process $2 \rightarrow 3$, $\Delta E_{th\ 2\rightarrow 3} = 0$ J and

$$Q_{2\rightarrow 3} = W_{2\rightarrow 3} = nRT_2 \ln\frac{V_3}{V_2} = (0.03 \text{ mol})(8.31 \text{ J / mol K})(2031.7 \text{ K})\ln\left(\frac{5.0 \times 10^{-3} \text{ m}^3}{1.0 \times 10^{-3} \text{ m}^3}\right) = 815.2 \text{ J}$$

For isobaric process $3 \rightarrow 1$,

$$W_{3\rightarrow 1} = p_3 \Delta V = (1.013 \times 10^5 \text{ Pa})(1 \times 10^{-3} \text{ m}^3 - 5.0 \times 10^{-3} \text{ m}^3) = -405.2 \text{ J}$$

$$Q_{3\rightarrow 1} = nC_P \Delta T = (0.03 \text{ mol})(\tfrac{5}{2})(8.31 \text{ J / mol K})(406.34 \text{ K} - 2031.7 \text{ K}) = -1013.0 \text{ J}$$

The total work done is $W_{net} = W_{1\rightarrow 2} + W_{2\rightarrow 3} + W_{3\rightarrow 1} = 410$ J. The total heat input is $Q_H = Q_{1\rightarrow 2} + Q_{2\rightarrow 3} = 1423$ J. The efficiency of the engine is

$$\eta = \frac{W_{net}}{Q_H} = \frac{410 \text{ J}}{1423 \text{ J}} = 28.8\%$$

(c) The maximum possible efficiency of a heat engine that operates between T_{max} and T_{min} is

$$\eta_{max} = 1 - \frac{T_{min}}{T_{max}} = 1 - \frac{406.34 \text{ K}}{2031.7 \text{ K}} = 80\%$$

Assess: The actual efficiency of an engine is less than the ideal or maximum possible efficiency.

19.63. Model: The closed cycle of the heat engine involves the following four processes: isothermal expansion, isochoric cooling, isothermal compression, and isochoric heating. For a monatomic gas $C_V = \frac{3}{2}R$.

Visualize:

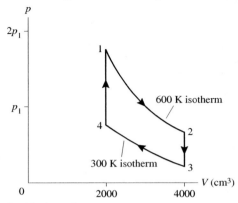

Solve: Using the ideal-gas law,

$$p_1 = \frac{nRT_1}{V_1} = \frac{(0.20\ \text{mol})(8.31\ \text{J / mol K})(600\ \text{K})}{2.0 \times 10^{-3}\ \text{m}^3} = 4.986 \times 10^5\ \text{Pa}$$

At point 2, because of the isothermal conditions,

$$p_1 V_1 = p_2 V_2 \Rightarrow p_2 = p_1 \frac{V_1}{V_2} = \left(4.986 \times 10^5\ \text{Pa}\right)\left(\frac{2.0 \times 10^{-3}\ \text{m}^3}{4.0 \times 10^{-3}\ \text{m}^3}\right) = 2.493 \times 10^5\ \text{Pa}$$

At point 3, because it is an isochoric process,

$$\frac{p_3}{T_3} = \frac{p_2}{T_2} \Rightarrow p_3 = p_2 \frac{T_3}{T_2} = \left(2.493 \times 10^5\ \text{Pa}\right)\left(\frac{300\ \text{K}}{600\ \text{K}}\right) = 1.247 \times 10^5\ \text{Pa}$$

Likewise at point 4,

$$p_4 V_4 = p_3 V_3 \Rightarrow p_4 = p_3 \frac{V_3}{V_4} = \left(1.247 \times 10^5\ \text{Pa}\right)\left(\frac{4.0 \times 10^{-3}\ \text{m}^3}{2.0 \times 10^{-3}\ \text{m}^3}\right) = 2.493 \times 10^5\ \text{Pa}$$

Let us now calculate $W_{\text{net}} = W_{1 \to 2} + W_{2 \to 3} + W_{3 \to 4} + W_{4 \to 1}$. For the isothermal processes,

$$W_{1 \to 2} = nRT_1 \ln\frac{V_2}{V_1} = (0.20\ \text{mol})(8.31\ \text{J / mol K})(600\ \text{K}) \ln(2) = 691.2\ \text{J}$$

$$W_{3 \to 4} = nRT_3 \ln\frac{V_4}{V_3} = (0.20\ \text{mol})(8.31\ \text{J / mol K})(300\ \text{K}) \ln\left(\tfrac{1}{2}\right) = -345.6\ \text{J}$$

For the isochoric processes, $W_{2 \to 3} = W_{4 \to 1} = 0$ J. Thus, $W_{\text{net}} = 345.6$ J.
Because $Q = W_s + \Delta E_{\text{th}}$,

$$Q_{1 \to 2} = W_{1 \to 2} + \left(\Delta E_{\text{th}}\right)_{1 \to 2} = 691.2\ \text{J} + 0\ \text{J} = 691.2\ \text{J}$$

For the first isochoric process,

$$Q_{2 \to 3} = W_{2 \to 3} + \left(\Delta E_{\text{th}}\right)_{2 \to 3} = 0\ \text{J} + nC_V\left(T_3 - T_2\right) = (0.20\ \text{mol})\left(\tfrac{3}{2}R\right)\left(T_3 - T_2\right)$$

$$= (0.20\ \text{mol})\tfrac{3}{2}(8.31\ \text{J / mol K})(300\ \text{K} - 600\ \text{K}) = -747.9\ \text{K}$$

For the second isothermal process

$$Q_{3 \to 4} = W_{3 \to 4} + \left(\Delta E_{\text{th}}\right)_{3 \to 4} = -345.6\ \text{J} + 0\ \text{J} = -345.6\ \text{J}$$

For the second isochoric process,

$$Q_{4 \to 1} = W_{4 \to 1} + \left(\Delta E_{\text{th}}\right)_{4 \to 1} = 0\ \text{J} + nC_V\left(T_1 - T_4\right) = n\left(\tfrac{3}{2}R\right)\left(T_1 - T_4\right)$$

$$= (0.20\ \text{mol})\left(\tfrac{3}{2}\right)(8.31\ \text{J / mol K})(600\ \text{K} - 300\ \text{K}) = 747.9\ \text{K}$$

Thus, $Q_{\text{H}} = Q_{1\rightarrow2} + Q_{4\rightarrow1} = 1439.1\,\text{J}$. The thermal efficiency of the engine is

$$\eta = \frac{W_{\text{net}}}{Q_{\text{H}}} = \frac{345.6\,\text{J}}{1439.1\,\text{J}} = 0.240 = 24.0\%$$

19.67.   Solve: (a) A heat engine operates at 20% efficiency and produces 20 J of work in each cycle. What is the net heat required and the net heat exhausted in each cycle?
(b) We have $0.20 = 1 - Q_{\text{C}}/Q_{\text{H}}$. Using the first law of thermodynamics,

$$W_{\text{out}} = Q_{\text{H}} - Q_{\text{C}} = 20\,\text{J} \implies Q_{\text{C}} = Q_{\text{H}} - 20\,\text{J}$$

Substituting into the definition of efficiency,

$$0.20 = 1 - \frac{Q_{\text{H}} - 20\,\text{J}}{Q_{\text{H}}} = 1 - 1 + \frac{20\,\text{J}}{Q_{\text{H}}} = \frac{20\,\text{J}}{Q_{\text{H}}} \implies Q_{\text{H}} = \frac{20\,\text{J}}{0.20} = 100\,\text{J}$$

The heat exhausted is $Q_{\text{C}} = Q_{\text{H}} - 20\,\text{J} = 100\,\text{J} - 20\,\text{J} = 80\,\text{J}$.